ELEVENTH HOUR

Alexander B. Adams

A HARD LOOK AT

ELEVENTH HOUR

HOUR

CONSERVATION AND THE FUTURE

G. P. Putnam's Sons, New York

To

CARY W. BOK

GEORGE R. COOLEY

ELEANOR HOUSTON SMITH

Dear Cary, George, and Eleanor:

If ever a book belonged to anyone, this book belongs to you. You may not agree with its conclusions, you may not even like it, but it is still your book.

It is yours for many reasons. Not the least of them are your long and imaginative interest in conservation and your concern for people.

Alex

Contents

Conservation in the Seventies—The Outlook 9
1. This Land of Ours 17
2. Death Threatens the Everglades 35
3. The Dam Builders 65
4. No Stopping Except for Emergency 94
5. The Affluent Deterioration 120
6. More People and Worse Cities 155
7. The Tale of Three Parks 185
8. Toward Better Use of Our Land 217
9. The Need for Cooperative Effort 254
10. The Part of Government 280
11. The Private Agencies 298
12. The Conservationists 324
Acknowledgments 349
Notes 351
Bibliography 361
Index 369

Conservation in the Seventies—
The Outlook

"You might just as well say," added the March Hare, "that 'I like what I get' is the same thing as 'I get what I like'!" . . .

"It is the same thing with you," said the Hatter, and here the conversation dropped, and the party sat silent for a moment. . . .

The Hatter was the first to break the silence. "What day of the month is it?" he said, turning to Alice; he had taken his watch out of his pocket, and was looking at it uneasily, shaking it every now and then, and holding it to his ear.

Alice considered a little, and then said, "The fourth."

"Two days wrong!" sighed the Hatter. "I told you butter wouldn't suit the works!" he added, looking angrily at the March Hare.

"It was the best butter," The March Hare meekly replied.

January, 1970, was a month in which the curious logic of the March Hare seemed to grip the country. We could not distinguish between what we liked and said we wanted, and what we were actually receiving. The month should have been marked by hope and the setting of attainable goals for the new decade; instead we wasted it on minor tinkering in an attempt to remedy the major mistakes of the sixties. It should have been a time in

9

which we squarely faced the issues of our era; instead we devoted it to burying our past errors in rhetoric. It was a period when we should have been looking ahead; instead we were busily occupied glimpsing back over our shoulders.

Confusion reigned everywhere, and words seemed to have lost their meaning. We recognized the horrors of our slums, but the administration recommended more economic aid to South Vietnam and less for rebuilding our own cities. It pressured one conservation agency to rid itself of a single public information officer as an economy move. At the same time, apparently with administration approval, the Pentagon was pushing a request for $29.5 *million* for a one-year public relations program. When asked by Congress how they intended to spend that much money, the admirals and generals were unable even to supply a detailed breakdown. The administration announced what it labeled the largest water pollution abatement program in America's history —but expected to achieve it by substantially reducing current federal expenditures for that purpose. The President preached economy to every department of the government and then himself spent $16,000 on comic opera dress uniforms for the White House police. And so it went throughout January, 1970.

That was the month we put the butter in the works.

Unfortunately, conservation was one of the victims of the type of thinking that prevailed. In spite of numerous magazine and newspaper articles, television broadcasts, Presidential proclamations, and the growing awareness of what we loosely call our environment, the water and air were just about as bad as ever; many of our latest national parks—already dedicated with much fanfare—had little hope of being completed; and the Land and Water Conservation Fund, which is the source of most federal money for the purchase of government-owned open space and grants to states and municipalities, was sadly below the scheduled amount. There had been some slight progress here and there and masses of legislation and thousands of speeches. But the words had led people to believe more had been accomplished than was the fact. Our surroundings were steadily getting worse, not better, and the outlook for the future was poor.

When President Nixon entered the White House, uncoordinated planning, the high cost of supporting the military, and the low priority accorded the environment were already taking a heavy toll of every conservation program. Although federal spending is not necessarily an accurate measure of the effectiveness with which we are handling a problem, it does tell something about the order of importance assigned to it. As an example, we had been spending far more—billions more—on our network of highways alone than on all our conservation programs put together. The cost of the latter amounted to such an insignificant proportion of the total federal budget that it could hardly be shaved further.

Nevertheless, that is what the new administration immediately proceeded to do. It professed to take a firm stand on water pollution but attempted to reduce the scheduled authorization by approximately 78 percent. If it had succeeded, it would probably have put an end to all further effort in this field. It bore down harshly on the acquisition of lands for more parks and other open space and almost destroyed that critically shrunken program. It did tighten the regulations controlling offshore drilling, and it took action to change the location of the airport whose existence threatened the Everglades National Park. But in spite of the wide publicity given the latter step, it represented the removal of only one threat to one national park. Worthwhile as the action was, it could hardly be regarded as a conservation program or even the salvation of the Everglades.

The President's State of the Union Message, which he delivered on January 22, 1970, contained many references to the environment and to "reparations for the damage we have done to our air, to our land, and to our water." But the only specific proposal it contained was a $10-billion program for the abatement of water pollution. Even if ending water pollution should have been our first priority—and it well might not have been—the President's proposal had to be weighed against the need. Of the $10 billion, only $4 billion was to come from the federal budget; and in spite of the President's statement that "we must do it now," this money would have been spread over such a long period of time that it would have represented a sharp reduction in annual expenditures from the appropriation Congress had just voted.

Shortly after the President had delivered his message, I was in Washington. His message had aroused no optimism among any of the agencies that I visited. Most conservationists I talked to had not been encouraged by the President's speech. They wanted action, not talk.

Their fears were borne out by the budget message. In preparing his recommended expenditures for the year, the President had faced serious problems. He had not ended the war in Vietnam, and that expense, along with other projects of the military, was sapping all our domestic programs. He had opened his administration—and his war against inflation—by approving sizable pay increases for himself and the members of Congress, and he had also during the year approved tax decreases for the American public. Having abandoned both taxes and wage-and-price restraints as a means of controlling inflation, he had to have a tight budget. This was understandable. The disappointment was the absence of any appreciable change in direction. With a few minor alterations, the President proposed giving the nation about what it had received in the past.

There was a slight increase in the amount requested for the purchase of park lands, but it was far less than the amount requested for a year's development work on the supersonic jet transport. Highways still reigned supreme. The nation was asked to spend far more on concrete and asphalt during the fiscal year 1971 than on all its conservation programs put together! The message was devoid of any fundamental thinking about our environment and left little cause to believe the government would assume a role of imaginative guidance.

Perhaps the pessimism engendered by this outlook could have been offset by the knowledge that more and more people were becoming interested in conservation. I discussed this with a man whom I consider one of the best informed in the field. He pointed out—and rightly so—that much of the current awareness was founded on either misinformation or lack of information. He also pointed out that the sudden popularity of conservation was attracting publicity seekers, who had not bothered to study the problem before attempting to assume positions of leadership. He handed me a copy of a magazine that listed a number of people it considered effective in conservation. Only one in the entire list had made a real contribution. All the others had been quite indifferent to the question until a short time previous. The clamor of self-appointed experts did little but add to the already-existing confusion.

This is not helping the cause. As this book points out, one of conservation's most desperate needs is people, but not people who are seeking publicity, satisfying a personal lack, or trying to increase their earnings. It needs practical idealists, men and women who know how to analyze a problem carefully, set priorities, and get a job done. It is one thing to become emotional over the ecological importance of our tidal marshes; it is quite another to devise a realistic plan for preserving them. We have done too much of the former, too little of the latter.

There is reason for grave concern, but not for gloom. Although time is running out for us—and running out fast—I do not hold with those who predict only the eventual destruction of the American environment, and I grow weary of reading or listening to their lamentations. The situation is far from good. but it will not be improved merely by decrying it. Enough time does remain, if we quickly seize our opportunities and act intelligently, to accomplish much and to make many drastic changes from the directions in which we are presently heading.

But we do know that many of the methods we have used in the past have not been generally successful. One look around us tells us that. The purpose of this book is to study some of the successes—and failures—that have occurred and to point out some fresher approaches we might take and new paths we might either explore or expand.

This is not a book of doom; it is a book of hope. I believe that if we Americans will apply our ingenuity and resourcefulness to the solution of the problems facing us, we can solve many of them in the seventies. But the achievement of success will demand more of us than we have given before—more understanding, more new ideas, more willingness to make sacrifices, and above all more intelligent application of the lessons we have learned in the past.

In the seventies, I believe, we can start to get what we like instead of foolishly pretending that we like what we get. We can remove the butter from the works.

ELEVENTH HOUR

1

This Land of Ours

THE land we were given is so rich in beauty and variety that no poet, writer, artist, or photographer—no matter how great—has ever succeeded in capturing it as a whole and confining it to paper. It resists confinement. All that the best of them has accomplished is to take a sample here or a sample there; and being good at their art, they are also wise and know it is only a sample.

It may be a bit of Maine they have given us, a spruce-covered island with the waves of the North Atlantic churning at its granite base, waves that can move hundreds of tons but cannot shake the rocky shore. They crash against it with the sound of thunder and then, defeated, retreat to the ocean in a swirl of white foam and green water. It may be the long beaches of Cape Hatteras, the playground of children in the summer sun, where they can build their castles near the tides and wade in the gentle waters, but a place of horror for mariners, when the hurricanes race out of the south, and safety can only be found in a tight harbor or in the open sea with room to maneuver. It may be a coastal island in Georgia, where pirates once landed their treasure on the sandy shores and where the ducks and geese take refuge in the marshlands, and the limbs of the live oaks are shrouded with Spanish moss. Or it might be the mysteries of a mangrove swamp on the coast of Florida, with the strange roots of the trees interlaced in the water and forming a pattern so intricate and impenetrable that even an Indian in a dugout cannot pass through it.

Unlike most nations, we have a second ocean, too, and there is little resemblance between the Pacific pounding against the state of California at the Big Sur and the Atlantic beating against the eastern shoreline. Here the mountains drop into the ocean as though defying it to destroy them, proud graceful mountains, covered with blossoms in the springtime and often lying in the wisps of fog that drift in from the sea. To the north, we have the Great Lakes. No other nation but Canada has anything like these bodies of fresh water, so large it comes as a surprise when no tide rises or falls. The word "great" is a misnomer; it should be "greatest." And to the south we have the Gulf of Mexico.

As if that were not enough waterfront for a single nation to be blessed with, we have other lakes, thousands and thousands of them. We have so many in Minnesota alone that it is easy for the canoer to become lost, as he passes from one to another through the waterways of the state. We have famous lakes like Okeechobee and Pontchartrain and Reelfoot, which was carved out of the Mississippi by an earthquake while John James Audubon was living on the frontier, and Crater Lake, which rests like a sapphire in the mouth of an extinct volcano, thousands of feet above sea level. And we have smaller, lesser known lakes, hidden in our forests and plains, where a camper can pitch his tent and, during the night, hear no sounds but the weird voice of a screech owl echoing in the distance and the crash of falling trees that the beavers have cut.

We have rivers, some of the greatest and most majestic in the world. The Hudson which reminds travelers from Europe of the Rhine, the Missouri, the Yellowstone, the Colorado which has carved out that marvel, the Grand Canyon—the only canyon like it in the world—the Klamath, the Columbia, and, the largest of them all, the Mississippi, which pours billions of gallons of water into the Gulf of Mexico, a river that is life-giving but unpredictable. Few nations are so blessed with water.

For those who do not like water, we have deserts, miles and miles of them. Death Valley in California, where the temperature often rises above 120 degrees and even the animals venture out only at night, the Mojave, which lies to the south, and the deserts of New Mexico and Arizona, where snowcapped mountains border the hot lands. In the winter, the land may look barren to those who do not know and love it, but in the spring the arid soil gives birth to thousands of flowers. They sprout from the arms of the giant cactus and from the fiercest of all cacti, the cholla, known as the leaping cactus because of the ease with which it attaches itself to anyone who brushes against it. At that time of year in the desert, even fences made of the cut stems of some of the plants become covered with flowers.

We have forests, also, forests with ponderosa pines and Douglas firs and eastern hemlocks and shortleaf pines, and mountainsides covered with aspens that turn to gold at the fall's first touch of cold. We have what no other nation in the world possesses, the giant sequoias of the West, the largest trees that grow anywhere, and the coastal redwoods. Nothing grows taller than the coastal redwoods.

We have plains. Our early settlers, when they trekked westward, sometimes thought we had too many plains. They stretched miles and miles ahead of the covered wagons and the men on foot and horseback who were seeking a new life in a new world. There were so many miles of plains they formed a barrier between East and West.

Rising above the plains and the seas are the mountains. We have the Green Mountains of Vermont and the Smokies of Tennessee. They form part of the Appalachians, which once, in a simpler day, divided East from West and nearly split us as a nation. We have the Rockies of Colorado, the Cascades and Olympics of Washington; and in the Olympics, we can find alpine flowers growing within sight of the ocean. Few countries possess a miracle like that. We have the Tetons, great blocks of rock thrust from the earth's entrails, and we have Mount Desert in Maine, the place where the sun each day first touches American soil.

In this land of ours, we have many natural wonders. We have

Niagara Falls, one of the greatest waterfalls in the world. We have Old Faithful in the Yellowstone, spouting its spray of steam into the air with the regularity of clockwork. We have the Natural Bridges of Utah and Virginia, the strange carved red rocks of the Valley of Fire, and the view from Glacier Point in the Yosemite, a view that cannot be painted or described. Here the artist or the writer or the photographer can take only a sample of the sample. The whole is too large to encompass with its many waterfalls, canyons, mountain peaks, and rounded rocky summits, and in contrast the green floor of the Yosemite Valley lies many feet directly below.

As if this were not gift enough—this beauty and variety—we were also given commercial resources almost beyond count. We have waterways down which ships can pass and secure harbors where they can safely anchor. We have forests that make us one of the great producers of lumber. We have rich deposits of oil and almost every mineral. We have fields that will produce wheat and cotton and soybeans and almost every crop that a civilized nation could desire.

We like to imagine that we earned all this with our plows and guns and axes, but that belief is only a partial truth. We took advantage of it, but we did not earn it because it was already there. Anyone with courage, ingenuity, and good fortune could have taken it. We were the ones that fate chose. Never before in history has so civilized a people advanced upon a land so rich in resources and been able to claim it as their own. Our fore-fathers understood this in a way that we do not. Today we use our pioneer tradition as an alibi for our actions. We have forgotten that there is a tradition older—and more truly American—than that. Many of our earliest settlers regarded the land and its resources with a respect that we soon lost and only now are beginning to regain. They did not use such words as "conservation" and "land-use planning," but they practiced those concepts in their most modern sense.

Anyone traveling through New England can immediately recognize this. Each of the older towns has its common or green, a piece of land that was set aside at the time of the town's establishment to be held in common for the use of every resident. This was an integral part of town planning, a custom that was practically taken for granted. Even the poorest resident, who might not own an acre in his own right, had a claim on the common ground. Today these plots of land, laid aside through the foresight of the earlier settlers, provide restful open space in busy cities. But moving westward, this conception of land planning disappeared, because the communities were founded after we had lost our land-use ethic.

Not long ago, I was in a small town in Wyoming and visited their newly purchased park. The man who supervised its administration was rightly proud of it because it represented a personal achievement for him. He had been almost alone in wanting it. As he explained, there was so much open space outside the town limits that few but he could see any point in preserving land within them. Such an attitude was foreign to the early settlers of New England. Although they were surrounded by wilderness and although the continent stretched for miles and miles behind them, they still kept common ground in their midst.

Many of them had the same attitude toward our seashore. In Massachusetts, the beaches belonged to everyone. They were a common resource that all shared for pleasure, for fishing, and for launching a boat. "No trespassing" signs were nonexistent. And to assure future access to the water, many towns reserved rights-of-way, so any resident could reach the shore. Owning waterfront property did not give the owner exclusive rights to the beach in front of him. The Cape Cod National Seashore in Massachusetts is the direct result of this early respect for Americans' right to reach the water. If it had not been for the numerous town beaches and rights-of-way, as well as an important state park, the national seashore probably would have been impossible to create. Cape Cod would have been built up like so much of the rest of our shorefront, and the expense of condemnation would have been prohibitive.

Respect for the rights of all the people, rather than the fortunate few, was not limited solely to the land itself. It applied also to what grew on the land. As early as 1626, the colony at Plymouth passed an ordinance prohibiting the cutting of trees on land within the colony unless the cutter first obtained official consent.[1] In 1710, the people of Newington, New Hampshire, established the first community forest in the United States. Over the years, the 110 acres owned in common have supplied fuel for the public buildings, planks for bridges, and helped in building the church, the town hall, and the library.[2] Protection and management of our forests was not limited, however, to New England. In 1777, North Carolina passed a law restricting the burning of woods and, with remarkable insight, declared that forest fires destroyed the soil.[3]

Common rights to the rivers of America were also closely guarded. In 1773, a man named Hunt tried to take exclusive possession of a section of the Housatonic River, which runs south from Massachusetts through Connecticut. He had set up a "fishing place"—to use the quaint language of the time—on the east bank of the river from which he could draw his seine. When other fishermen set up a similar operation on the opposite bank, he brought a suit of trespass against them, claiming as his own property all those fish that he could reach with his net. The court wasted little time over the case. The river, it said, was a public river, and the fishing rights belonged to everyone in common.[4]

Some of the early charters were specific about land-use planning. The New Jersey Concession and Agreement of 1664 gave to the General Assembly the right to decide the amount of land that would be allocated to houses in each town and specified the maximum width of streets and made provision for the construction of wharfs, churches, forts, and even public houses. It also guaranteed to every man the right to travel on any body of water that eventually led to the ocean.[5]

The Fundamental Constitutions of Carolina, written in 1669 by John Locke, went even further in protecting our natural resources. They expressly placed on government the responsibility for preventing air or water pollution.[6] Although he did not use the word "pollution"—he called it "infection and corruption"— he was, in this as in many things, ahead of his time. He even recognized that air and water are common property and referred to them in those terms. Three hundred years later, we are just beginning to catch up with his thinking.

The charter of Georgia, written in 1732, went far in land planning by placing a specific limit on the amount of land any one man could obtain. It was 500 acres. If through some subterfuge he succeeded in securing more than that, his title was to be declared void.[7] When William Penn laid out the city of Philadelphia, he was more specific than most modern zoning commissions about the sites of houses. He wanted each one placed in the center of its lot so that it would be surrounded by orchards or gardens. His purpose, he said, was to make Philadelphia "a greene Country Towne." [8] He also restricted the farmers' rights to cut trees. For every five acres cleared, one acre had to be left in timber. The ordinance was difficult to enforce and finally lapsed, but Penn's intentions were clear.

Thoreau, who visited Cape Cod before 1850, devoted several pages of his book about the Cape to the subject of soil conservation. Timothy Dwight, whose *Travels in New England and New York* had appeared in 1821–22, had reported that the citizens of Truro were required to plant beach grass every April to help in the preservation of the dunes and shoreline. By this measure, they had rebuilt the area between Truro and Provincetown. Thoreau wrote, in words that might describe many a later conservation project, "I was told that about thirty thousand dollars in all had been appropriated to this object, though it was complained that a great part of this was spent foolishly, as the public money is wont to be. Some say that while the government is planting beach-grass behind the town for the protection of the harbor, the inhabitants are rolling the sand into the harbor in wheelbarrows, in order to make house-lots." [9] But he recognized, as did many other people, that beach grass and other cover was essential to the survival of the Cape. Without it, the Cape would be destroyed by the waves or carried away by the wind. We had to relearn this lesson in the 1930's, when much of the Midwest blew away because we had broken the protecting sod that held it together.

Daniel Boone, who might be taken as the epitome of the pioneering spirit, was also a conservationist in the modern sense. When the first settlers arrived in Boonesboro, Kentucky, 200 or 300 buffalo had been grazing nearby. With wanton destructiveness, the settlers had each been shooting from 3 to 6 of them, leaving most of the meat to waste. This incensed Boone, who found that it was necessary for a good hunter to travel 15 or 20 miles to obtain game. In 1775, when Boone was elected a delegate to the convention setting up the laws for the new settlement, one of his first acts was to introduce legislation restricting hunting. His bill passed, and his brother, Squire, also introduced legislation to protect the range. This passed, too.[10]

Today we often blame the sorry condition of much of our countryside on what we call our pioneer tradition. But this alibi is only partially valid. Many of the earliest settlers had a modern concept of land use and believed in communal rights to many of our resources. That attitude began to change with the westward expansion, especially after the Louisiana Purchase in 1803. Settlers began to move west in streams, across the Allegheny Mountains, down the Ohio and Mississippi rivers, then across the Missouri, and finally into the Far West. There were many reasons why they went. Some, like the Mormons, made the long journey to escape religious persecution in the East. Some moved westward in flight from the law officers of their eastern homes; this is not just a fiction of television. Some went in search of adventure. Some were naturally restless, constantly seeking whatever lay beyond the next range of mountains, the next plain, or the next river. But the majority traveled westward for only one reason—to make money. And there was money to be made. There was land to be bought and sold or farmed or mined or timbered or grazed. For it was the land that provided the prospect of wealth.

Each traveler to the West wanted as much as he could get, and we became greedy for land and less respectful of it. Soon a conflict in attitude developed between the East and the West. In 1829, Senator Samuel A. Foote of Connecticut proposed in Congress that no lands be offered for sale except those already designated for that purpose. His proposal drew howls of indignation from the West, and it was clear that Senator Foote did not know what was happening in the development of the country. He did not realize that if land sales continued at their current rate, the supply of public lands opened to entry would have been exhausted in about twenty years. He did not understand that surveyors and speculators were already exploring public lands that had not been put up for sale, selecting the best sites in expectation of the day when they would be opened, even though this activity was forbidden by a law passed in 1807. The economies of many western communities were based on real estate activities, and the phrase "land-office business" was entering our language.

America's preoccupation with its land was described by Senator Robert Y. Hayne of South Carolina in reply to Senator Foote's proposal. "More than half our time," he said, "has been taken up with the discussion of propositions connected with the public lands; more than half our acts embrace provisions growing out of this fruitful source. Day after day the changes are rung on this topic, from the grave inquiry into the rights of the new States to the absolute sovereignty and property in the soil, down to the grant of a few quarter sections to actual settlers. . . . A question that is pressed upon us in so many ways; that intrudes in such a variety of shapes; involving so deeply the feelings and interests of a large portion of the Union; insinuating itself into almost every question of public policy, and tingeing the whole course of our legislation, cannot be put aside or laid asleep." [11]

Two schools of thought existed in the following years. One retained the older American tradition of careful land use and planning, coupled with respect for our natural resources and a recognition that, vast as they are, they are not inexhaustible. In this school belonged the members of the Washburn expedition who explored the Yellowstone in 1870. Having heard of the wonders of the region, the group planned to verify them and then lay claim to the area for themselves. But on the historic evening of September 19, 1870, they sat around a campfire on the Yellowstone River and discussed what they had seen. The region was too remarkable, they agreed, ever to pass into private ownership, and they decided it should be preserved for the benefit of the entire American public. They were not content, however, to let the subject drop at that. When they returned to civilization, they and others lobbied hard and successfully for what became America's first national park—indeed, the world's first national park, for the setting aside of the Yellowstone in this fashion created an entirely new concept.

There were others, too, who put the common good above personal interest in the use of our land and resources. They worked to save our migratory birds against those who argued that federal laws designed to protect them would be unconstitutional. (They resolved the issue of constitutionality by persuading the government to enter into a treaty with Great Britain to protect the birds flying to or from Canada. Because the subsequent legislation was in fulfillment of the treaty's obligations, its constitutionality could not be reviewed by the courts.) There was also Gifford Pinchot, who did so much to establish our system of national forests and introduce wise forestry practices into this country. But people like these, although they were a great force for good, were the minority.

The majority believed in the rapid utilization of our resources. They saw in America a great treasure-trove that should be opened up for the benefit of present generations, and they did not believe in the reservation of at least part of it for the future use and enjoyment of others. They were the ones who caused the many scandals that have plagued our distribution of the public lands, the ones who cut down our forests and left the barren ground to erode, who cared only for immediate profit. They are best characterized by Secretary of the Interior Albert B. Fall, who, during the Harding Administration, was deeply involved in the Teapot Dome and Elk Hills oil scandals. Fall, who was in charge of the department entrusted with our natural resources, faced trial for having accepted a bribe of $100,000 from an oil company to give them favored treatment in the award of drilling leases. (For many years, he was the only secretary whose picture did not hang in the offices of the Secretary of the Interior. A few years ago, in the interest of history, his picture made its reappearance.) Unfortunately, it is this group of people who laid their mark on our land and are still doing it.

What we have done to this magnificent country of ours is a national disgrace. No people ever had a greater opportunity to use their resources wisely; no people ever threw that opportunity away more carelessly. Anyone who travels through our country must take pride in the beauty that is left and some of its conservation achievements, but they must also hang their heads in sorrow over some of the sights they see. Many of the rivers are so filthy they smell; the odor from them is almost unbearable. Much of our air is unfit to breathe. Our cities, many of them, have become shocking jungles of disorder and inhuman living conditions. Once-beautiful fields and woods are laced with the asphalt and concrete of highways, down which we drive at high speeds, scarcely conscious of the greatness around us. Some of our forests are lumbered according to modern practices, but only a short time ago I saw one that looked as though some timberman out of the nineteenth century had been at work—but with the even more destructive machinery of the twentieth. It was in a handsome section of the Rocky Mountains, and great gulleys were etched by erosion in the steep slopes that lay naked with no effort being made to replant them. I regret to say the area had once been a part of the national forest system and had been given to a state government. It did not look like one, but officially it was a state forest.

If we wish to visit our seashores, we are lucky if we can even reach the ocean. Usually the coastline is bordered by private residences through whose land we cannot pass or by commercial enterprises, more noteworthy for their neon lights and high prices than for their good taste. We construct buildings everywhere. When we have ruined one area with factories and slums, we simply move into a new one and make no provision to avoid repeating the same errors. Thus we swarm over the country, developing here and developing there, putting in airports without regard to their surroundings, creating residential centers without considering the water supply or whether the tracts chosen might have a better, and higher, use. As a final insult to this land, many of us cannot even place our trash in the containers that are provided for that purpose. We toss it out of our car windows; we drop it on our streets; we throw it into our creeks and streams. I am not writing now of the deprived who could be excused for not knowing better. I am writing about middle- and upper-class Americans who think they are respectable and tidy. At the Yellowstone National Park, I have seen a man finish some crackers and throw the empty box into one of the fascinating hot springs. If someone had dropped a similar box into the window of his car, where it would have done no harm, he would have been furious. But he thought nothing of partially destroying for others a rare and unusual sight.

His attitude typifies the thinking of many Americans. We are fierce in the defense of what we consider our own personal property, but we regard communal rights lightly and do not consider the effect of our actions on others. We have strayed a long way from the thinking of our forefathers, who regarded the land as an entity, not something to be subdivided with each person doing exactly what he wanted with his own. Most of them would have been horrified at the concept of rugged economic individualism, particularly as we have practiced it in the nineteenth and twentieth centuries.

In recent years, there has commenced a slow awakening to what we have done. More people have looked around them and disliked what they have seen. They have been disgusted by the foul air and the dirty streams, the invasion of parks by highways, the proliferation of industry into scenic areas, the exploitation of resources that should be used for the benefit of all the people.

More and more books and articles have been written on the subject, and more and more television time has been devoted to it. Most literate and concerned people are now at least aware that the problems exist and that the time left in which they can be solved is running out. Much of what is being said is being shouted in strident voices. Yet the message is not producing effective results. We are barely keeping up with the situation, much less getting ahead of it.

One of the reasons for this is lack of national purpose. Anyone who studies the conservation movement today quickly realizes that as a nation we have not yet decided what we would like our land to be, and therefore we constantly contradict ourselves. The very conservationist who is most irate over the building of a dam near his country home is the one who favors the construction of the superhighway that permits him to reach that home more rapidly. He is annoyed at the traffic jams that delay him and is unaware of the values of the land that has been destroyed to build the new highway. He may also be the one who wants the bigger and faster car that requires the larger and straighter road.

The camper who likes to spend his time in the forest and is angry when his favorite campsite is timbered may also have a workshop at home and spend his free time fashioning articles out of wood without seeing any connection between the two activities. The finest conservationist may also be a member of a private club that blocks others from access to the ocean. Contradictions like this are common, and they emphasize that even the conservationists are divided into several groups, often with quite different points of view and not always working in harmony.

The very word "conservation" is subject to many interpretations. To some, it primarily means cleaning our air and water. To others, it means setting aside areas for scientific research and therefore closing them to the public. To still others, it means developing recreational areas for skiing, snowmobiling, or boating. Some think of conservation as setting up wilderness areas and protecting our last remote regions from intrusion. And others consider it the preservation of our rarer species of birds, animals, and plants.

To me, conservation is all of these things, but it is also something more. I think conservation is largely a question of drawing lines. I was talking one afternoon to Ansel Adams, the noted photographer and conservationist, and most naturally our conversation turned to conservation. Suddenly he pointed to the view outside the window and said, "We can save that mountain, and the mountain behind it, and the mountain beyond that one. But we cannot save all the mountains. Somewhere we have to stop." That graphically expresses an idea with which I am in complete agreement. We cannot save everything, but we can save a reasonable part of it. And the objective of conservation is to draw the line. I do not believe we should leave every forest untimbered, but I do not think we should timber every forest. I do not believe that every single marshland in the United States should necessarily go unfilled, but I do not think we should continue our present course of filling them all indiscriminately. I do not believe that we should go without highways, but I also do not think we should cut down an irreplaceable grove of redwoods in order to build one.

Unfortunately we have failed to draw many lines. Instead we are using all our resources for all purposes with the result that they are all becoming downgraded to the lowest use. We employ our rivers as sewers for factories and towns, and at the same time we try to enjoy them for fishing and boating. But they are now sewers. We have only the mildest of local restrictions on the location of factories and other commercial buildings. As a consequence, if the present trend continues, we will have a land dotted with factories. We need dams for flood control, irrigation, and municipal water supplies, but we do not have to turn every river into a lake.

One reason for our failure to draw lines is that no one person or group of people is in charge of what we are doing with our surroundings. Even in the federal government, with its thousands and thousands of employees, no one has been designated to take charge. As a result, we consider each conservation issue as an isolated unit. And few conservation issues are. When we talk about conservation, we are talking also about our total environment; and most of the things we do eventually have an impact on the type of country in which we are going to live. Someone should be coordinating our activities and be responsible for the outcome. But in terms of our environment, we are a leaderless nation.

The self-designated practical man, whose vision for the future rarely extends more than a few years, thinks of conservation as impractical. He can see no reason why anything should be preserved if someone can make a profit by not preserving it. His practicality is indistinguishable from shortsightedness. There are many practical reasons for sounder conservation than we are practicing in this country, and I will list a few of them.

One, which the practical man should understand but often overlooks, is economic. The Bureau of Business and Economic Research of Montana's School of Business Administration would hardly be called a visionary institution. Yet here is what it said in a report commissioned by the state: "Travel appears to be unusually important to the state of Montana. There are many reasons for this. First, the state's strategic location athwart important travel routes, both east-west and north-south, assures Montana of a large and growing cross-state traffic. Secondly, Montana holds within her own borders *many and varied natural attractions in the form of national parks* [emphasis added], ski areas, hunting and fishing areas, and other natural attractions." [12] In other words, national parks and other natural attractions generate outright business, providing jobs and incomes for many people. They may, indeed, be the most continuously productive use for a particular tract, especially over the long run. Many of the travelers whom the bureau interviewed made comments like these: "This is the 28th state I have seen and it is, in my opinion, the most beautiful yet." "Some of the greatest scenery . . . to be found in the United States." "Very impressive—a relief after being in the city all year." "Montana once again renews the meaning of America the Beautiful." [13] These people were willing to spend money to visit these natural attractions that so appealed to them. In the twelve months from July, 1963, to August, 1964, out-of-state travelers alone spent more than $76 million there.[14]

Other states have had similar experiences. For the fiscal year 1966–67, visitors to California's great state parks spent an estimated $95 million in the immediate vicinity of the parks and another $71 million while traveling from their homes to their destinations.[15] Dr. Ernst W. Swanson, Professor Emeritus of Economics at North Carolina State University, in a report published in 1969, estimated that gross expenditures by visitors to our national parks amount to $6.3 billion.[16] From these expenditures alone, the federal government directly receives in taxes $952 million.[17] Our national park system, in addition to being a source of pride and pleasure for many of us, is an income-producing operation for the federal government, something that Congress might bear in mind at appropriation time—but does not. Natural attractions, properly protected, are big business in America.

Conservation and the wise use of our land has other economic advantages. It is an important factor in sustaining real estate values because people will pay more to live and work in pleasant surroundings. For example, homes close to parks or having nearby areas where people can walk or children play are more valuable than those that do not. I have seen instances in which the creation of a bird sanctuary has raised the prices of the surrounding real estate. This is true even in the hearts of our greatest cities. The eastern section of midtown New York used to be a slum area. When land was cleared for the United Nations building and open space was created—along with handsome views of the East River—prices rose. Today that is one of the most fashionable parts of the city in which to live.

There are other economic aspects to conservation. When we indiscriminately fill in our marshes, we adversely affect our fishing industry. When we cut down forests without following the best of modern forestry practices, we leave barren, unproductive soil that soon erodes. When we break the sod in areas where the sod should remain undisturbed, we not only destroy the farm that should never have been created in the first instance, we also —and this is a fact that many people do not know—run the risk of destroying other farms as well. Once the dust starts blowing, it is dropped by the wind on good farms as well as bad. The wind makes no distinctions.

Science, a subject that is likely to appeal to the practical man even if he does not understand it, also gains from conservation. We still have much to learn in the earth and life sciences. We will not learn what we should, however, unless the scientists have places to work. They cannot uncover many secrets of the world around us by examining a piece of asphalt paving. They need natural areas in a relatively undisturbed condition. These places also provide us with what the scientists call gene pools, stockpiles of widely diversified genetic material. When we breed domestic animals and plants, we eliminate some characteristics in favor of others. Often, because of certain circumstances such as a newly virulent pest, we need to introduce additional characteristics. The necessary ones can sometimes be found only in the wild. I have been told that the success of the cattle industry of western Canada was dependent on the simple fact that, in the end, we did not exterminate the buffaloes. Characteristics of the buffaloes were

THIS LAND OF OURS · 33

introduced into the great beef herds. This enabled the cattle to survive the rigorous winters.

Health, too, is benefited by conservation. Some aspects are more obvious than others. The people who died some years ago in Donora, Pennsylvania, made us all aware of the potential hazards of air pollution, but fewer people know about the positive effects of conservation on health. We live in an age of wonder drugs that have done so much to save human lives and alleviate human suffering. Approximately half these drugs have been obtained from botanical specimens, many of which might have been destroyed if we had been even freer with our use of bulldozers. The business in medicinal plants amounts to approximately $330 million every year. Cortisone and digitalis are only two of the many drugs that come from natural sources.[18] And we have only begun to explore the potentials of the many biological specimens available to us—if the practical man has not destroyed them before the researchers have discovered their uses. We do not as yet know nearly enough about the physiological and psychological effects of overcrowding or, conversely, open space.[19] We know that many people derive emotional and mental benefits from visiting the outdoors. We should know more about those benefits before we destroy all the open space that is left to us.

These are just some of the many practical reasons for conservation, but I am not a practical man. If I were, I would not have devoted years of my life without pay, trying to make a contribution to the conservation movement. Instead I would have spent the time providing a more comfortable existence for my wife and children. But neither they nor I think those years were wasted, because I have not mentioned what to me is the greatest reason of all for conservation—the sheer beauty of this country. Who can put a dollar sign on the wind blowing across the domed point of Cascade Head in Oregon? Who can say what the moonlight is worth as it reflects from the Colorado River at the bottom of the Grand Canyon or brightens the slopes of the Santa Rita Mountains of Arizona? Who can place a value on the sight of a deer and her fawn wandering through the Maine woods, or on the sound of a loon crying out on a Maine lake when darkness

is falling? Who can write a price tag for the weird, black lava
formations of the Craters of the Moon in Idaho? Or for the ebb
and flow of water in a tidal marsh with a wren singing in the
nearby cattails? Or for a glimpse of white herons rising like
ghosts in the early light of a Louisiana dawn? No one can establish prices for these because—they are priceless. No amount of
money could create them or duplicate them.

I want future generations to be able to share them, too, for
they are a part of the quality of life. Without them, there would
be a shabbiness to our existences that would be cause for despair.
And to pass them on to future generations is, I believe, one of
the greatest gifts we can give, a gift worthy of the inheritance
that we ourselves received.

There is no point simply throwing up our hands at what is
going on around us, disgraceful and shortsighted as it may be.
Too many people interested in conservation talk about what is
wrong and confuse the talk with real concern. Laments will not
preserve the country as it should be preserved. But action will—
constructive, well-informed, intelligent, and coordinated action.

One of the reasons we do not take such action lies in the
complexity of most major conservation issues. An excellent example can be found in our handling of the Everglades of Florida,
where the construction of a jet airport was arousing wide controversy while I was writing this book. But the jet airport, for all
the publicity it received, was only one of many dangers threatening that outstanding area. It may well be the Everglades National
Park will still be lost, not just as the result of what we are doing
today, but as the consequence of more than a hundred years of
indecision, poor planning, abuse, greed, and parsimony where
conservation is involved. From the point of view of conservation,
a summary of the complicated history of the Everglades can
illustrate, and thus help explain, some of the general problems
that we face throughout the United States and why they have
come about.

2

Death Threatens the Everglades

THE sun had long since begun its descent toward the narrow line where, off in the distance, the sky and the Gulf of Mexico merged into a mass of indistinguishable grayness, a meeting of one vastness with another. We had left behind us the mainland of southern Florida and beneath us now were the shallow waters of Florida Bay, in many places only a foot in depth and occasionally threaded by passes for which the Coast and Geodetic Survey will not vouch. Information on their existence, says the official notice, is "obtained from reports of local mariners and not verified by field surveys. Mariners are advised to use caution." Ahead, the sea glimmered in the sunlight, and as Ranger Pilot Ralph Miele of the National Park Service commented, this was truly wilderness.

Suddenly he banked; below us was Frank Key, one of more than a hundred islands that dot the bay. Each of them is rather like the others, their mangrove-covered shores barely rising above the surrounding waves, almost as though nature could not decide whether they should be land or water. When the hurricanes roar up from the south they become submerged, and no man can live on them, and no boat lie safely in their lee. But

35

when the water is calm, they become land again, and the green leaves of their trees make them appear to be substantial islands. Frank Key is one of these, a rectangular-shaped cluster of mangroves lying almost two miles off the coast, yet well within the boundaries of the Everglades National Park. Looking down, we could see numbers of the rare great white herons. These are the largest of all American herons, beautiful birds with their pure white feathers and long yellow beaks. But neither nature nor man has been kind to them. Their range is extremely small. They live and breed largely in the coastal swamps of southern Florida and are not often seen farther north than Miami. Thus they are almost completely dependent on this small section of the United States. Over the years, they have been the victims of many natural disasters and much human persecution; and by 1935, they had been reduced to approximately 150 individuals. Since then, they have been increasing again; and it was good to see them on Frank Key under the protection of the National Park Service. Mingled with them were white pelicans that later in the year would fly diagonally across the country to spend the summer in the Northwest, roseate spoonbills with their pink feathers and flat bills, and bald eagles, which are growing rarer and rarer but which still breed in the Everglades. (There had been fifty-five nests that year inside Everglades National Park.)

Never before had I seen a sight such as this, the great birds roosting and flying below us in the slanting light, but Ranger Miele was somewhat disappointed. A stiff wind had been blowing for much of the afternoon, and so the profusion of birdlife had not been as visible as usual. Yet it had been Ranger Miele's assignment—and personal desire—to show me why the Everglades National Park deserved protection. And also why its continued survival was in such serious question. No other national park is so seriously threatened with complete destruction. In southern Florida, the absence of a sense of purpose is clearly evident, and the area now presents a problem so complex that it may never be satisfactorily solved.

We had taken off earlier in the afternoon from the small airport near the park's headquarters at Homestead, Florida, and headed east over Route One, which runs down across the Florida

Keys, and had then turned back over the coastal mangrove swamps. These waters are extraordinarily fertile, as the park personnel kept impressing on us. They are rich in fish and bird-life and essential to the important shrimp industry because they harbor the shrimp during four critical months of their life cycle. Without them the shrimp could not exist—nor the men who make their livelihoods fishing for shrimp. The waters also provide a home for crocodiles, which are so close to extinction that they have been placed on the federal government's endangered species list.

Birds had been next among the sights that Ranger Miele wanted us to see, and this was the reason he had turned south over the bay. We had flown low over several eagles' nests in the hope of finding one that still contained the young; we finally did. We had passed over rookeries of spoonbills and one used by that extraordinary bird, the wood ibis, the only American stork. We had seen pelicans flying along the coastline and had crossed over rafts of coots lying in the water. We had seen the stretches of mangroves that had been wiped out by Hurricane Donna, their whitened trunks and tangled roots lying like lacework beneath us. Now we had seen the myriads of birds on Frank Key, and I was beginning to understand why Superintendent John Raftrey had told me that the best way to see the Everglades first, if you are trying to comprehend them as a whole, is from the air. They are so vast, so generally inaccessible, so strange, and so unique. Unlike most national parks, which contain one, two, or three central, dramatic features, the Everglades are the Everglades— acres and acres of sawgrass, mangrove swamps, hammocks of hardwoods, and miles of waterways and bays, the only park of its kind in America.

We had left Frank Key and the other islands of Florida Bay and were heading west along the coast when we saw beneath us several campers on the beach, their motorboat anchored in the mouth of a small inlet. To me, the scene was a happy one. Here, I thought, were young Americans finding peace and happiness in the outdoors, but Ranger Miele is not quite as naïve. He brought the plane down over them to check them out, wondering if they had obtained a fire permit. (For all the water that is associated with the Everglades, fire is a constant hazard.) But as the campers waved to us, we noticed something unusual. Several of them were wearing helmets, which seemed like strange dress for either boating or camping. So Ranger Miele turned eastward, circled, and then came back for a low pass alongside them. This time we saw that they had motorcycles with them, obviously intending to scramble on the beach. In country like that, where a difference of even a few inches in elevation can produce profound changes, the ruts left by fast-moving, fast-turning motorcycles could be disastrous. So Ranger Miele radioed to headquarters, asking them to send out a boat. At the same time, I gained an understanding of the difficulty of patrolling the park. Although it contains few roads and trails for the casual traveler, its miles of coastlines, bays, and rivers offer easy access to anyone with a small boat. The park's eastern and northern boundaries are almost as difficult to protect. Few roads penetrate them, but there are also few geographic obstacles to prevent entry by anyone willing to struggle through the swamps or to battle with the sharp-bladed sawgrass. Those experienced at traveling through the Everglades—and that includes poachers—can enter the park and, under the cover of darkness, move about freely without detection. Only by daylight and from the air is it possible to determine accurately what is going on in that vast wilderness.

I was about to comment on this to Ranger Miele, when he silenced me and told me to look out the window, for we were approaching a sight that he particularly wanted me to see. We were flying almost due west. Suddenly in a great curve we rounded East Cape, the southern elbow of Cape Sable, and could see the smooth sand sweeping to the northwest with the surface of Lake Ingram glistening behind it. Here were miles of practically virgin beach, a view not to be duplicated anywhere in the United States.

As we turned inland again, we passed once more over the coastal mangrove swamps and a section of flat, grassy plain that is so typical of the Everglades, and on to Whitecap Bay, dotted with islands that looked as though they were the disassembled pieces of a jigsaw puzzle, set out for some mythological giant to put together. Farther north, we saw the valley of the Shark River, one of the longest of those that run from the Everglades National Park into the Gulf of Mexico. Then we left the park, flew over the Tamiami Trail, the highway that crosses Florida from east to west, looked at the construction taking place at the new Dade County Airport, saw the gates through which water passes from the conservation districts into the park, and noticed an Indian village with its thatched roofs of palm leaves.

Daylight was fast disappearing as we turned again into the park and headed back toward the landing strip. But there was still time to dip low over an alligator hole (we could see the track the reptile had made going in and out), to circle a flock of white ibis, and to watch a deer standing in the sawgrass and casting a long shadow in the falling light. Shortly afterward the airstrip appeared before us, and we heard the sound of the wheels as they touched the grass.

Of course, one cannot learn much about the Everglades in a single plane flight, even with a guide as experienced as Ranger Miele. But one can gain an understanding of them as a whole, and it is as a whole that they must be understood. In few places are so many elements of life so closely intertwined or so dependent on interrelated factors. It is this quality that makes them unusually vulnerable to destruction. And destroyed they may well be, in spite of their vast size, the miles and miles of mangrove swamps, and the great, seemingly endless, acres of sawgrass. Indeed, the Everglades could be the first national park in the history of our country to be abandoned. Within a short time, they might not be worth keeping.

The Everglades are often called the river of grass, but the description is misleading because it implies that the grass itself forms the "river," perhaps by swaying in the wind like a Western grain field. Actually the Everglades are a real river—the broadest and shallowest one in the United States.

Its headwaters are to the north of Lake Okeechobee, one of the largest lakes in the country. Although it is extremely shallow, in many places only a few feet in depth, it is more than 30 miles in diameter and covers more than 700 square miles. Therefore

it has a large water-holding capacity. This is filled by the rains
that fall on its surface and by drainage from farther north.

From Lake Okeechobee southward, for approximately 100
miles, the land slopes imperceptibly but steadily at a rate of a
few inches a mile. This is not great, but it is sufficient to make
the water move. On the east, the area is bounded by an eroded
ridge of limestone, and on the west by a mass of relatively higher
land. This geologic formation makes of southern Florida a giant
trough, running from the north to the south and southwest and
opening into Florida Bay and the Gulf of Mexico. Because the
trough is composed of limestone covered with marl and peat that
help contain the water, it is an excellent conduit—a perfect
riverbed for the overflow from Lake Okeechobee. Except for
occasional floods, when the rainfall is heavy over Lake Okeechobee and the lands to the north, the water does not come in a
rush. The grade is so gentle and the width from bank to bank so
great (approximately 100 miles in places) that the water seems
to drift southward along its course, dragged over that expanse
by the slight tug of gravity. Its motion is barely noticeable, and
to the casual observer it appears to be standing still. Yet this is
a real river, as real as the Ohio or the Mississippi or the Columbia. As real as any of them. Yet unlike anything else in the
United States.

In this river grows the sawgrass, a tall plant whose blades are
sharp enough to tear the flesh of a man. It is from the sawgrass
that the Everglades received their name. Earlier they had been
known by the Spaniards as *El Laguno del Espiritu Santo,* "the
Lake of the Holy Spirit," a mysterious place, perhaps holding the
promise of the great riches the Spaniards wanted, but almost
impenetrable to Europeans. The descendants of British settlers,
however, called them glades, a word meaning a grassy place.
Sometimes they called this area the river glades, but because the
sawgrass of southern Florida goes on forever and ever, often as
fas as the eye can see, the land came to be known first as the
Ever Glades and then the two words became one.[1] And truly
they are Everglades. They stretch unbroken for mile after mile,
the sawgrass standing like grain stalks in a field, catching the
sunlight and waving in the wind. Here and there are pools of

water, looking from a distance like lakes in a meadow until the observer sees that the water, except in the dry season, does not stop at the edge of the lake but extends in among the blades of the sawgrass.

Every so often, the flat expanse is broken by the small "heads" or groupings of a particular tree, such as a "willow head"—or the larger, mixed groves that are called hammacks. In the heads and hammacks, the world is utterly changed. Outside, the sun may beat down mercilessly; in the hammack, there is shade and protection from the winds. Outside, the Everglades are fertile in fish and birds; in the hammacks, the soil itself is fertile; and years ago, settlers occasionally planted them. I have eaten lemons from a tree that is all that remained of the efforts of one such venturesome soul. These changes in the total environment—and that is what the hammacks and heads represent—result from the slightest of causes, a small deviation in altitude. These deviations are so minute they are measured in inches, not feet. A botanist who had studied this question told me that in one area the average difference in elevation between the hammacks and the Everglades was twelve inches and never more than eighteen.[2]

In the centers of many of these hammacks and heads, particularly those where the willow trees stand, are holes that have been eroded in the underlying rock. These and other holes are essential to life, for when the river starts to dry up, as it does regularly every year in early winter, the water still stands in these places, which are known as survival holes. Here the fish, the alligators, the birds, and other wildlife of the Everglades congregate, and here also the observer can see the interdependence of life in the glades. In considerably oversimplified form, the mosquitoes supply food for the smaller fish, who in turn are eaten by the larger ones. These larger ones provide food for the birds and the alligators. (Although alligators will occasionally devour birds or even small dogs, one of their principal sources of food is gar fish.) It might appear that the alligators were merely the final beneficiaries of the interbalance of life in the Everglades, but they are more than that. They are also vital contributors. In the dry season, they keep the survival holes open with their massive bodies, digging out the muck and debris that might otherwise clog them. This is something neither the birds nor the fish could do for themselves. So without the alligators, those strange-looking, generally phlegmatic reptiles, the other life could not exist, at least in such large numbers.

In the world of the Everglades, even the dry seasons, which commence in November and usually end in May, have a role to play. Although the word "dry" often connotes disaster, here the reverse is true. Too much water in the dry season is almost as serious to the wildlife of the Everglades as too little water in the wet. When the water is high, the fish are dispersed over hundreds of square miles and are therefore more difficult for the birds to find. This is especially true for those birds that grope for their food. When the young are hatching, however, and the need for food is greatest, it is within easy reach, concentrated in the survival holes.

As the water drifts slowly down the gentle slope to the sea, it comes at last to an area streaked with rivers, dotted with lakes and islands, and covered with mangrove trees. At this point, the salt and the fresh water are in fine balance, each exerting pressure on the other and intruding into each other's territory. When the tides are running high or a strong onshore wind is blowing, the salt water creeps up the slightly rising land, and water that was brackish becomes salty, and water that was fresh becomes brackish. But when the rains fall over the Everglades or Lake Okeechobee overflows its banks, the fresh water moves with greater mass against the salt and pushes it back. And so the seesaw battle wages back and forth in the fertile and productive waters, while overhead fly the birds from the great rookeries of the mainland and the offshore islands.

Just as it is difficult to determine the margin between salt and fresh water in the Everglades, it is also difficult to decide on the climatic zone to which it belongs. On the map, it lies well within the temperate zone, but maps and other such rigid measures are not completely useful in the Everglades. The temperatures of southern Florida can fall low enough to damage some animals and plants, but the country is generally warm enough to permit many tropical species to live there. Blown by the winds or carried by the currents of the ocean, they have arrived in southern Florida as chance refugees from the West Indies. Because they are prevented from moving farther north by the barricade of cold weather, they remain on the tip of Florida, adding another unique quality to this unique area.

White men were a long time coming to the Everglades. They built settlements on the coasts of southern Florida and on the long chain of islands that forms the Florida Keys, but their expansion inland was temporarily checked by the miles of sawgrass and shallow water that covered the interior. Except for a few hunters, trappers, and adventurers, the only humans who lived in the Everglades were Indians, descendants of the original Indian tribes, other Indians whom the whites had driven from farther north, and numerous escaped slaves who found there greater justice than in supposedly more civilized communities. Traveling through the Everglades in their dugout canoes and making their encampments on the many hammacks, they kept these lands as their own domain, one of the few places in the East where they could live in safety and freedom. But this peace, which had already been broken by intermittent fighting, was shattered in October, 1834.

Yielding to pressure from the citizens of Florida for more land and fewer Indians, the United States adopted a new policy: All the Indians must move to Arkansas. By the year 1836, not a single Indian was to be left in Florida. The Indian agent, General Wiley Thompson, called a meeting of the leading chiefs to announce the government's plan and was greeted by a flat refusal to go and a reminder that the Indians were living up to the agreements they had already made. Another meeting took place in the spring of the following year. This time General Thompson was more adamant. He demanded that each chief sign a paper agreeing to move his men and their families to the West. Eight chiefs did so, but the others said no, and one even stepped forward, whipped out his knife, and drove it through the paper on the table. General Thompson, still not sensing the depth of the Indians' feelings, insisted that they must be ready to move by January, 1836. On December 28, 1835, just a few days before the deadline, General Thompson and another officer were taking a walk a mile from the fort. Bullets whistled through the air;

both men fell dead; their scalps were divided between the attacking Indians; and the Seminole War had begun.

The years that followed were bloody and bitter. More than one general tarnished his reputation fighting the elusive Indians, and at least one sullied America's honor by deliberately breaking a flag of truce. Yet even treachery, combined with the most massive concentration of troops in the United States, could not bring about the total victory that so obsesses the American military mind. By June, 1842, almost eight years after General Thompson had issued his original ultimatum, the army and navy had lost 1,555 men, the cost of the war had amounted to $40 million, and there were still Indians in southern Florida—not a large number, but there were some. Many people in Florida, who had become economically dependent on the war, wanted to continue the fighting until the last Indian had been exterminated or removed, but the country as a whole was growing weary of the pointless and expensive battling. The army was ordered to disengage, and the remaining Indians were told they could stay, provided their behavior was good.[3]

The Seminole War had a profound effect on the Everglades. As the fighting continued, the Indians were driven farther and farther back into the wilderness, and the soldiers came in pursuit. Thus for the first time, the Everglades lost some of their mystery, and white men became familiar with their vastness. Almost immediately they began to suggest that the Everglades might be drained and then converted into habitable lands. Few saw any difficulty in accomplishing this. One authority thought that the entire feat could be completed at a cost not to exceed $500,000, and his optimism was backed by the views of army officers who had fought in the war. The collector of customs at Key West was one of the few who had a different opinion. He had traveled extensively throughout the Everglades, carefully measuring the depth of the water with poles that he had marked for this purpose. As a result of his studies, he had concluded that much of the Everglades was at sea level and therefore never could be drained. He thought the best use for part of the land was small-scale farming. The remainder of it, he believed, should be left undisturbed.[4]

His view might have prevailed for a time if it had not been for the apparently unrelated demands of the citizens of Louisiana. By 1849 they had built 1,400 miles of levees along the Mississippi and its tributaries, thus making several million acres of land available for cultivation. They thought that 5 million more acres could be protected from flooding, but the lands belonged to the federal government. Since Congress at that time had no intention of constructing levees itself, it passed a bill that gave to the state all federal lands that were either subject to flooding or were swamps. During the following year, an agent of the General Land Office visited Louisiana to make an on-the-spot survey. He recognized the futility of constructing levees in Louisiana alone and realized that other states, such as Mississippi and Arkansas, should be included in the program. Out of his recommendations came the Swamp Act of 1850. The purpose of this act was to provide a means of financing drainage and flood-control projects. Under its provisions, any state could patent federal lands considered unsuitable for cultivation because of excess water; the proceeds from these lands were to be devoted to drainage and flood control. But the wording of the act and subsequent revisions were not clear, for they did not include an adequately refined description of the type of lands that might be patented. This loose wording led to many interpretations, much debate, and considerable scandal. In many states, in order to save expense, individual land agents were appointed on a commission basis, receiving in return for their services a percent of the lands they were able to secure from the federal government. In Missouri, the land commissioners, even by following the most liberal policy, could allow only 64 percent of the state's claims; and the surveyor general for Arkansas discovered that some of the lands selected were indeed unsuitable for cultivation; they were situated so high in the Ozarks that they were too steep.[5]

Florida lost little time in taking advantage of the new law. The legislature passed the necessary enabling act and established the Board of Internal Improvement, which was to handle all the funds received from the sale of the lands and to supervise the economic development of Florida. The state then took claim to some 500,000 acres of the Everglades, but there was no rush to settle them. Indian fighting had broken out again, although on a smaller scale; and it was followed by the disruption of the Civil War. When peace was concluded, Florida, like the rest of the South, was in economic trouble.

The Internal Improvement Fund, too, was in sorry condition. Before the war, it had issued millions of dollars' worth of bonds for the construction of some 400 miles of railroads, all of which were now ruined. Interest on this debt had been accumulating; land in the Everglades would not sell for even thirty or forty cents an acre; and one creditor alone was presenting a claim against the fund for $1 million.[6] Failing to obtain cash, he entered suit for 14 million acres of the Everglades and pushed the Internal Improvement Fund to the verge of receivership.

In 1880, William Bloxham became governor of the state, and his first step was to look for outside capital. One of those whom he interested in the development of Florida was Hamilton Disston of Philadelphia, who purchased 4 million acres of the Everglades for a million dollars, thus enabling the Internal Improvement Fund to regain its solvency. Disston and some associates formed the Atlantic and Gulf Coast Canal and Okeechobee Land Company, which planned to drain the country west of Lake Okeechobee. At about the same time, two other entrepreneurs, Henry B. Plant and Henry M. Flagler, also began making Florida investments. They were particularly attracted by the purchase and construction of railroads because a Florida law passed in 1879 provided that generous allotments of swamp lands be given railroads for each mile of track they laid down, allotments that ran from 3,840 to 10,000 acres for each mile.[7] Thus with each railroad they purchased or built, they acquired additional claims in the Everglades.

Like the Civil War, the Spanish-American War interrupted the economic development of Florida, and at its conclusion the state of the Everglades was just about what it had always been. Flagler's operation was going on successfully, and he owned much of the Everglades, but Disston's experiment had demonstrated that a few dredges building a few canals were hardly the answer to the seemingly endless water. Everglades lands were commercially worth little, and the Internal Improvement Fund had no money. Furthermore the trustees had been allotting acreage to the railroads before, not after, the tracks were laid. As much of the work had never been completed, these claims should have been invalid. To complicate the problem further, the trustees of the fund had given out acreage totaling more than the fund supposedly controlled, and the federal government had not yet actually patented the land to the State of Florida.[8]

As the governor told the legislature in 1903, there was really nothing to do but start over again. A patent was secured from the federal government for 2 million acres.[9] (By 1966, Florida had obtained more than 20 million acres under the Swamp Land Acts.) [10] The railroads pressed their claims against this acreage, but the governor took the case to the courts and eventually won.[11] One writer has said this was probably Flagler's luckiest day. If he had retained possession of his Everglades holdings and gone on with his plans to drain them, he would have undoubtedly ended in bankruptcy.[12] The people of the state now had the idea that they would drain and sell their own lands instead of having the railroads do it for them. Governor Napoleon Bonaparte Broward, former sheriff of Duval County, was the man to lead them in this ambitious enterprise. In his campaign for the governorship, he had compared the Everglades with the Mississippi River, stating that control of water in the Everglades posed a much simpler problem; he had likened Florida to Holland; he had spoken of the harnessing of the Nile; and he had challenged the people to join him in what he considered an easy task. The cost, he estimated, would be considerably less than a dollar an acre.

In November, 1905, the dredges went to work. The mud was piled along the edges of the canals. Where rock stood in the way of drainage, it was blasted. Land prices in the Everglades began to soar. One man bought 25,000 acres at two dollars an acre and sold them at thirty. Governor Broward persuaded a land developer from Colorado, Richard Bolles, to buy 500,000 acres of land in Dade and Lee counties at a dollar an acre on condition that the state would dig five canals for him.[13] Taking advantage of the inherent American desire to speculate in land, the developer sold 10,000 farms in ten-acre tracts for prices ranging from twenty to twenty-four dollars an acre. Some of the people came to settle on their lands; but the majority had bought only in the hope of making an immediate profit.

As he watched the economic development of the Everglades, Governor Broward must have thought that he had reason to congratulate himself on his foresight. But Florida had been passing through a relatively dry cycle of weather. Then the rains came and with them floods. The water poured over the rim of Lake Okeechobee, and people had to be rescued from their houses in boats. It was suddenly apparent that 142 miles of canals, two locks, and the expenditure of more than $2 million were not sufficient to drain even a portion of the Everglades. Homeless families and unemployed men ranted and stormed against the state and against real estate speculators; and in the aftermath of disillusion, several land promoters, including Bolle, were indicted for fraud. Bolle was subsequently acquitted and given more time to pay for his holdings, thus permitting him to continue with his development.[14]

While the majority of people were looking at the Everglades as a potential source of revenue, a small number of others were contemplating its natural wonders and considering whether they might be preserved. Several botanists, particularly impressed by the palms on Paradise Key, spoke of making the area a national park;[15] and in 1901, the president of the National Association of Audubon Societies, aroused over the slaughter of birds by the plume hunters who supplied feathers for the millinery market of New York, came to Tallahassee and persuaded the legislature to pass a model law protecting nongame birds. Since each county had only one game warden (and the warden for Monroe County had to cover the Florida Keys, Florida Bay, and part of the mainland), enforcement of the new law would have been impractical without additional personnel. So the Audubon Societies agreed to pay the salaries for four more men.[16]

One of these was Guy Bradley, a young man whose father was a land agent for Flagler. Bradley lived with his family at Flamingo, the small town on Florida Bay that is now an important center in the national park; and from there he patrolled the keys and the southern tip of the mainland. His job was no sinecure.

More than once, the plume hunters threatened his life, and on several occasions they shot at him. Among the worst poachers were Walter Smith, whom Bradley had once arrested, and Smith's two sons, Tom and Dan. One day in 1905, the same year that Governor Broward's dredges were penetrating the upper stretches of the Everglades, Bradley noticed Smith's schooner off Oyster Key, an island almost due south of Flamingo. Then he heard shooting. Knowing that Smith was raiding the rookery, he climbed into his skiff and rowed out to make an arrest. It was Bradley's last act. Smith shot him in the breast, left him dying alone in the skiff, and sailed directly to Key West. He did not deny killing Bradley, but he claimed that Bradley had fired first. In support of this assertion, he relied on the unanimous testimony of his sons and two other men who were on the schooner, and he also pointed to a bullet hole in his mast as further proof. Although he was held and brought to trial, the state was unable to break his story, and he was acquitted. Regardless of the jury's decision, public opinion was outraged; and it became further enflamed with the murder of another warden, Columbus G. McCleod three years later.[17]

The answer to the plume hunters clearly did not lie in local regulation. No warden could be sure of safety in the Everglades or among the keys of Florida Bay, and once the plume hunters had taken the feathers, it was relatively easy to ship them out of the state. So the Audubon Societies began to attack the market in New York City by lobbying for the passage of the Audubon Plumage Act by the New York State Legislature. (The size of this market is revealed by the testimony of one millinery firm that reported the sale of $200,000 worth of egret plumes in a year.) Alfred E. Smith spoke strongly against the bill, saying it threatened 20,000 workers with unemployment and might destroy $17 million of investments. In spite of this opposition, the bill passed both houses of the legislature, and Governor Charles Evans Hughes signed it on May 7, 1910. The Audubon Societies could consider they had won the battle, but they had not. The plume hunters were still active in the Everglades; but now, instead of shipping the feathers directly to New York City, they sent them abroad and then brought them back into the country as imports, which were still allowed. Federal legislation finally put a stop to this practice.[18]

Nevertheless the land in which the birds had their rookeries was still far from safe because the craze for development continued to sweep Florida. The Florida Federation of Women's Clubs, however, became concerned about Paradise Key and attempted to save it by interesting the state in it. Largely through their efforts, the railroad company that owned part of it gave 640 acres for the creation of a state park, and the state itself gave 960 acres, later adding another 2,080.[19]

Although a relatively small state park was better than no park at all and certainly represented a major step in an important direction, others still thought that a larger area should eventually be included and that it should be given national park status. They continued to work quietly toward this end and were so convincing that Stephen T. Mather, then Director of the National Park Service, officially recommended such action to the Secretary of the Interior in 1923. But in the twenties, the minds of people were not on the preservation of their national heritage but on the economic development of the Everglades and the surrounding country. Land prices were soaring even beyond the visions of Governor Broward. One developer spent $20 million filling in swamp and pine land south of Fort Lauderdale. He brought potential purchasers by the busload from Miami and sold his first division before the fill was completed. One estate north of Miami sold for $30,600 an acre. Few of these transactions were made for cash. The down payments were generally small, and often more than one mortgage was involved. It was a gay world, a mad world. Enormous profits were quickly and easily made, but the profits were mostly on paper,[20] and they blew away in 1926.

Early in September, the Weather Bureau warned of an approaching storm and then announced that it had moved out to sea. But on the morning of September 17, the barometer dropped to 26.71, the lowest reading recorded in Florida's history. By noon, the wind started blowing from the northeast and kept increasing until midnight. At Miami Beach, one wind gauge is said to have registered 132 miles an hour before it blew away. When the storm finally roared off on the morning of September 18, it carried with it the dreams of many men and women, and left behind it only the wrecked and flooded houses. Long before southern Florida had had a chance to recover, a second storm struck on October 19. The wind blew almost as strongly as before, and the rainfall was even heavier.[21]

As the state slowly took stock of itself, it could only realize that it had not yet mastered the Everglades. Its canal system had now cost some $14 million and was completely inadequate either to supply water in dry times or to prevent flooding in wet times. The governor now called for the establishment of an Engineering Board of Control to build further canals and to construct a levee at the southern rim of Lake Okeechobee. He also asked for a bond issue that would raise $20 million more to carry on the work. But counties like Dade, already impoverished by over-investment in ill-conceived drainage projects and the effects of the storm, protested strongly.

Nevertheless by 1928, the total cost of draining the Everglades had reached $18 million. Some of Florida's optimism had returned, and people proudly said that the Everglades were worth $106 million. But once again a hurricane struck. This time, instead of staying close to the coastline, it turned inland from West Palm Beach toward the Lake Okeechobee area. The waters in the lake rose higher and higher and swept down their natural water course over the southern edge and into the Everglades, where hopeful farming communities had been established. When they could, men and women took refuge in boats; the boats were overturned and smashed by the weight of the water. Some people fled to schoolhouses; the schoolhouses were ripped from their foundations and set adrift. Those who remained in their houses or climbed the few trees were no better off than the others. At dawn, when the first rescue boats started in search of the living, their crews found a sight of incredible ugliness. They collected the bodies and piled them up at the railroad stations. Later, as the waters fell, the whole area smelled of decaying flesh. For all the boasts of Governor Broward, the Everglades had taken their revenge. About 1,800 people had died.

The Everglades had defeated the State of Florida. All those years of work, all those dollars of expense had brought profits to a few, death to many. If men insisted on living on the flood plain of Lake Okeechobee, Florida had to enlist the support of the federal government in a more comprehensive flood-control project than any envisioned before. Rarely reluctant to enter a major public works project, regardless of cost or purpose, the federal government agreed to help build a massive dike around the lower end of Lake Okeechobee. As part of the plan, the Caloosahatchee River to the west was dredged out to provide drainage in that direction, while the St. Lucie Canal provided it to the east. The water in the lake dropped five feet below its normal level; the water table in the surrounding country dropped seven. Many of the fields dried up. Now that the Caloosahatchee was wide open, the tides began creeping up it. Where once the wells near the river had given forth fresh water, they now gave salt. Fruit groves were deserted. Cypress trees died. Money could still be made in farming part of the Everglades, although more and more only on large farms. The little farmer was being driven out.[22]

During World War II, the Everglades passed through another dry season, much like the one that had inspired unwarranted optimism in the heart of Governor Broward. The flow of water down through the sawgrass became less and less. The fish collected in the pools and often died. The birds searched for water. Then the fires started. The Everglades have always been subject to fire, and it may be that a certain amount of fire is helpful to their well-being. But these were not natural fires in normal amounts. Almost anything could start a fire. The lookouts in the towers saw the smoke curling skyward and often, even as they made their reports, knew that nothing could be done; there were too many fires to fight them all. The Tamiami Trail, which runs across Florida, was sometimes closed for weeks; the smoke was so dense the drivers could not see where they were going. Next the seawater, no longer held back by the fresh water, began to move inland.[23] Oldtimers could remember when the water in the Miami River was fresh about a mile and a half from its mouth.[24] With the continuous dredging, however, the salt water had mounted farther and farther, and the fresh water springs near the coast stopped flowing. The salt water now began moving inland faster and faster. In 1942, it was advancing at a rate of about 200 feet a year; two years later, the rate had increased to more than 800.[25]

By 1945, the situation was desperate, and the people were protesting—but against what, they were not sure. A plan for state control of drainage was defeated in the legislature; and although Dade County voted to take away the authority of the local drainage board, similar measures were defeated in other counties, largely at the instance of the large growers who did not want to lose their discretionary powers. Yet some degree of reason was beginning to prevail. In 1933, the University of Florida had been studying the soils of the Everglades, and later the United States Soil Conservation Service and the United States Geological Survey also conducted surveys. Although these studies, valuable as they were, did not explain all the mysteries of the Everglades, at least men were beginning to think about this area scientifically for the first time since they had started bludgeoning it with dredges. Two facts emerged. First, in spite of the blatant claims of the earlier real estate speculators, much of the Everglades, whether drained or undrained, was unsuitable for agriculture. Second, the water supply had to be regarded as a whole. Each area was related to every other area and therefore could not be treated independently.[26] Therefore in 1949, the federal government joined the state in establishing the Central and Southern Florida Flood Control Project, with the design and construction to be handled by the Corps of Engineers and the operation and the maintenance to be the responsibility of the Flood Control District.[27]

Farther south, the Royal Palm State Park had also not been faring well during this period. The Florida Federation of Women's Clubs had devised various means of earning the money needed for its maintenance, such as the operation of a lodge for paying guests; but none of these had produced sufficient revenue, and the federation had had to seek additional assistance from the state and from the federal government.[28] But the idea of creating a national park had not faded. In 1929, the state legislature established the Tropical Everglades National Park Commission with the authority to acquire land by purchase or condemnation

ELEVENTH HOUR · 54

—but with no funds allocated for this purpose. In a related action that year, Congress set up a committee to report on the desirability and possible location of such a park. The committee submitted its recommendations to the Secretary of the Interior in 1931. He approved them and turned them over to Congress. About three years later, in the fall of 1934, Congress passed a bill calling for the establishment of an Everglades National Park. With its customary consideration for the public purse when conservation measures are concerned, it included a provision that no money could be spent for five years. By 1938, the state's commission was practically out of existence, and World War II ended any further planning. In 1946, the commission was reactivated; the federal government agreed to establish the park if Florida would provide $2 million for the purchase of land; Daniel B. Beard of the United States Fish and Wildlife Service (and later superintendent of the park) was authorized to patrol the area and make arrests for poaching; and the land speculators moved in and attempted to drive prices upward.[29] In June, 1947, the state gave the federal government the $2 million; and in December, 1947, the park was dedicated, even though all the land had not been bought.[30]

Twenty-four years had elapsed since the Director of the National Park Service had officially recommended the establishment of the park, sixteen years since Congress had set up its study group, and thirteen years since the original authorization passed Congress.

More than twenty years later than that, Congress was still unable to find the funds to complete the Everglades National Park. Not that the money does not exist. Millions of dollars have been poured into southern Florida (to say nothing of the amounts that have been poured into Cape Kennedy), but in such a haphazard fashion that many serious observers doubt that the park can survive the onslaught of the bad planning and ill-conceived programs of land use. All the lessons of the past seem to have gone for nothing.

One of the most obvious examples is provided by the rapid destruction of the alligators.[31] In twenty years, their numbers were reduced 95 percent by draining and poaching.[32] Draining is now a complicated problem, but poaching is not. Although alligators have a reputation for ferocity, they are a relatively easy animal to kill. Except when they are teased or when they have become accustomed to being fed, they do not become excited at the approach of a human being. Knowing this, the poachers enter the Everglades at night, go to the sloughs and alligator holes, blind an animal with a flashlight, and then either shoot it or kill it by striking it with a machete on the back of the neck. The job is done quickly and easily and, when a machete is used, silently. No number of rangers can prevent the poachers from coming in. These people know the Everglades well and, because of the flat topography, can enter them from any direction. (They even come by bicycle down the road that leads from the north to the National Park Service's lookout tower.) Once inside the glades, they can move in almost any direction and, before daylight breaks, be outside again. On the rare occasions when one is caught, the penalties imposed by the local courts are light. The rangers are still talking about the night they captured a man suspected of killing seventeen alligators. A ranger on " 'gator watch" saw a pickup truck drop off a man with a skiff in the dark of night. In time, the man returned, and seventeen alligator hides were in his boat. But when the ranger attempted to arrest him, he fled into the tangle of mangroves and was not flushed out until the next day. Because the ranger could not positively identify him as the person he had seen in the nighttime, the man, of course, was acquitted. The courts acted properly, but the rangers remember this case as an example of the difficulty of obtaining convictions. Even when a poacher is found guilty and fined, alligator-hide prices are so high he can often earn the penalty back in another night of poaching. Although today's poachers are less bloodthirsty than the plume hunters of Guy Bradley's day, they pose a similar problem that could be solved in a similar way. Local controls, although helpful, did not stop the shooting of egrets at the turn of the century. Neither will they stop the slaughter of alligators. What is required is legislation prohibiting the transportation of alligator hides and their use in manufactured articles. Once this is done, the slaughter of the alligators will probably be checked; and these animals will have a better chance to continue their vital role in the life of the Everglades, digging the holes in which the fish and birds can gather in the dry season.

If the problem of the alligators might be relatively easy to solve, the question of the in-holdings—those parcels of land that Congress did not appropriate the money to buy—is complex. Many of them are in a tract of land called by the National Park Service the "hole-in-the-doughnut," which lies in the eastern part of the park. When the park was established, the owners of these lands claimed they were too valuable as agricultural property to be included. Therefore they were excluded under an agreement that provided they could not be used for any purpose other than farming. Then the federal government, working at cross-purposes with itself as it so often does, lent $400,000 through the Federal Farm and Home Administration for the development of part of the area for home construction.[33] This contradiction was finally cleared up through the threat of condemnation, and the land was retained for farming. Although earlier it had been assumed that such use would be compatible with the park's purposes, it is not. Various pollutants such as pesticides have drained from the farmlands into the park's waters with damaging results. Although this is not among the park's most critical problems, it should never have been permitted to occur. (At the time I write, there is hope that the service may be able to pick up options on this land, most likely using a loan from the Nature Conservancy's revolving funds to be repaid when Congress finally repairs the error made years ago.)

The other in-holding problem is more serious. Some years ago, the family of Barron Collier, the New York advertising man after whom Collier County is named, gave to the National Park Service thousands of acres in the Ten Thousand Islands on the west coast of Florida. Congress accepted the handsome gift but did nothing about purchasing the in-holdings with which part of it is dotted. Many of these are now being divided into small lots and sold as sites for hunting camps and vacation cabins. Aside from the undesirability of having such development within the boundaries of any national park, this one poses special difficulties, particularly in connection with patrolling the area and with disposing of the sewage. Because the value of the in-holdings is mounting and Congress has still not acted, it may be necessary to abandon this part of the park altogether. That would be a sad loss to the American people and would certainly discourage the gifts of other lands to the National Park Service in the future. That is a penalty for Congressional inaction.

None of these problems, however, is nearly as serious as the one that has haunted all experimenters in the Everglades: drainage and water. Ever since the 1940's, the Corps of Engineers has been digging and building; and southern Florida is now crisscrossed with a series of canals, some completed and some merely projected. Their diagram on a map looks like a fantasy created out of a child's set of tinker toys.

The types of questions that can arise and how they develop can be illustrated by Canal 111, located at the eastern end of the park. Eventually it will connect with a network of additional canals leading down from the north, but at present it ends at the site of a manufacturing plant. The manufacturer wanted to transport solid fuel rockets from there to Cape Kennedy by water, so Congress provided the funds, and the Corps of Engineers dug the canal. The canal was used three times. Then Congress discontinued the program, and the plant lay vacant. Meanwhile the salt water crept from Florida Bay up the canal and dispersed into the nearby area. As so often happens in the Everglades, one slight change begot another greater one. So the Corps of Engineers, after considerable negotiating with the National Park Service, spent more money and erected a salt water plug to make the unused canal less damaging to its surroundings.

Farther north, in the area between Lake Okeechobee and the park, the Corps of Engineers has wisely recognized that not all of the land can be drained and cultivated or developed. Three large tracts, called conservation districts, have been set aside. Together they comprise 1,345 square miles or an area larger than the State of Rhode Island. One district is leased to the United States Fish and Wildlife Service. The other two are managed by the Florida Game and Fresh Water Fish Commission.[34] All these areas are surrounded by earth dikes, so they are able to retain both the water that falls on them and that which runs from Lake Okeechobee during the rainy season. This represents a significant change from earlier thinking. Unlike Governor Broward, the Corps of Engineers and the Flood Control District have learned the lesson that drainage by itself is insufficient. There must be provision for the storage of water; and this in turn means, contrary to the optimism rampant at the beginning of the century, that much of the Everglades can never be used for any other purpose. In fact, the Flood Control District points out that the three conservation areas represent 49 percent of the original Everglades region. There is now enough water being held so that the Everglades are not subject to the ravaging fires of some years ago. Nevertheless there is still not enough.

As the superintendent of the park, John C. Raftrey, told the Florida Academy of Sciences, "Man is bleeding life from the Everglades National Park. In the interest of flood control, agriculture, and real estate development, he has constructed an elaborate system of canals, dikes, and levees, designed to divert much of this water from its natural course. Drainage has greatly reduced the Everglades' phenomenal productivity, destroying habitat and food supplies for many creatures. Aquatic animals that once found refuge in water holes during the short dry season have diminished, their reservoirs become dry. The million and a half wading birds that nested here 30 years ago now number less than 50,000." [35]

By 1966, the situation had become so serious that a federal-state agreement was reached in March of that year. Under its provisions, the park is to receive water at the rate of 1,000 cubic feet a second, but only when the water in Lake Okeechobee is above a certain level. That was the basic fault of the plan. The delivery of water was tied, not to the needs of the Everglades or their normal cycle, but to the height of the water in the lake.[36] Thus the park could receive considerable water in its usual dry season and almost none in its wet. Because of the delicate interrelationship between life in the Everglades and the seasonal flow of water, this was hardly a satisfactory arrangement. Furthermore, changes in the flow of water could occur abruptly. In a few hours, the amount delivered could be reduced from 1,000 cubic feet a second to 140. Under natural conditions, such a change would take weeks or even months.

The interim plan, as it was named, had little to do with the needs of the Everglades. It provided enough total water for the possible survival of the area, but the water might well be delivered at the wrong time and in the wrong amounts. About $70 million had gone into the flood-control project, and it was still not working right.

In 1968, Congress authorized additions to the program for southern and central Florida that will probably cost about $70 million more. The Corps of Engineers will dig more canals, build more pumping stations, and attempt to recirculate some of the water. Whether this will work, nobody really knows. They can just guess. And the history of the Everglades since the Seminole Wars is replete with guesses that turned out to be wrong. Under the modified plan, the name by which this one is known, the park would receive 315,000 acre-feet of water a year in all but the driest years, and the water would be delivered in the proper seasons. The amount should be sufficient to support life in the park, although many think 500,000 acre-feet a year would be a more realistic figure. But because of the enormous amount of construction work that must be done, the plan will not go into effect until 1976 and perhaps not by then.[37]

Furthermore, the plan offered only a partial solution to the area's problems. Collier County, which lies to the north of the park (some of the park is within its boundaries) and which is an integral factor in the distribution of water, was not included in the plan at all. All the money and work was being invested on one side of the river but not on the other. This left much of the future distribution of water a virtual question mark. To complicate the situation even further, Miami, which is in Dade County, had plans to become an international transportation center with facilities to handle the large new jets of the future. The more enthusiastic promoters of this idea envisioned international flights terminating at the Dade County Airport with the passengers taking domestic flights from there to other American cities. But the proposed Dade County Airport was not to be in Dade County, according to their thinking. It was to be in Collier

County, outside the Flood Control District, outside the plan of the Corps of Engineers, and not far from the northern boundary of the park.

In 1968, construction had already started on the first runway, the black strip that we saw from Ranger Miele's plane. It was to be two miles long and capable of being extended to six. Ostensibly it would be used solely for training, but provision was made for building several other runways in the future. If the airport became the center that its supporters desired, it would pose a host of problems. As man has seen again and again in that flat country, any sort of massive construction will change and distort the flow of water. In addition, pollutants are likely to drain off, and the noise from the giant jets could make the park unbearable. With careful planning, these problems might be controlled, but the airport could not exist in isolation. A transportation corridor would have to be built across the Everglades between Miami and the airport along which passengers, freight, supplies, and personnel could move. Nothing existed there at the time of the proposal capable of handling a load of this magnitude, and so the Department of Transportation proposed the construction of a high-speed railroad at an estimated cost of $100 million to $150 million.[38] (Compare this with the investment that the government has been willing to make in the park itself. The comparison demonstrates our sense of values and produces a grotesque picture of what tomorrow's America may be like.)

One thing leads to another, and the development of the airport and fast transportation to Miami could also have been expected to produce a community that might within a few years number 1 million to 1.5 million persons. Their houses, stores, and other facilities would probably occupy parts of three counties—Dade, Collier, and Monroe. These three governments showed a willingness to work together and called for a two-year moratorium on rezoning around the airport area until further studies could be conducted on the environment.[39] One real estate developer immediately registered a strong protest, stating that every man has a right to do with his property as he wants regardless of the effect on the whole.[40] This attitude, which places personal profit above the nation's good, is unpatriotic. It also overlooks a basic economic fact: Without the expenditure of those millions of dollars by the American taxpayer, that man's lands might not become worth more than he paid for them. Nevertheless his view may prevail in spite of dedicated citizens' groups like Conservation 70's, Inc., formed to develop better management of the environment of Florida. If it does, the development will probably be like that of the past, haphazard and relatively uncontrolled. The water supply alone could present serious difficulties. One estimate places the water needs of Dade County at 1.4 billion gallons a day by 1995.[41] This would require a holding area as large as the entire Everglades. This figure shows the enormity of the problems that face southern and central Florida. And by then, unless more foresight has been shown, there will probably be no more Everglades National Park. Even the relocation of the airport will not save it. That removes only one of many threats.

It could be argued that in the long run this is not important, that the extermination of the birds and animals that live there is of no consequence, nor the destruction of the shrimp industry, nor the effect on fishing, nor the disappointment of the more than a million visitors who come to the park every year. Superintendent Raftrey has put it differently. Speaking of these visitors, he has said, "Perhaps through their experience here they will ultimately recognize a personal responsibility to the environment, if only because they are a part of it. The fate of the Everglades National Park depends entirely on man's recognition of this responsibility. Outside forces control its destiny. South Florida is changing rapidly—and haphazardly. South Florida desperately needs an environmental design that will strike a balance with the natural environment.

"We can no longer afford the luxury of changing the environment without prior planning if we are to assure optimum benefits to all. We must insure that any change we make results in minimal damage to the environment. A systematic management plan based on ecological understanding and environmental responsibility will achieve that end. But it involves the concern of everyone. Only when we learn that we are part of nature's intricate web and not the weavers of it, only when we concede the necessity of environmental unity—here, as everywhere—will we preserve the integrity of Everglades National Park, and, subsequently, the quality of our own existence." [42]

In his statement, Mr. Raftrey underlines the real significance of the Everglades problem. It is not just a question of whether the park itself can and should be saved; even those who love it might agree that the point could be debated. But the park is part of a much larger whole and thus serves to dramatize a situation that is much more universal than we care to admit. It is a prominent example of incredibly bad land planning. Thus it highlights a problem that we have elsewhere and for which we must find a solution.

When we look back over the history of the Everglades, certain points become abundantly clear. For one thing, lack of human and financial resources had nothing to do with the predicament. Counting the 1,555 sailors and soldiers who died wresting the land from the Indians and the 1,800 people who drowned in the flooding of Lake Okeechobee, the nation has spent well over 3,000 human lives in central and southern Florida. We have also invested large amounts of funds. The park was by far the cheapest element. It cost the State of Florida a gift of land that was almost valueless at the time and the payment of $2 million, which our thrifty Congress felt unable to afford. The flood-control project has so far required an investment of approximately $70 million and will probably end up at double that price. The transportation corridor was estimated at $100 million to $150 million, and that figure did not include the airport itself, to say nothing of the cost of the buildings lost because they had been built in flood and hurricane areas. A conservative estimate of the total amount that the people had already spent or were prepared to spend in and near the Everglades would add up to several hundred million dollars. That is enough in money and human lives to have acquired at least a degree of the environmental unity about which Mr. Raftrey spoke. But the expenditures did not achieve it, and the reasons are not difficult to ascertain.

One reason is the large number of governments and departments, many of them with conflicting interests, that are involved in the Everglades. In the federal government, the Departments of the Interior, the Army, and Transportation all have vital, but limited roles. The Department of the Interior certainly has the most concern for the overall environment, but it also has the least authority and the least money. Its right to intercede is based on its interest in the park, which is at the end of the river, not the beginning, and thus provides it with little negotiating power when it comes to the other two. The Department of Transportation, with far more money and with the promise of more immediate economic impact, can exercise considerably greater influence but has far less concern for the total environment. The Corps of Engineers, the pet of many Congressmen, undoubtedly has the greatest influence of all but is concerned only with water control. In spite of occasional interdepartmental meetings, no one in the federal government coordinates their activities, so Congress happily votes money for the maintenance of a park that gives enjoyment each year to more than 1.25 million people.[43] Then it votes money to dig Canal 111, which will flood and partially destroy part of that park. Then it votes to discontinue the expensive solid-fuel rocket program it had started and which was the immediate reason for digging Canal 111. This sort of confusion is not only disastrous in its effect on the Everglades and elsewhere, it is expensive. I do not know whether anyone has ever attempted to estimate the amount that is wasted each year by programs that eventually cancel each other out, but it must be considerable.

Add to this the involvement of other governments. The State of Florida also has a say in the handling of the Everglades and so do Dade, Monroe, and Collier Counties. Each of them, of course, has a somewhat different interest. The closer they are geographically and the greater their hopes for growing, the more immediate their economic concern. The businessmen of Miami want the airport where it will be of direct benefit to them; the State of Florida wants it where it will stimulate the growth of the state, and that could be somewhere else; and the federal government, except for political pressures and debts, would probably be willing to have it located anywhere that it would best serve the largest number of people. (That might well be a location more influenced by the distribution of our traveling population.) Thus each person and each government comes to the problem with a considerably different point of view.

These conflicts might be resolved, however, if there were any determination by the American people to look at their country as a whole. The basic questions about the Everglades not only have not been answered; except by the few, they have not even been raised. Do we place any national value on the species of life that inhabit the Everglades? Do we want an Everglades National Park for its scientific, educational, and recreational purposes? Should the Corps of Engineers be using important human and financial resources, paid for by the American taxpayer, to develop an area that has historically proved expensive and difficult to develop? With the extensive, unfulfilled needs of this country, should not these resources be used for some other purpose? And among other fundamental questions comes this one: Why do we continually try to solve complicated problems such as the treatment of this area with such inadequate planning and no coordination of effort? Everything we have learned in the past should have taught us to do otherwise.

The questions posed by the Everglades are unfortunately not at all unique. They are the same questions that surround almost every conservation issue in this country, and they underscore the most important question of all—the question of purpose. As a nation, we have not made up our minds what it is we want to become. The story of the Everglades is a classic case history of what is wrong with American conservation.

3

The Dam Builders

THE involvement of the Corps of Engineers of the Army in such delicate problems as the environment of southern Florida, unlikely as it is, results from a historical accident that we have not gotten around to correcting. It dates back to 1802, more than a century and a half ago.

At that time, President Jefferson, realizing the United States had few engineers capable of constructing fortifications against the impending British invasion, signed a bill establishing the corps. Its first assignment was to found an academy at West Point to provide technical training for army personnel. The War of 1812 revealed how badly this mission had been performed, so the academy was reorganized and revitalized. Soon it became one of the finest technical schools in the country and one of the few sources of adequately trained engineers.

In 1818, the House of Representatives directed John C. Calhoun, who was then Secretary of War, to draw up a plan for constructing a system of roads and canals as part of the national defense. It was only natural that an ambitious man like Calhoun should expand on the directive given him and include the commercial, as well as the military, aspects of such a program. It was also only natural that he should contemplate that the work would be done by the Corps of Engineers. After he had submitted his report, Congress authorized the expenditure of $5,000 for a study to improve navigation on the Ohio and Mississippi Rivers, and in 1822 appropriated $22,700 for actual work on rivers and harbors. With the exception of the year 1823, appropriations have been made with regularity ever since, and the Department of the Army has continued to remain in a field that has little connection with its other responsibilities.[1]

During the Civil War, the efforts of the corps were concentrated on its military functions; but in 1866, after hostilities had been concluded, Congress asked the corps to study all the public works projects for which appropriations had been previously voted and resubmit cost estimates for them. The same bill also provided that the corps make its report directly to Congress.[2] Thus the executive branch of the government lost control of the program; and water projects, instead of being developed on a national basis, became a victim of logrolling and political bargaining. One Congressman could trade support with another for projects within their home districts, establishing a tradition they have faithfully followed ever since.

With a hesitancy that does not usually mark its activities, the corps was reluctant about undertaking any but the most limited responsibility for controlling floods, although it had now become the agency to do so. That hesitancy lasted until the Taft Administration. At the time, Senator Francis G. Newlands, who had been working for better coordinated control of water in the United States, formed a coalition with Congressmen from southern states bordering on the Mississippi. They had been protecting their lands with a hodgepodge system of levees, usually built and maintained by local levee districts. These had proved insufficient to prevent repeated flooding. The idea that the federal government should engage in extensive flood-control activities immediately ran into opposition—on constitutional grounds—from the states that had no flood problems in which the government could assist. But the states on the Mississippi argued back, with considerable logic, that much of the water that ended up in their fields and backyards originated outside their boundaries; and they agreed to work with Senator Newlands, if he was willing to include flood-control provisions in his bill. Although the coalition eventually collapsed and Senator Newland's plan failed, temporarily at least the coalition exerted pressure on the corps to engage in more flood-control activity.

By the 1920's, the corps had become increasingly committed to this type of work; but its thinking on the subject had remained static. Particularly along the Mississippi, which represented the division with the largest appropriations, it continued to rely on levees, and levees only. This concept of flood control had long been criticized by many experts; and in April, 1927, the Mississippi itself substantiated the criticism. Floods broke the levees in at least seventeen locations, more than 250 persons were drowned (although that number was fewer than in the less publicized flood in southern Florida), 700,000 persons were made homeless, and the damage amounted to somewhere around $500 million. The publicity that the disaster created opened the way for a more constructive and imaginative approach to the problem of flooding. Various plans were proposed, and Gifford Pinchot, the conservation leader who was then serving as Governor of Pennsylvania, harshly criticized the corps. After fifty years of responsibility for flood control, he said, they had failed to come up with a workable solution. Nevertheless the traditional view of the corps about levees prevailed, largely because of a study ordered by the Chief of Engineers. He attempted to prove that more and better levees would be adequate and showed that they would cost about one-fifth of what the proposed alternatives would. The economy-minded Coolidge Administration accepted his findings.[3]

Meanwhile, two years earlier the corps had been instructed by Congress to study more than 200 rivers from the point of view of irrigation and water power as well as flood control and navigation. This was probably the most comprehensive directive the corps had ever received; and in 1927, the year of the great flood, Congress included a provision in the Rivers and Harbors Act that work be started immediately on the corps' recommendations. Because the economic policies of the Hoover and particularly the Roosevelt Administrations relied heavily on public

works projects in the combat against the Depression, the corps'
new program was richly financed, and the corps emerged as
a prominent factor in the control of our environment.[4]

Its official duties are now many, and often unrelated. In addition to providing engineering services for the Department of the
Army, the Department of the Air Force, and other agencies, it
also has this official assignment: "Under the supervision of the
Secretary of the Army, the Chief of Engineers has responsibility
for construction, operation, and maintenance, and real estate
necessary for the improvement of rivers, harbors, and waterways
for navigation, flood control, and related purposes, including
shore protection; administration of the laws for the protection and
preservation of the navigable waters of the United States. . . ." [5]
This is one of the broadest mandates in government for the control of our environment, although the officials charged with carrying it out report directly to the Secretary of the Army, whose
principal obligations are entirely different. The arrangement is
an organizational absurdity with roots in history, not in logic.

More than once, the suggestion has been advanced that the
Corps of Engineers should be transferred to the Department of
the Interior, not the whole corps, but those sections of it devoted
to civilian projects. At first glance, this seems like a sensible solution. After all, the Department of the Interior has responsibility
for many of our environmental and land-use programs. Perhaps
it, better than any other department of government, would be
equipped to direct the corps's activities. This was one of the proposals made after World War II by one of the Hoover Commissions on the reorganization of the federal government, but
nothing came of it.[6] It has been suggested again since then, but
the corps is determined to stay where it is, functioning almost
as a semi-independent agency and maintaining its own strong
relationship with Congress. It has, therefore, resisted the change;
and as one senator said to me, never underestimate the ability
of the corps, when it is dealing with representatives and senators.
It is also questionable whether such a transfer would result in
any marked change of overall policy, for the Department of the
Interior already has its own mammoth dam-building group, the
Bureau of Reclamation. And in many respects it is subject to the

same criticisms as the Corps of Engineers. Its origins go back to a different aspect of our water policy; but it has followed almost as circuitous a route to its present position of power; and it, too, demonstrates that from the very beginning, we have never been able to consider our water policy as a whole.

A significant obstacle to the settlement of this country was the area called the great American desert. This included the plains region west from the hundredth meridian, which passes through western Kansas, to the foothills of the Rockies and the vast reaches of desert in such states as Nevada and Utah that lie on the other side of the mountains. This comprises an enormous area; but in the view of explorers and settlers, it was uninhabitable wasteland whose only function was to prevent easy travel from East to West. By the 1850's, farmers had moved into Kansas; but one argument advanced against Kansas' admission into the Union by a senator was the worthlessness of the lands beyond the Missouri, an argument that could have been supported by some of the settlers who had struggled to raise crops and take them to market on the Missouri and Kansas rivers. According to one of them, the corn, pork, and hides shipped out of the country barely paid the cost of the whiskey drunk there. Many men simply lived on their savings until they were forced to return to the East.[7] To move even farther west was unthinkable.

Only the Mormons found the desert areas hospitable. Persecuted in the East, they thought they might find freedom at Salt Lake City and commenced an incredible exodus to reach it. In the years 1857–59, 5,200 Mormons made the long journey to Utah by wagon team. Another 3,000, in a heroic effort to get to the new Zion, walked from Iowa, pushing their stocks of belongings in handcarts.[8] They could move westward in such numbers because the Mormons had discovered the obvious secret of living in American desert land—irrigation. Although the principles of irrigation had, of course, been known for thousands of years, they had never been widely applied in the United States;[9] but by 1878, Utah had invested almost $2.5 million in the construction of dams and thousands of miles of canals and ditches.[10]

Others also began to see possibilities in irrigation. Some

Fifty-Niners, who had come to Colorado in search of mineral wealth, remained to farm. By 1866, they were irrigating thousands of acres.[11] At Garden City, Kansas, the citizenry erected a grist mill on the Arkansas River. When dry weather ruined the crops before it could be used, many of the inhabitants moved away; but one who was familiar with irrigation asked, and received, permission to use the water from the millrace. He obtained an excellent crop, and soon others followed his example. By 1890, Kansas had invested approximately $3 million in major canals. (But the dangers of haphazard, local water planning soon revealed themselves. The people of Colorado, by virtue of their geographic location closer to the headwaters, took so much water from the Arkansas River that soon the fields of Kansas again lay bare and scorched under the sun.) [12]

To encourage further irrigation, Congress in 1877 had passed the Desert Land Act. This provided that any citizen or anyone with his first papers could enter 640 acres on payment of twenty-five cents an acre. At the end of three years, if he had irrigated the land, he could receive final title to it by paying an additional dollar an acre. The measure was intended to help the small farmer but rarely did; few of them were able to incur the cost of irrigation. Stockmen and land speculators, however, found in the new act a bonanza. By using dummy entrymen, two interconnected companies in Wyoming made fifty-five desert entries for a total of more than 35,000 acres. Nor did they even install the required improvements in spite of the sworn affidavits they had submitted in accordance with the law.

Widespread scandals such as this helped convince Congress that the act needed to be rewritten. As a first step, it directed the Geological Survey in 1888 to study all public lands that might be irrigated and determine the location of future reservoirs and canals, so those areas might be withdrawn from entry. But the survey took so long to accomplish this task that the head of the survey came under heavy criticism.[13]

In the meanwhile, many conflicting attitudes toward irrigation arose. Some wanted the arid lands turned over to the states for their disposal; some wanted to continue to rely on private efforts, which under favorable conditions produced good results; some wanted the federal government to intervene and undertake the cost of building the necessary facilities.

Finally in 1901, a voice of authority in Washington spoke up and outlined a comprehensive policy. In his State of the Union Message that year, President Theodore Roosevelt said: "Great storage works are necessary to equalize the flow of streams and to save the flood waters. Their construction has been conclusively shown to be an undertaking too vast for private effort. Nor can it best be accomplished by the individual States acting alone. Far-reaching inter-state problems are involved; and the resources of the single States would often be inadequate. It is properly a national function. . . ." [14] The basis of a national irrigation program had been laid down.

Francis G. Newlands, who had been interested in all water problems, was then serving in the House as a representative from Nevada. In 1902, he introduced the Newlands Act, which Congress passed without much opposition. The act provided for the establishment of the Reclamation Fund, a fund into which the government was to put the proceeds of public lands sold in the sixteen Western states that had arid or semiarid lands. The money in the fund was to be used for the construction of irrigation projects. Those who used the water were to repay the cost into the fund, and the Secretary of the Interior was permitted to withdraw temporarily from entry any land suitable for irrigation. Then, when the irrigation project was built, he could make it available for entry under the Homestead Act of 1862. The homesteader could not gain title to the land, however, until he had irrigated at least half of it and paid the cost of all the water he had used. As a final condition, no one land owner could obtain water for more than 160 acres. This last provision was intended to keep out the land speculators and to break up any large landholdings that already existed in the areas to be irrigated. Because the money initially placed in the fund included all the receipts from sales in the fiscal year 1900–1, by June 30, 1902, the Reclamation Fund contained a large sum, and it was growing fast. [15]

At the time, there were other agencies of the government engaged in other aspects of our water problems. The Corps of

Engineers, of course, had accumulated considerable experience in the building of levees, canals, and other engineering projects to control water. The Department of Agriculture had been gathering information about irrigation in the various states. And the Department of the Interior, through the Geological Survey, had been conducting excellent studies of the geology and water resources of the country. But as usual, no one was coordinating these efforts. As a result, many questions were overlooked. Little attention was paid to the quality of the soils that might be irrigated, whether they would stand up under continued irrigation and cultivation, and what the market would be for the crops raised. If anyone really thought that the problem of irrigation had now been solved, they were mistaken.

The Reclamation Service was first placed in the Geological Survey and then set up under its own director in 1907. None of these organizational changes took care of the real difficulties, which were basic to the program itself; and by 1910, the program was in trouble. Although the Land Office had been given authority to withdraw land that might be used for reservoirs and canals, the pressure of individual congressmen had prevented it from doing so. This failure gave many speculators an opportunity to make a profit. They took up lands they thought would be needed for irrigation projects and then sold them back to the government at inflated prices. Others waited until the Reclamation Service had publicized its programs for a given area and then moved in. When one project was announced for the Snake River near Twin Falls, Idaho, 1,000 of the available tracts were taken up within a few months. In instances such as this, some of the claimants were legitimate farmers, who intended to cultivate their holdings as soon as the project was completed. But many times, the farmers were intermingled with people who had no interest in farming at all and were merely making entry for the purpose of resale later. These people impeded the development of the area by not doing their share of the work in digging subsidiary canals or assuming their share of the expense.[16]

Another problem arose from the manner in which the Reclamation Fund could be spent. The Secretary of the Interior had discretion to establish projects but with one severe limitation:

He was required to spend the major portion of the funds in the state from which they had come. The wording was imprecise, but in practice it was interpreted as meaning 51 percent. This provision had a serious impact on the program. It forced the Secretary of the Interior to spread the available funds throughout many states and prevented him from concentrating the money on a few large projects and bringing them to completion. Sometimes, therefore, a project would be announced, legitimate settlers would take up land and then be forced to wait for as long as five years with no water and no means of support. Sometimes the director had to search for projects in order to satisfy the requirement. Thus in desperation he developed a system in Kansas for pumping water from an underground stream that proved too expensive for economical farming, while Nebraska, which had little public land that could be sold, received relatively few irrigation projects. Furthermore the Reclamation Service had not given sufficient consideration to the soils to be irrigated, drainage questions, and the markets for crops.

These and other charges were leveled against the service in 1910 by Sereno Payne, a representative from New York.[17] In the debate that followed, a measure was introduced that provided $20 million from other sources for the Reclamation Fund, so that projects could be hastened. In the same measure, Representative Payne also provided for the repeal of the provision that the major portion of the money be spent in the states where it was obtained.

Opposition to the bill came from Oscar Underwood, a representative from Alabama. Using figures supplied by the Director of the Reclamation Service, he pointed out what was perhaps the most fundamental of all the faults of the program. It was not benefitting the small, poor settlers, who possessed no acreage, as much as it was the people already wealthy enough to own land. In the thirty projects undertaken by the service, only slightly more than one million acres were in the public domain and thus open to settlement, while approximately 1.4 million were in private ownership, and some 130,000 were owned by the states. In the areas covered by six of the projects, including the most expensive one, not a single acre was in the public domain.[18]

Startling as they were, his figures did not affect Congress, which overwhelmingly approved the new measure with no further amendments. The passage of this bill subverted two of the original purposes of the reclamation program. By not providing that most of the acreage should be in the public domain, it failed to help the poor settler; and by appropriating additional funds, it prevented the program from being self-sufficient.

In 1921, the Director of the Reclamation Service, again under Congressional fire and trying to present his agency in the best possible light, pointed out that the average value of the lands irrigated by his service had increased by $200 an acre for a total of $350 million. To that he added another $100 million for the land in private projects supplied with government water. Thus, he attempted to argue, he had increased the value of part of the American land by a total of $450 million and had done so at a cost of only $130,742,488. What the director did not emphasize was the small return the government had received from the beneficiaries of the program. The sum amounted to only $10,677,-250, and much of this represented income from the sale of electric power.[19] Individual landowners had benefitted greatly, but the general taxpayer was footing the bill.

By 1923, criticism of the service had become so sharp that Hubert Work, Secretary of the Interior, appointed a special committee to look into its problems. The committee found numerous faults. Expenses had been grossly underestimated, a common technique of government agencies, which are certain that once Congress has made an initial investment in a project it will not allow it to remain incomplete for lack of further funds. (This practice has cost the American taxpayer billions of dollars, and the time has long since come when Congress should put a stop to it by imposing severe penalties on the offenders.) The service's estimated cost for an average acre was $30.75; the actual cost by the time the acre was under irrigation had mounted to $117.94. Only 10 percent of the construction costs had been paid by the water users; and many payments, both for construction and for operation and management charges, were in default. The acreage covered amounted to only half the original estimate, and many of the farmers were facing insolvency in spite of the extensions they had received on their payments. Aside from the inaccurate estimates of construction costs, many of the problems arose from inattention to agricultural considerations. Prices for the use of water were fixed without thought to the value of the crops that might be raised on the irrigated land and were often too high to make profitable farming possible. Many of the people owning the land were not experienced farmers; many more had insufficient capital.

Worst of all, as might have been foreseen, the land speculators still received major benefits. The Reclamation Service, with many millions of dollars to spend on public works projects, had been subjected to pressures from the individual states, congressmen, and real estate interests. Again, instead of concentrating on developing the public domain and thus providing an opportunity for the small settler, three of the projects on which payments were being made contained no public land at all, and overall only 37 percent of the land had been in the public domain.[20] Congress had not yet accomplished its original purpose of providing a means to make irrigated arid and semiarid public lands easily available to the general public.

In 1923, the Secretary of the Interior began to reorganize the Reclamation Service. It was placed under a commissioner, Elwood Mead, who had been a member of the special fact-finding committee. Mead was dedicated to irrigation, and under his leadership the Bureau of Reclamation (as it was now called) undertook more and larger projects in the states in which it operated. He built Hoover Dam (then named Boulder), which ultimately cost more than all the reclamation projects undertaken until 1929; and the Bureau of Reclamation continued to grow in spite of the complaints of agricultural experts, who in the thirties were desperately trying to stabilize falling agriculture prices. The depression did not spare the farmers on reclamation projects. The crops they raised in 1929 were valued at more than $161 million; by 1932, their value had dropped to one-third that amount, or slightly more than $50 million.[21] But the dams, now used as an integral part of the public works relief program, continued to be built, making more and more land available for agriculture. Thus, once again, one agency of the government was busily canceling out the efforts of another. By this time, the Department of the Interior had on its own an equivalent of the Corps of Engineers. Although the basic responsibilities of the two groups are somewhat different, they have often come into jurisdictional conflict with each other. And they are both among the great dam builders of the world.

Two dam-building agencies in separate departments of the government are enough to complicate our water problem, but anyone familiar with the topsy-turvy growth of the federal government, usually promoted by special interests, will realize that this is not the end of the story.

As a by-product of the irrigation projects undertaken by the Bureau of Reclamation, the Department of the Interior, which is principally charged with the conservation of our natural resources, got into the electric power business. The department is now also in the business of marketing power. Besides the Bureau of Reclamation, it contains the Bonneville Power Administration, the Southwestern Power Administration, and the Southeastern Power Administration, whose purposes are generally related to the development and sale of power.

The Department of Agriculture is also in the electric power business through the Rural Electrification Administration, which makes loans to finance distribution, transmission, and generating facilities to bring electricity to rural areas where it is not available. In connection with this activity, it also supplies technical assistance. (The Department of Agriculture also has the authority to build dams, although smaller ones, through the Soil Conservation Service.)

The Federal Power Commission, too, enters the picture of water use. Among its major functions under the Federal Power Act is the issuance and administration of permits and licenses for the planning, construction, and operation of nonfederal power projects that affect many of our rivers. The Tennessee Valley Authority builds dams on the Tennessee River and its tributaries for the purposes of both electric power and flood control. The latter activity naturally affects flood control on the lower Ohio and Mississippi rivers, a problem that is otherwise

under the jurisdiction of the Corps of Engineers. Water standards, however, are not set by any of these departments or agencies. They are set by the Department of Health, Education, and
Welfare. But the Federal Water Pollution Control Administration is in the Department of the Interior.[22]

Among those who have been concerned with this proliferation
of responsibility and authority is Senator Frank E. Moss of Utah,
who summarized his concerns on March 7, 1969, when he told
his colleagues in the Senate: ". . . 4 years ago . . . I was frankly
motivated by the lack of coordination and long-range planning
in the management and development of our water resources.
I was concerned by the fact that each water resource agency in
the Federal government was surrounded by competing agencies,
with each agency striving to utilize our water resources in a way
which would benefit its particular clientele and that as a result
we were dissipating and wasting and polluting these precious resources at an alarming rate. We still are. We had no basic overall
water policy, and we are still moving at a snail's pace to formulate one. . . .

"In the last Congress, we established the National Water Commission . . . The purpose of the Commission is simply to provide
a comprehensive review of national water resource problems and
programs and to submit to the President its recommendations
for legislation needed for the proper development of our water
resources. I supported the establishment of this Commission,
too, but I did so with the conviction that if the policies it drafts
are to be fully implemented, this can best be done if the agencies
involved are in one Federal department subject to the action of
one Secretary who can take an overall, broad view.

"Water problems still illustrate most effectively the need for
a Department of Natural Resources. The first Hoover Commission reported on this need as follows:

" 'Incomparably the greatest opportunity for economy lies in
the imposition of precautions to eliminate wasteful water development and to assure the soundness of the projects finally
adopted. In the past, projects have been carried through which
should never have been undertaken at all. Others have been

wastefully constructed and without regard to important potential uses.'

"Probably their most important conclusion was that developing the entire river basin is difficult, if not impossible, as long as independent bureaus with traditional loyalties and jealous clientele carve up the development and management tasks.

"The Nation faces a twofold task in developing overall river planning. First the Nation must find, and find quickly, greatly increased supplies of clean water. Second, we must manage with far more wisdom than we have thus far the water supplies we now have.

"Total management of water resources involves a variety of functions. Among others are watershed protection and management, flood control, river and harbor improvements, irrigation, fish and wildlife, recreation, desalination, and pollution. This whole package must be tied together. We must plan for entire river basins from their sources to their mouths.

"However, even should authorities successfully be established for every river basin, the basins are interrelated. Precipitation, pollution, and water use in one basin can vitally affect the others. Coordination in their development and management is essential.

"Interbasin transfer cannot even be considered without both river basin planning and overall planning of water programs of many basins and States. Ideally, we should have a long-range plan for the management of water resources in the United States. The national plan would then be the starting point for the river basin plans. . . .

"On the basis of expenditures, the most extensive Federal activity in the water resources field is conducted by the Department of Defense through the Corps of Engineers. They first were given the job of maintaining navigable waterways—which has some connection with the national defense—at least a better connection than the Navy has in operating petroleum reserves. . . .

"The Engineers operate in every State. Though commanded by a few Army officers, the workforce is composed of civilians. Since it has such a tenuous connection with the Army, it is virtually autonomous.

"Until 1936, the bureaucratic tangle, while confused, was at least limited. Up to that time, authority to harness rivers for storage and electric power was a function of the Bureau of Reclamation. But the jurisdiction of the Bureau was and is limited to the Western States. Following the great floods of 1936, President Roosevelt asked the Corps of Engineers to build flood-control projects. At the same time, TVA was beginning the development of the Tennessee River Basin. Shortly after, Agriculture was given authority to construct small upstream and tributary check dams, and another agency entered the water picture.

"In 1944, legislation logically provided that water projects should be multipurpose whenever possible. This brought the Army into irrigation, power generation, and recreation. . . .

"Congress recognized the dangers in this situation when it passed the Water Resources Planning Act. This act creates a Water Resources Council to coordinate our water resources planning. But this instrument will be an awkward one at the best. The Secretary of the Army, whose time presumably is occupied by Vietnam, and the Secretary of Health, Education, and Welfare, who should be concerned about our tremendous problems of health and education, are now asked to plan our natural resource development.

"It is clear that the basic work is being done by the staff, but the decisions must be made by the Council. The Council cannot devote sufficient time to this. One Secretary could do it and accept the responsibility of those decisions." [23]

Earlier, Senator Moss had underlined even more sharply the inherent weaknesses of the Water Resources Council. Testifying before a Senate subcommittee, he said of the Water Resources Planning Act, "It provided for consideration of water resource needs—on a national scale—by a council consisting of the Secretaries of the Army, Agriculture, Interior, HEW [Health, Education, and Welfare], and Transportation, and the Chairman of the Federal Power Commission. Its functions include preparation of a biennial report on the adequacy of the Nation's water supply, and a review of all developmental plans made by river basin authorities.

"Even though it was a step forward, the weakness of such an arrangement will be evident to this subcommittee. First, it places authority in a committee of Cabinet Secretaries, rather than in an individual whose primary responsibility is resource protection and development. Secondly, it involves a number of men who have more than full-time jobs running their own departments, and who usually serve on several other high-level committees.

"Such an arrangement might have worked quite well years ago. But it can hardly be expected to function adequately when overall planning of water resources is essential to prevent actual deficiencies in many areas of the Nation." [24]

Thus responsibility for the protection and development of our water resources, one of the most vital resources that we have, has been dispersed among several departments and agencies of the federal government. No one department was in overall control, only a loosely knit committee of busy men whose major preoccupations generally had little to do with the environment or with our national resources. This has been the pattern of many of our conservation actions. We have failed to face the issues squarely and instead have obscured them with a bureaucratic superstructure.

It is small wonder that the Everglades—and many other sections of our country—have suffered so badly. We have no policy for their management.

In discussing the situation in the Everglades, Senator Moss directed the following question to Lieutenant General William Cassidy, Chief of Engineers: "The Engineers have built massive levees to contain the runoff from Lake Okeechobee and constructed 1,400 miles of drainage canals in the name of flood control. Park Service officials complain bitterly that the Engineers have drained Everglades National Park almost dry in their effort to halt wetlands flooding and reclaim glade country for agriculture.

"Flood control advocates have said that reclamation is for people and Everglades Park is 'for the birds.' But I do not believe that is the question. The Park is for people, and the farms are for people. The real question is how shall priorities be established for the best use of limited resources."

The question was a pertinent one because it went to the core of the difficulty: Who established the priorities?

General Cassidy's reply showed that there was no answer. "I think the last sentence is a true statement," he said. "How shall this be handled?

"Now, actually the central and south Florida flood control project was established because of the enormous loss of life in that area. . . .

"The major system was authorized just about the same time the park was authorized and created. Before the park was created the water was cut off by local Florida land owners draining their land. The corps project has been underway 20 years. The construction has gone on and we are about 50 percent complete. We have looked at this problem for many years. It is a problem of water use, and part of the problem must be solved by working with the State of Florida which really has authority in the use of the waters of Florida. . . .

"There is a great deal of talk about what is happening there. The glades go through a periodic cycle of drought and wet. There were losses in the glades at that time. This is the natural cycle. And, really, what we are looking for now is an even ecological cycle, a flow of water all the time that will prevent historic droughts. We think we can probably give it to them, but it is going to take just a little bit of time."

Later on, when Senator Abraham Ribicoff of Connecticut asked, "How much consultation is there with the National Park Service?" General Cassidy replied, "We work with the Park Service constantly, sir, and with the State of Florida, to try to reach solutions to problems.

"But we have to reach solutions that are agreeable to the State and to the Park Service, and this has been rather difficult until just recently." [25]

General Cassidy's reply pinpointed two important facts. After twenty years, the corps had not found a solution to the problem of the Everglades; it might require another twenty. And no one had the final responsibility for the environment of southern Florida.

Some of the confusion—and disregard for other values—that

can result is evident in the proposal of the corps in 1965 to construct a dam on the Buffalo River in Arkansas in an area that the National Park Service had proposed preserving as a national river. On reviewing the corps's recommendations, Governor Orval E. Faubus had this to say: "Already created dams and lakes are to be found on every side of the beautiful Buffalo River within a distance of 30 to 100 miles. The creation of another such facility would add little to the attraction of the area as a whole. . . . Were there not already dams and lakes for flood control, generation of electric power, and recreation, this would be a different proposition. . . . It is well to point out also that by a conservative estimate, 90% of the thousands of visitors to Buffalo River State Park favor the National River over the dam and lake." He continued by saying that another survey by a local businessman showed that business in the area would benefit more from a national river than another dam.

But Governor Faubus did not limit his argument against the deployment of dams simply to economics. "A conscious effort on the part of society must be made to preserve a part of our God-given beauty," he said, "or very soon there will no longer be left a sufficient number of these 'little corners of this earth put aside by nature to be discovered' by small boys, to bring pleasure to their pure, fresh minds, and joy to their innocent hearts.

"Unless this effort is made, under the leadership of the people's government, soon there will no longer be a sufficient number of accessible places where families can have a wholesome pleasure and adventure together. This will constitute a loss to society, for which all the material wealth cannot compensate." [26]

In making that last statement, Governor Faubus emphasized a point that is often ignored by the dam builders. Wherever a dam is erected, a lake is formed; and although we may gain flood control, water for irrigation or drinking, electric power, or a place for water sports recreation, we always lose something else. Even the water recreation, which the dam builders particularly stress, usually replaces some other form of recreation that was already there—an excellent trout stream, perhaps, or a canyon to hike through. The value of what has been destroyed will vary from location to location. It may be, as Governor Faubus pointed out, a place where families can have fun together or a spot to be discovered by a small child. It may be an area like the Sangamon River in Illinois, which botanists considered invaluable for research and which 20,000 persons signed petitions to protect.[27] It could be the Indian relics that were covered by the waters backed up by the Kinzua Dam near Warren, Pennsylvania. (Fortunately experts from the Carnegie Museum in Pittsburgh and the New York State Museum, aided by an emergency appropriation from the National Park Service, were able to save many of them.[28]) It may be only a stream beloved by fishermen, or it may be the magnificent gorges through which the Snake River flows in Idaho. In 1958, there were no dams on that part of the river. Only ten years later, the Corps of Engineers had built four dams for flood control and electric power downstream from Lewiston, Idaho; and the Idaho Power Company, following a bitter controversy over public versus private power, had built three dams above Hells Canyon. (Seven dams in ten years on the same river, even though it is a long one, indicates the speed with which we construct obstacles to the free flow of our rivers.)

In the early fifties, a group of private utilities filed a petition with the Federal Power Commission to erect yet another dam in Hells Canyon, one of the most unusual areas in America. The canyon is more than 6,000 feet deep, and at its bottom runs the Snake River, cutting its way through strange basalt and granite formations, a sight that can never be forgotten. But the group was opposed by a coalition of public utility companies, who claimed priority under the Federal Power Act. The issue was further complicated because the Bureau of Reclamation decided that it, too, would like to build a dam, except at a slightly different site. Its attitude placed the Secretary of the Interior, who should be the defender of our natural values, in the position of defending his own dam. By then we had two groups of utilities arguing before the Federal Power Commission for permission to build a dam at various sites on the river, and the Department of the Interior arguing for still another. The complexities of the legal questions brought the matter up to the Supreme Court, where Justice William O. Douglas wrote the decision, one that again underscored the disorganization of American water policy.

"The test," he wrote, "is whether the project will be in the public interest, and that determination can be made only after an exploration of all issues relevant to the public interest. These include future power demand and supply in the area, alternate sources of power, and," he added, "the public interest in preserving reaches of wild river in wilderness areas, and the preservation of anadromous fish for commercial and recreational purposes, and the protection of wildlife." [29] Justice Douglas's decision, which set the Federal Power Commission on a course of holding public hearings, emphasized a point that again and again is overlooked in establishing water policies for this country. The public's interest must come first, and that interest is not limited to a single locality or to a single purpose. There are many other considerations.

The discussion over Hells Canyon also demonstrates why the difficulties of the Corps of Engineers cannot be solved simply by handing over its civil works functions to the Department of the Interior. The department already has its hands full trying to control the Bureau of Reclamation. One of the best examples can be found in its handling of the Colorado River and its proposal to build a dam that might have flooded a part of the Grand Canyon.

The day was warm and clear, as it should have been, because we were in the magical desert of northern Arizona at the edge of the Navajo Indian Reservation—a mysterious and, until recently, remote land of bright colors and majestically carved landscapes. For a short while, we paused in our journey at Marble Canyon, where the Colorado River has cleaved the desert floor. To the Conquistadors and other early travelers, this canyon with its sharply cut walls presented an almost impenetrable barrier. Then we crossed the bridge into the reservation, followed the road over the plain, and began the climb up the mountains. Below us, we could see miles and miles of the vast stretch of desert and the narrow slit of Marble Canyon, twisting and turning over its surface.

Finally we came back to the river again at Glen Canyon Dam. Below it, the river and the canyon vanished in a natural and beautiful curve. Above it, the canyon had disappeared in the backed-up waters of the man-made lake. On the bridge itself was a sign that boastfully proclaimed it to be "the highest steel arch bridge in the world" but said nothing about the wonders of the canyon, as though the works of God were nothing beside the works of man.

That afternoon we purchased tickets for the boat ride to the Natural Bridge, once a distant place reached only by foot or on horseback. The marina looked strange with gaudily colored powerboats moored at the piers and a display of fake captain's hats offered for sale in the desert country.

The next day we boarded the excursion launch and slowly swung into the channel and up the lake, while the pilot of the boat pointed out areas that had been used in the making of two movies, *The Greatest Story Ever Told* and *The Planet of the Apes*. His tone of voice indicated greater respect for Hollywood than for the natural beauty surrounding us, for he barely mentioned the latter. Soon we entered the river's canyon with finely polished rock cliffs rising from the water's surface on either side of us. Underneath us, we knew, were equal marvels now buried in water and silt. Never again would they be part of the magnificent whole.

After a time, we turned from the main channel into Bridge Canyon, its walls high and sheer and yet molded into curved shapes. Like most boats, ours stopped at the National Park Service's marina and store, where tourists can purchase ice cream and soda to supplement the lunches they have brought with them. Then we reembarked to continue up the canyon. "Go Slow" signs reminded us of the danger of erosion to the weirdly patterned rocks, a danger that is increased by the wake of fast-moving boats. We left the boat again at the float at the foot of the short trail to the Natural Bridge and walked up it in the hot sun.

As anyone who has seen the bridge can attest, it is one of the great natural wonders of the world. It crosses the canyon in a graceful arched span that reaches a distance of almost 300 feet. Its height is only about 25 feet greater than its span; but the proportions are perfect, because the water, with the skill of an artist, placed the abutments differently on either canyon wall and varied the thickness of the span itself in a way that gives it an appearance of lightness. The viewer can quickly understand why the Navajos, who were once the only people who knew of its existence, gave it great religious significance. He can also sympathize with the conservationists' alarm at the thought of the lake rising high enough to come beneath it and perhaps in time destroy it. (There is a strong possibility and hope, however, that the Bureau of Reclamation has overestimated the amount of water that the lake will collect.)

As soon as everybody in our party had finished their box lunches, they began taking pictures of the bridge, usually with their wives or husbands standing in the foreground. One man even mounted his camera on a tripod and with the elaborate use of a self-timer managed to get himself into the picture alongside his wife.

After this tourists' ceremonial was completed, we returned to the launch and headed for home. On the way up, the pilot, who seemed so indifferent to the natural scenery, had taken some time to explain that the float at the National Park Service marina had been brought up in three sections. One of the passengers was certain that he had been referring to the Natural Bridge, and now that she had seen it, she thought it indeed a remarkable achievement. Her husband argued with her, saying that it would not then be the "Natural" Bridge, but she remained silently unconvinced.

On the return trip, we entered Cascade Canyon, where, before the lake was formed, a waterfall had dropped into the river far below. Now it was gone. We turned into another canyon, where the river had carved out an enormous and echoing rock in the cave. If the Bureau of Reclamation is correct in its water estimates, this cave, too, will be drowned.

Then we came back to the broader reaches of Lake Powell. A wind was blowing, and a sharp chop marked the water. The launch's pilot was obviously in a hurry to get home, so he did not slow his boat. Consequently several of his passengers in the stern were soaked in a manner that better seamanship could have prevented. Altogether, it had been a day marked by curious contrasts: a lake and typical marina in the midst of the desert; tourists taking pictures of themselves in front of a sacred symbol of an ancient tribe; one of America's greatest wonders threatened by an invasion of man-collected water; fake captain's hats for sale in the land where the Navajos work with silver and turquoise. It had been a conglomeration of sensations with the tawdry and the magnificent piled one on top of the other.

How the lake came to be there under the auspices of the Department of the Interior, and how the department was induced to support another dam farther downstream at Marble Canyon, which would have flooded that wonder, and another even farther down the Colorado River that would have flooded part of the Grand Canyon, is a complicated story. It tells much about the Bureau of Reclamation and the nation's lack of a water policy.

To understand what happened, it is first necessary to know something about the history of water use in that part of the country and also to realize that the attitude of the West toward its water is quite different from that of the East, largely because the West has less of it. Easterners may, and do, pollute their streams and line the banks with industrial installations. But they are not resentful, as Westerners often are, if some of the water reaches the ocean; some Westerners speak of such water as "wasted."

Early in the West's history, the tradition became established that those who first use water obtain a vested interest in it. Those who come later can take only what remains after the first users have drawn their supply. Throughout the West, the early settlers got the water; the later settlers did not. Thus the date of first use is important in establishing ownership. In parts of the state of Colorado, for example, water rights dated in the 1890's, when water was relatively plentiful, were often poor rights in later times of drought.[30] The principle that water is something to be owned outright and that ownership is established by prior use pervades Western water policy and underlies the suggestion to dam the Colorado River and flood parts of the Grand and Marble canyons.

The Colorado River is one of the mightiest in the nation. It drains one-twelfth of the area composing the first forty-eight states, and, with the dividing line at Lees Ferry, Arizona, is composed of two basins, the upper and the lower. The Upper Basin states include Arizona, Colorado, New Mexico, Utah, and Wyoming. The Lower Basin states again include Arizona and also California and Nevada.

One of the areas that early wanted to use the Colorado's waters was California's fertile Imperial Valley. The word "early" should be stressed because of the implications of prior use. In 1901, the California Development Company completed the construction of a canal that would divert water into the valley. This was a dangerous undertaking because much of the region lies below sea level (approximately 280 feet below toward the north). Should the water get out of control, the whole river might empty into the pocket of the valley instead of into the Pacific Ocean.

In the spring of 1904, a flood left part of the canal so badly silted that in the fall the California Development Company dredged a bypass so the flow of water could continue. Because there had been no floods in past winters, the company did not build a regulating gate, thinking the bypass could be closed before the usual spring floods. But that winter proved to be an exception to the general rule. (We constantly take action on our rivers without sufficient information.) By March, 1905, the river had been flooded three times, and the company was frantically trying to plug its bypass. A fourth and then a fifth flash flood destroyed the dams the company had constructed, and erosion in the bypass was changing the normal course of the river, which was out of control until November. Then in December, another flood sent water running through the original irrigation canal into the valley. The water was out of control again until February, 1907.

By this time the natural flow of the river had been so altered that it could not be returned to its former condition; and in 1910, the government, in an effort to help the people of California, invested $1 million in the construction of a levee. The levee did not work satisfactorily, although expenses for controlling the river had mounted to $500,000 a year, the money being spent for preventing both flooding and sedimentation. Meanwhile similar problems were developing in the Yuma Valley to the east, where the Reclamation Service had instituted another irrigation project. In 1906, in spite of hundreds of thousands of dollars spent on levees, water stood four feet deep in the City of Yuma, Arizona. The answer seemed to be to construct a dam farther up the river basin and thus regulate the flow of water through the river. Hoover Dam, a marvel of engineering, was the result.[31]

But the prospect of such a dam raised many fears among the states of the Colorado River Basin. What, under Western law, would prevent California from taking the major share of the Colorado's water first and thus establishing prior rights to it? [32] It was already a major water user. The only solution seemed to be to reach agreement in advance on the amount of water that belonged to each state and to do this before the dam was built. No agreement was reached, however, until President Hoover offered a compromise: to divide the water between the Upper Basin and the Lower Basin states without dividing it between the individual states.[33]

The final result was to apportion 7.5 million acre-feet to each group of states and 1.5 million acre-feet to Mexico. Because the Lower Basin states could not agree among themselves on the further subdivision of the water allocated to them, Arizona filed suit in the Supreme Court. The court appointed a special master, who heard testimony over an eight-year period and reported his findings to the court, which in 1962 issued its ruling. Of the 7.5 million acre-feet allocated to the Lower Basin states, California was to receive 4.4 million; Arizona, 2.8 million; and Nevada, 300,000.[34]

There were several basic problems with this arrangement, but perhaps the most fundamental was that there was not that much water in the Colorado River. Everything had been predicated on an annual flow of 17.5 million acre-feet a year, or a million acre-feet more than the allotments, but from 1906 to 1965, the flow averaged only about 15 million acre-feet a year—2.5 million acre-feet short of the amount anticipated when the agreements were signed.[35]

That was problem number one. Problem number two—and this gets complicated—resulted from the lack of inexpensive electricity necessary to pump Arizona's share into the state. (Because of the topography, a considerable amount of electricity was needed.) Like most desert states, Arizona would like bigger cities and more farms, whether or not they are really compatible with its natural environment; and the principal untapped source of water is the Colorado. Therefore, to help it realize Arizona's ambitions for growth, the Bureau of Reclamation had to find the power for the pumps. Furthermore the price of the electricity had to be low enough to be included in the costs charged to the water users. Particularly for irrigation projects, this had to be extremely low to be feasible.

That was the reason behind the dam that drowned Glen Canyon and the proposal to build two more dams downstream, one of which would have drowned Marble Canyon and the other, part of the Grand Canyon. None of these construction projects was intended to hold water for irrigation—the basic purpose of the Bureau of Reclamation; they were designed solely to provide hydroelectric power. (Note that the bureau could not consider alternate sources of power; its activities—and thinking—are limited to hydroelectric power only.) Sufficient power could be generated at the dams, the Bureau of Reclamation argued, so there would be a surplus over the amount needed for the pumping. This surplus could be sold at a relatively high rate, the bureau continued, to subsidize a much lower rate for the power used for pumping water. In this way, it could obtain the inexpensive power it needed and keep the costs to the water users down.

But the economics of these operations can always be questioned, and these were by many experts. In the first place, interest computed by the Bureau of Reclamation for the capital invested in construction is often less than the interest rate actually paid by government for borrowing money; the difference is eventually borne by the general taxpayer. Any recreational, wildlife, or flood-control values assigned to a project are deducted from the costs paid by the direct beneficiaries; these expenses, too, are paid by the general taxpayer. Consequently the projects are not truly self-supporting. Furthermore in the undertaking along the Colorado, serious questions were raised about the Bureau of

Reclamation's ability to sell the power not used for pumping at the price it set in its proposal. Numerous persons thought the price unrealistically high.[36]

Yet the proposal, in spite of its expense and the destruction it would cause, still left the project without sufficient water, those 2.5 million acre-feet that were omitted from the original calculations of the Colorado's capacity. This shortage would also be aggravated by the increased seepage and evaporation caused by more dams. Extra water, therefore, would have to be brought from outside. The nearest source of additional water lies far to the north in the Columbia River Basin, which includes most of Oregon, Idaho, and Washington, as well as parts of Montana, Wyoming, Utah, Nevada, and British Columbia. The idea is to persuade those states to release some of their water, carry it through a tunnel, empty it into the Colorado River Basin, and then irrigate Arizona.

Fortunately, the proposal to flood Marble Canyon and part of the Grand Canyon was at least temporarily defeated, largely as a result of the Sierra Club's effective campaigning, but only after extensive hearings in the House and the Senate. (The testimony for and against the proposal fills volumes.) Secretary of the Interior Stewart Udall finally found the solution by arranging to purchase power from a thermal plant at low enough rates to make the cost of the electricity used in pumping, reimbursable from the water users.[37] But before he did that, he had had to appear as one of the most important advocates of the dam. That demonstrates the strength of the Bureau of Reclamation. It can generate as much political power as it does electricity.

As an additional commentary, any discussion of the Bureau of Reclamation should also consider the effect of its actions on agricultural surpluses. An acquaintance of mine in eastern Washington, who is highly knowledgeable about farming problems, described to me the intricate regulations by which the bureau attempts to prevent the use of irrigated lands for raising crops that are in surplus. He added, however, that such regulations can be circumvented. At his suggestion, I asked for the crop summary report at the very next bureau project I visited. Wheat farming occupied more than 22 percent of the total acreage. Only alfalfa hay was using more of the irrigated lands.[38] As I write this, I have before me a clipping from the New York *Times* that says the wheat surplus is as bad as ever.[39]

Studying America's water policy—or rather, lack of it—is somewhat like sitting next to the dormouse at the famous tea-party. For brief moments, the arguments and discussions appear as though they might be about to make sense. Then they drift off again into a wonderland logic all their own in which we are building canals to drain an area like the Everglades that we are asking another agency to keep intact. Or we are constructing dams to sell electricity to subsidize pumping more water from a river than the river has in order to irrigate land that may be used to raise surplus crops.

Any attempt to restore order to our water policy will most certainly meet strong opposition. Too many vested interests stand in the way. But it could be done if the American people as a whole decided they wanted it done.

Several solutions could be found. One logical step would be to remove the civil works functions of the Corps of Engineers from the army's jurisdiction and place them in a civilian agency where they belong. But I am not sure they should be combined with those of the Bureau of Reclamation and placed in the Department of the Interior. That would create a giant capable of gobbling up the whole department. The problem with both agencies is that they have limited basic purposes and responsibilities but heavy economic impact, directly and indirectly. Thus the Bureau of Reclamation fundamentally can only build dams and dig canals, but its actions can affect a whole region, both through its expenditures on construction and the results that it achieves. But it cannot perpetuate itself unless it continues to build dams, so like any other government agency in a similar situation, it will continue to build dams as long as there are rivers that still can be dammed. Perhaps its excellent engineering skills should be combined with those of the corps in a new Agency of Public Works with this provision—that the new agency could initiate no projects by itself and could act only as a servant of other depart-

ments of government that need its assistance. Authority for formulating an overall water policy could be vested in the Secretary
of the Interior; and particularly if that department is converted
into a Department of Natural Resources as some desire, he could
be given veto power over any project he believed would adversely
affect the environment. He would also make decisions on flood
control and recreation and receive recommendations on irrigation from the Secretary of Agriculture, on rivers and harbors
navigation from the Secretary of Transportation, and on power
from the Federal Power Commission.

There are certainly many other ways that the problem could
be solved effectively, but basic to any solution is an attitude of
nationalism, rather than sectionalism, toward the use of our
waters. Do the Everglades really belong to the State of Florida
or to the American people? Does the Grand Canyon and the
river that carved it really belong to the State of Arizona or to
the people as a whole? Are not some of the great natural wonders
and resources of this nation the possession of all the people, not
just a small part of them? Too often, each individual, each industry, each town and county, each state and region is out to get
what it considers its own for fear that someone else might get it
first—and without consideration for a balanced country as a
whole. That may be the way to make a short-run profit, but it is
not the way to build a nation. The sectionalism and the parochialism that pervade conservation questions is nowhere more evident than in our handling of the water resources of the United
States. The subject also provides a clear example of our lack of
overall planning and the great danger of one-purpose agencies.
We cannot solve conservation problems by looking at them from
a single point of view. That lesson has been made abundantly
clear to us again and again, and our experience with the dam
builders once more emphasizes this point. Why are we unable
to learn this?

4

No Stopping Except for Emergency

W E had spent the night at Chambers Lake, high in the mountains of Colorado, and had then crossed Cameron Pass and dropped to the plains on the other side. On the outskirts of Walden, Colorado, the road came to the head of a T, and we had to turn either right or left. There were no signs and nobody to direct us, so after studying the map, we turned to the right and in a few minutes had left the town and were surrounded by the sage of the cattle country. Ahead was a range of mountains that lay like an impenetrable barrier. Nothing on our map showed such an obstacle, and we began to suspect we had chosen the wrong turning. But there was no one to ask. We had not passed another car the entire time; and although we could see for miles in the clear air, we could not locate a single ranch house. In the distance, I had noticed through a break in a ridge a wide stretch of river bottom, and any nearby ranch would probably be located close to the water. Before we could make up our minds whether to continue in search of information or return to Walden, the first car we had seen came down the road. There was no need to hail them. With typical Western courtesy, they stopped without being flagged down and confirmed our thought that we had made a mistake.

On our return to Walden, we again did not see another car, and even after we were once more on the main route, we passed only a few. Traffic could not be heavy, for the country was dominated by large ranches. The range of one ran for miles on both sides of the highway, and at the entrance to another, a small sign indicated that the ranch house was eight miles down the private roadway. Apparently visitors in search of it had sometimes despaired of finding it because of the distance. After passing through another small town, we entered a little valley, a colorful place of bright red hills, yellow flowers, and gray-green sage with purple hills in the distance. To add to our pleasure, the place was so remote that the only traffic on the road was an occasional pickup truck belonging to a rancher.

Then ahead, we saw a flagman signaling us to slow down because of construction, except we soon realized it was not a flagman, but a flagwoman, a handsome Indian. There was probably a washout, I thought to myself, or some other local repair. Then I noticed on either side of the road, silhouetted against the clear sky, gigantic earth-moving equipment, more than was needed for any minor improvement. Drawing closer, we noticed an ugly scar crossing our quiet road, and we knew what was happening. In this distant valley, a major highway was being built, one of the many that have slashed the face of America with concrete and asphalt and steel trestles and cloverleafs.

The signs of it are everywhere. The visitor to Waterbury, Connecticut, is amazed to discover that large sections of the town are engulfed in a network of overpasses. A traveler to Norwalk, Connecticut, in the summer of 1969 would have found that the center of the town looked as though it had been bombed by one of the raids going over North Vietnam. Acres and acres of naked dirt lay on a site once occupied by some low-value houses but also by a few dating back to the eighteenth century as well as some fine examples of the best of the Victorian era. Because there are so few of these houses left, real estate agents tell me they command premium prices, if they have been properly restored. But Norwalk had not been subjected to an air attack. The highway department was simply building a connection between two routes.

Portland, Oregon, commands one of the finest sites of any city in the United States, with its harbor, the Willamette River, the hills behind it, and Mount Hood in the distance. But the freeways arch above it like strings of spaghetti, twirling off in every direction. At least when I was there, it was hardly possible to locate any particular street below, because the signs only pointed to the next town that the exit might lead to. When occasionally I descended to get instructions from one of Portland's friendly and courteous citizens, I was always directed to "get on the freeway" but discovered it was almost impossible to find the right one. In Portland, I have covered more mileage trying to reach a simple destination than in any city I have ever visited, obtaining in the meanwhile a rather comprehensive view of the community over the guardrail.

Newcomers to New York had best leave their cars behind them. It requires first-hand knowledge and long experience to navigate the maze of highways and cloverleafs that take up so much space in that already overcrowded city. And the traveler can almost always be certain that at least one important sign will have been omitted from an important location. When I direct drivers from our house to La Guardia Airport, I always point out to them that first they will see signs saying NEW YORK AIRPORTS. Then they will come to one saying KENNEDY to the left. That is where they should be sure to turn right, even though they will see no sign saying so, or they will miss La Guardia, and it may be hours before they get back again.

Driving down the Owens Valley in California, I met little traffic, certainly not enough to cause the slightest concern or even to break the mood of that wonderful place. But as I passed over Dead Man Summit, there again was a concentration of construction equipment and the scars left by the preliminary preparations for another superhighway. In the New Mexican desert around Santa Rosa and Tucumcari, another four-lane highway, lined at night with the blazing lights of motels and gas stations, lies across the landscape. In the little town of Mack's Creek, Missouri, the bulldozers, when I was there, were piling up dirt for another four-lane highway. It was going through the backyards of some of the houses. In the Connecticut town in which I am now writing, the view from my room overlooks a road labeled a turnpike, but the name goes back to Revolutionary times, and the road itself is small, winding, and only two lanes wide. One of the environmental problems worrying the residents living on it is whether the town will widen it and cut down the trees that give the area much of its character.

In every corner of America, the highway builders are at work, in small hamlets and large cities, in the deserts and the forests, in heavily populated areas and those that are remote. For America is engaged in the greatest highway construction program of all time, one that profoundly affects our environment, our health, and our society. And like many such programs, it was started with no consideration of any of these factors but for reasons that were entirely unrelated to them.

On a July morning in 1919, a group of notables, including the Secretary of War and the Chief of Staff, gathered just south of the White House at a marker labeled Zero Milestone. They were conducting farewell ceremonies for an army convoy that was departing for San Francisco.

The army was being motorized, and the generals wished to call attention to the poor condition of the nation's roads. From the start, the journey was marred by difficulties. The first day the coupling broke on the Trailmobile Kitchen, and the magneto gave out on a truck. The next day some of the covered bridges on the route were too low for the trucks, brakes wore out, several trucks had difficulty climbing the steep grades, and another magneto collapsed. So it went the whole long, slow journey. In places, the trucks even broke through the road surfaces and had to be hauled out with tractors. Finally on September 6, the convoy arrived at its destination; and the army had proved two points. The equipment it used was faulty, and the roads of that time, if they were to be the principal means of military transport, needed improvement.

Probably by now the journey would have been forgotten except for a quirk of fate. One of the officers assigned to the convoy, an officer who welcomed the task after the tedious duty of demobilizing soldiers at Camp Meade, Maryland, later became President of the United States. Dwight D. Eisenhower never forgot his experiences on the trip he took in 1919; and when he became President he felt deeply and personally that the nation should undertake a mammoth highway-construction program.[1] On February 22, 1955, he sent a special message to Congress, requesting legislation to implement the recommendations of a special presidential commission. These called for a ten-year program of highway construction at a cost of $101 billion. A bill passed the Senate but failed in the House.[2] In his State of the Union Message of 1956, he again emphasized the need for a mammoth highway program; and this time, Congress passed the Federal Aid Highway Act, which President Eisenhower signed into law on June 29.

Commenting proudly on this achievement of his administration, he later gave these statistics: Completion of the program would require enough concrete to build eighty Hoover Dams or six sidewalks to the moon. Enough dirt would be moved to cover the entire State of Connecticut to a depth of two feet. The area finally paved would be large enough to park two-thirds of all the automobiles in the United States. It would be the largest peacetime construction project ever undertaken by any country. It would, he said, change the face of America more than any other single government action since the end of World War II.

He was correct particularly in that last statement, but the change may be for the worse, not the better. In his memoirs, he makes it clear that he carefully considered two aspects of the program: its potential impact on the economy by providing employment and opening up new areas to development and also the use of the highways in evacuating civilians in the event of an enemy attack. But he makes it equally clear that he did not consider alternate ways of moving people and goods (the word "railroad" does not even appear in the index of his book) or the effect on our total environment.[3] It may well be that these considerations should have outweighed those he did take into account.

To implement the program, a major change was made in the handling of federal tax monies. Until 1956, all highway-related excise taxes, like most other taxes, went into the government's general fund, and expenditures for highways were appropriated from that fund. Legislation enacted in 1956 completely altered this basic concept. From then on, the majority of highway-related excise taxes were diverted from the general fund and segregated in the newly created Highway Trust Fund to be used for building highways. Furthermore, some of these taxes were subsequently raised as much as 100 percent, and additional taxes were imposed.[4] One thing was certain. The federal highway program would not run out of money.

Once again, we had established a powerful, one-purpose agency—like the Corps of Engineers or the Bureau of Reclamation—with its own source of funds, and the future was clear. The more highways that were built, the more motorists would use them, and the more revenue they would produce. This would result in building even more highways and lessen the chances of developing alternate means of transportation.

By 1966, only ten years later, here was the program in which we found ourselves engaged as described by the U.S. Department of Commerce: "Construction of the 41,000-mile National System of Interstate and Defense Highways. Approximately half this mileage is now open to the public. The Federal Government cooperates with the States in the construction of this system and pays approximately 90 percent of its cost.

"The Federal-aid primary system of more than 265,000 miles. Here the States contribute approximately 50 percent of its improvement costs. These are main highways and arterial streets, most of them in the State highway systems.

"The 601,000-mile Federal-aid secondary system. About half of these are State highways; and the rest are county and local roads. The Federal Government likewise contributes 50 percent of the cost of these improvements. The Federal-aid primary and secondary systems include more than 38,000 miles of arterial

streets in urban areas." [5] The highway program was well under
way, and the end was not in sight.

President Eisenhower, in 1955, envisioned a ten-year program. In view of the politics involved in a construction project
of this magnitude, his estimate was unrealistic. Soon the deadline
for completion was 1972; and in August, 1968, President Johnson signed a bill that would extend the deadline until 1974. In
part, this extension was designed to compensate for rising construction costs. Instead of increasing the highway-related taxes,
the government thought it would be more politic to levy the taxes
at the same rate but over a longer period of time. But also in
part, the extension resulted from an enlarged highway program.
In the same bill, 1,500 more miles were added to the interstate
system (the House version called for 3,000 miles), and it authorized $12.3 billion in additional funds.[6] To this enormous amount
of money spent by the federal government must be added, of
course, the taxes levied by the states for highway construction
and maintenance. In the State of Connecticut, where I live, we
paid the usual four cents a gallon to the federal government and
seven cents to the state. In the summer of 1969, this was raised
to eight cents. This tiny state needed $10 million more for its
highways.[7] Generally speaking, the vast federal expenditures are
more than equaled by the states themselves.

Anyone who thinks that this gigantic undertaking will termi-
nate even in 1974 is a political innocent. With all that money
to spend, with all those jobs at stake, the engineers and the
politicians will between them devise ways to keep it going—
special high-speed highways, scenic and recreational roads, the
new ideas may be limitless. But already there is a growing questioning and uncertainty among many members of the general
public. The highway program, at least in the manner in which
it is now being operated, seems to be creating more problems
than it solves.

Rye, New York, is a quiet residential community of 15,000
people and is located on the edge of Long Island Sound within
commuting distance of New York. For years, its citizens have
devoted themselves to preserving the qualities that attracted them

away from the city in the first place; they have maintained facilities for boating; they have kept more than 20 percent of their limited land area as parks and bird sanctuaries, all of them open to the public; and what is more unusual, they have kept in public ownership more than 10,000 feet of their shoreline, thus giving any citizen access to the waters of Long Island Sound, something all too few towns can do.[8] In a region that is becoming increasingly urban, Rye remained an oasis.

Then Rye learned that it was slated for virtual destruction, not by an atomic bomb, although an atomic bomb would hardly have caused less damage to the essential character of the community, but by the dreams of the highway planners. Rye had been selected as the terminus for a proposed bridge across Long Island Sound.

Alarmed and agitated, the people of Rye began to take stock of the possible effects on their community, and here is what they found: The bridge would consume 2,000 feet of their coveted shoreline; its entrances and exits alone would occupy 120 acres within their small city limits;[9] $5 million worth of property would have to be destroyed, $5 million worth at the tax assessment valuation, not the market price;[10] one suggested location for the bridge would occasion loss of part of the Rye Town Park beach, which served four communities with a total population of 80,000 people; through their quiet community would roll each year almost 6 million automobiles and trucks, or approximately 400 automobiles and trucks for every resident; and much of what was not destroyed outright would be destroyed by the fumes and the noise.[11]

Indeed, the City of Rye as it was would be gone. In its place would stand an enormous steel and concrete structure, whose sole purpose would be the transportation of the ever-growing stream of automotive traffic that is slowly strangling America and destroying the nation's beauty and culture. For building a road is no longer a matter of laying down two lanes of paving; it is a major engineering task, consuming acre after acre of land and dollar after dollar of the public's money. The cost of the bridge alone was estimated at $130 million and that price did not include the approaches or the changes that would have to be made in the existing highways into which the bridge would feed.[12]

Furthermore, the consulting engineer whom the citizens hired to advise them stated: "These areas in the vicinity of the proposed bridge are residential in character, with some industry in areas beyond the immediate vicinity, and they are now served with adequate streets and arterial highways where required.

"The necessity for a vehicular crossing of the Sound via a bridge at the proposed location had not been supported by any public demand for its construction. In the past, ferries operated between points on Long Island and Westchester [the county in which Rye is located], but the demand was not very great and they were abandoned for lack of patronage." [13]

This proposal, which, as I write, is still being argued over, illustrates several dominant characteristics of the attitude of our highway builders: their determination to build, the high cost of their programs, the inadequate processes for the selection of routes, and the large amount of land they are consuming.

This latter characteristic should in itself be a worry to anyone concerned about the future face of America. As in the case of Rye, so much land can be taken by a highway that the nature of a community can be profoundly altered. Probably no other form of transportation is more inefficient in its use of space. This stems from the efforts of the builders to make the highways safer and, at the same time, susceptible to high-speed driving. These are commendable objectives, but the price for attaining them may be greater than we realize.

The recommended minimum widths of the rights-of-way for modern highways run from 150 feet for a two-lane highway without frontage roads to 300 feet for an eight-lane divided highway with frontage roads.[14] On a modern highway, a reasonable hour's drive is certainly 60 miles. The acreage required to make such a drive possible with a 300-foot right-of-way is approximately 2,184 acres. Compared with railroads, for example, this is a large amount of land over which to move passengers and freight. The Penn-Central Railroad, running through Connecticut from the New York line to the Rhode Island line, extends a length of 115.63 miles. To cover this route, it occupies 1,191 acres.[15] The Connecticut Turnpike, which more or less parellels it, extends 129 miles. It occupies 4,694 acres, not including entrances and exits,[16] a difference of more than 3,000 acres. In the heavily populated, popular shore area of Connecticut, that amount of land could provide much-needed open space and many opportunities for passive and active recreation. The complete trackage of the Penn-Central Railroad in Connecticut extends 713.31 miles and in its entirety occupies only 1,197 acres more than the one 129 miles of throughway. Yet its capacity is enormous. Within a single year, it has actually carried more than 86 million passengers and hauled more than 38 million tons of freight.[17] Obviously the railroad, especially at this time, cannot replace the highway system, but it certainly does provide an example of more effective use of land for transportation purposes.

But it is not only the car in motion that takes up land; it is also the car at rest. To park and store America's millions of automobiles requires miles of streets and acres of parking lots, most of them smears of black asphalt spread across the nation's landscape. They contain no trees, no soil, no architecture, no place for the water to seep into the ground, nothing of beauty or human significance; they are hard, empty blackness broken only by the white lines showing where each car should be placed. And in some suburban communities, they take up more space than the buildings they are designed to serve.

As every shopping center merchant knows, the desirability of a location is directly dependent on the availability and the convenience of parking space. There must be room to hold the cars of his customers, generally one car to each customer and not on a staggered basis. There must be room to hold them all at the peak hour. No one wants to shop where he cannot park and park easily. Marketing studies show that the average customer is reluctant to walk even the length of the shopping center.[18] If she stops at the grocery store at one end, she will not go to the bakery at the other end unless she can park there, too. Wherever an American goes, he must take his car with him. So when an architect draws the plans for a shopping center, he knows that the most important land use is for parking; he generally must provide more land for that one function alone than for the stores and the people who work in them or use them.

Nor is the need for parking space limited only to commercial organizations. Many churches in suburban communities now devote more land to the care of their parishioners' cars than they do to the worship of God, for it takes far more space to store the car than to pray. Civic organizations also require it. In spite of the unrecognized irony, the very group that meets to plan the town's future in terms of open space and beautification has to have room for its members to leave their automobiles.

Across the country, averages have been calculated for the number of parking spaces needed for each seat in a public auditorium. These vary considerably, depending on the locality, the usual attendance at the auditorium, and how likely it is to be filled to capacity. In general, they run from one parking space for every twenty seats up to one parking space for every three seats.[19] In actual practice, the higher number of parking spaces seems more common. Indeed, one town, whose zoning regulations prescribe that a parking space be provided for every five seats in an auditorium, discovered that this figure was unrealistic. What it required for its high school auditorium was actually one space for every two seats. Nor could the parking area be far removed from the building. A five-minute walk from the car to the auditorium was considered out of order.[20] In practice, this means that many parking lots cannot serve a double function. There must be one attached to each individual meeting hall or business center because people will not walk.

A few major cities have at least made an attempt to force the great mass of parked automobiles underground to get it off the streets and out of sight. Boston has built a large parking garage underneath its historic Common, leaving the surface still covered with trees and grass. At Pittsburgh's Mellon Square, modeled after a somewhat similar square in San Francisco, the cars enter the parking garage through relatively inconspicuous portals and then go down ramps through several levels underground. The ground surface is open space and fountains, a relief in the middle of a large city.

But many major cities have just thrown up their hands in

despair at the magnitude of the problem. On many of New York City's streets, the moving traffic cannot move because the parked cars and trucks block their passage. To handle residential parking, the city has adopted an "alternate side of the street" regulation. This simply means that parking is permitted on one side of the street on one day and on the other the next. Its purpose is to shake up the mass of cars at least once every twenty-four hours and to prevent cars from being deserted for weeks at a time. It also facilitates street cleaning. Every morning, in thousands of New York households, while the wife makes breakfast, the husband dashes down to the street and moves their car to the opposite side. He dashes—and that is part of the ritual—because if he does not arrive early, all the spaces may be taken and he will have to drive for blocks through the city on the time-consuming task of locating another place to leave his car. Thus his day always starts, not with concern for himself and his family, but with concern for his car. It provides him with his most important job on awakening every morning, and because so many other people are also keeping their cars on the streets and playing the same game, if he decides actually to use his car within the city, he will undoubtedly have difficulty finding a place to park at his destination.

But if some cities have given up trying to solve the problem, the suburban and rural communities have not. They still believe that room can, and must, be found for the endlessly growing stream of cars. Every merchant demands it; every professional man demands it. Without parking close at hand, the store goes bankrupt, the doctor loses patients, and the church, parishioners. Parking, in the society that we have created, is necessary to economic survival.

Yet the cost of providing space for it is enormous. Assuming the usual standards of an area 9 feet wide and 20 feet long in which to leave each car and a 24-foot wide driveway to get them in and out, it requires something over 11,000 square feet of land to park forty cars—11,000 square feet devoted to that one purpose alone and generally used only part of the time. This is usually expensive land, too, because of its proximity to the buildings that draw the traffic. How high that price can be, both in actual dollars and relative values, can be illustrated by the experience of one of Connecticut's shoreline towns.

The town is a semisuburban community located on Long Island Sound. Much of its population commutes regularly to New York City, but much of it works within the community itself or nearby. What draws the commuters, in addition to the town's outstanding schools and excellent library, is its fine recreational facilities. It has a large town beach and some years ago bought a country club whose members were offering it for sale. Thus the residents who want to play golf and tennis or go swimming and boating can do so in areas owned by the town. But because those facilities were becoming somewhat overtaxed, much thought was being given to enlarging them. Just offshore was one of the relatively few islands in Long Island Sound. Held by the same family for many generations, the island was undeveloped and served, almost, as another town park, for every summer it was used by hundreds of town residents who camped there, picnicked on its beaches, anchored their boats along its shores, or went fishing near the reef that extends from its eastern side. With the death of its owner, the island was offered to the town for the bargain price of $75,000, but at the moment, because of increasing educational costs and the need for other new town facilities, its government thought that amount of money could not be included in the budget. (Several years later, it regretted its decision and contracted to purchase the island from a new owner at a much higher price.) Shortly after its refusal to buy the island, the town—under pressure from its citizens—made a study of the adequacy of the parking space at one of its junior high schools. The town already had two schools with sufficient parking space for their auditoriums' capacities, but complaints had been received about this one. To bring it up to the standard the town considered adequate, 125 more parking spaces were needed to accommodate possible crowds without making them walk more than five minutes. The estimated cost of acquiring the land and preparing it? The sum of $111,600.[21]

That is typical of the choice facing America. The sum of $75,000 for an island that could be enjoyed by thousands of families for generations to come; the sum of $111,600 for a place to leave occasionally 125 cars whose owners will either not walk or not double up with other drivers. We face again the problem of purpose.

A high-speed highway leads from New York City down the center of Long Island. It was intended to provide fast, economical transportation to an area that was relatively remote even though geographically near the nation's largest city. Today a driver who is able to elude the police can move down its broad surface at 90 miles an hour—at some periods of the day. At others, he will average, if he's lucky, 5 miles an hour—somewhat slower than he could do on horseback. If an accident occurs, and accidents are not infrequent, he will average less than that. He will be brought down to walking speed—if he moves at all, that is.[22]

Such conditions are not in the least unique. Los Angeles is noted for its numerous freeways; it is equally noted for the length of time required to get from one part of the city to another. On a few occasions when I have attempted to leave New York City on the eve of a holiday weekend, I have decided that it might be easier to escape from Alcatraz than from the city. If at moments the traffic approaches the speed of a man walking, the motorist sighs with relief. It is good to get moving again.

In Albuquerque, New Mexico, one day I happened to skirt the downtown section around the hour when the stores and offices were letting out their employees. A young girl stepped out of a doorway beside me, crossed the street, stopped to talk with a friend, and vanished around the corner two blocks ahead of me before I could reach it in a vehicle capable of going 80 miles an hour. As a form of transportation, automobiles are not only inefficient in their use of space; they are often extremely slow.

Building more highways, at least on the basis that we are now building them, is not the answer. Our recent history has demonstrated that. Particularly around our large cities, the more highways we build, the more traffic develops, and the greater become the snarls. One reason for this is expressed by the consulting engineer employed by the citizens of Rye. "Besides the normally expected increase," he said, "experience has shown that the opening of a new highway, bridge or tunnel tends to attract substantial traffic volumes which, prior to the construction of the new facility did not exist. This is known as 'Facility Increase' which, in the case of motor vehicle transportation facilities, has ranged from 10% to 200%." [23] In other words, the building of highways automatically and of itself creates additional automotive traffic.

It also can increase traffic by changing the nature of the communities it serves. The Long Island Expressway provides a case in point. When it was constructed, much of Nassau County was already fully developed. It cut through those municipalities, as one resident put it, like the Great Wall of China, bisecting them almost completely. Emerging at the eastern end of the county, it gave access to the once-rural village of Plainview. Light industries chose to settle there, and in ten years the population multiplied thirteen times. Twenty-five thousand more people now used the expressway as a principal access to New York City. And so it continued, as the expressway pushed itself across the countryside. Everywhere it went, it created additional traffic to ride over the six original lanes that are now probably impossible to expand sufficiently.[24] One transportation authority says that by 1985, it would be necessary to have a fifty-lane highway if the area continued to rely on automotive transportation to the extent that it now does.[25] It looks, consequently, as though the people of Long Island, like people in many other sections of the country, can look forward to traveling at five miles an hour for many years to come. Unless drastic changes occur, they will not move faster than their great-great-grandfathers.

Even on the open highway, where the cars can move quickly, they are not efficient in use of their passengers' time. The driver can do nothing but drive. He cannot sleep, he cannot read, he cannot listen to serious discussion on the radio, he cannot concentrate on his own thoughts. He can do little else except devote his attention to the manipulation of his automobile, keeping his eyes fixed on the ribbon of asphalt or concrete in front of him and on his mirror to prevent his being hit from the rear. His passengers fare somewhat better. At least they can sleep if they want to. They can engage in some serious thinking or discussion. And they may be able to look at the landscape, although that is

often difficult to do from the modern highway. It is too far distant from the right-of-way. Although it is now possible to drive
from Connecticut to Florida, for example, in approximately
twenty-four hours, those twenty-four hours are likely to be a
blank in the lives of the drivers. The total time lost this way
across the country must be enormous.

If automotive transportation is inefficient in its use of both
space and time, it can also be accused of endangering health and
even life. In testimony before a subcommittee of the Senate, Dr.
Arthur M. Bueche, a vice-president of the General Electric Company had this to say: "The U.S. Public Health Service has
pointed out that of the 133 million tons of 'aerial garbage'
dumped into the nation's atmosphere each year, an estimated
85 million tons—almost two-thirds of the total—comes from
sources under the general heading of transportation. I . . . have
mentioned our lack of definitive knowledge about which contaminants cause the most harm; therefore, it may not be fair to
say that two-thirds of our air *problems* come from the internal
combustion engine.

"However, in any case, it is safe to say that this engine—the
most-engineered product in human history—*is* a major problem
as well as being a key factor in our economy and our entire way
of living. (Incidentally, this is not just a problem in the car-
crammed United States. For example, the World Health Organization reports that no fewer than 50% of the motorists in Paris
are 'on the threshold of intoxication'—not from wine, but from
carbon monoxide.)

"One possible solution to the problem of the internal-combus-
tion engine is, of course, to keep on improving it, with great
emphasis on more complete combustion and cleaner exhausts.
You are familiar with efforts in this direction, although it is
generally acknowledged that even with the best of luck it may
only be possible to keep the present situation from getting worse.
In the long run, I believe we must look toward other ways to
convert chemical—or other kinds of energy—into mechanical
energy." [26] Other experts are even less optimistic than Dr.
Bueche. In 1966, one stated that unless the emission of pollutants

from automobiles could be reduced by 99 percent—he thought this unlikely—big cities would have to find a different propulsion system; [27] and another in 1967 said that air pollution by automobiles would be critical within ten or fifteen years unless active steps were taken now to handle the problem. [28]

Various attempts are being made to alleviate the problem. The federal government, while building more highways through one department, has passed legislation restricting the permissible emission from new cars and has spent small sums for research on more efficient engines. California, in parts of which the question has already reached critical proportions, has taken a lead in initiating legislation. The state is exempted from federal law in this respect and is allowed to set up its own even more stringent standards, which have often been adopted by the federal government for the use of the country as a whole. Whether these laws requiring better control of automotive pollutants will work well enough to confound the more pessimistic experts and give us clean air to breathe remains to be seen.

It can be argued, and has been, that the new highways increase the safety of driving. Yet recently, I was traveling on a divided highway near Washington, D.C. and saw four serious accidents in approximately that many miles. (Road conditions, I should add, were completely normal.) In 1967, to select a year at random, motor vehicle accidents cost the staggering sum of $10.7 billion—an amount far greater than the total natural resource items in the federal budget. An average of 225 people were killed every Saturday; and altogether, during the twelve-month period, 53,100 people met death in automotive accidents, and another 1.9 million were seriously injured. [29] The automobile, even with our new highways, does not provide us with safety.

These basic impracticalities in the use of both trucks and automobiles that I have outlined are so great they should give us pause. Certainly in the future it is likely that we will be forced to find supplemental forms of transportation of quite a different nature, for the automobile, as we now know it, is in many respects already out of date. The only reason we do not recognize this fact is that we have spent so little energy and money in a search for a substitute and therefore, seeing no substitute at hand, do not believe there is one. In the meanwhile, we continue to spend billions of dollars of federal and state funds each year on the construction and maintenance of highways that do as much to aggravate the problem as they do to solve it. Furthermore, the routes are laid out with little overall consideration of their impact on the regions through which they pass.

When he signed the 1968 highway bill, President Johnson rightly praised many of its features. It provided more assistance to people dislocated by highway construction; it permitted the advance acquisition of rights-of-way to reduce land speculation and local disruption; and it contained provisions to experiment with parking facilities on the outskirts of heavily congested areas. But he was also severely critical of some of its other provisions. It lessened the protection afforded small parks and privately owned conservation lands, and it extended the interstate system by 1,500 miles without adequate studies of the routes needed.[30]

These criticisms were well taken. In their haste to create more roads, the highway builders have isolated themselves from modern social and environmental questions. Their attitude toward the selection of routes belongs more to the 1920's when automobiles were few and life was simpler, than it does to the 1960's, when conditions have grown unbelievably complex. Old-fashioned in both their training and their outlook, the highway builders still seem to predicate their choices of routes on three limited concepts developed in the early days of the automobile: the shortest distance between two given points, the expense of building on a particular terrain, and the cost of the land itself. Taken in combination, these three factors affect the cost of each mile of the highway, and on this basis they are defended by the builders. But they completely overlook many other factors that may, in the end, prove far more expensive; and they lead to choices of routes that in this day of growing awareness of our environment are incredibly behind the times. Much of the trouble comes from the concept of low-cost land.

Parks, wilderness areas, privately held conservation preserves, and other such lands retained in their natural state automatically become the targets of the road builders. They are cheaper in an

immediate dollar-and-cents sense than those used for other purposes, for there are no buildings to destroy. The temptations that
this undeveloped land raises can be illustrated by hundreds of
examples. In 1937, in California, there had been some doubts
about the authority of the highway builders to seize park land,
but those doubts were removed by the passage of specific legislation that stated: "The real property which the Department [of
Public Works] may acquire by eminent domain, or otherwise,
includes any property dedicated to park purposes, however it
may have been dedicated, when the commission has determined
by such resolution that such property is necessary for State highway purposes." The legislation gave the Highway Commission
absolute authority to enter any park lands that it wished. That
year also marked the start of the planning for the first expressway
in California, the Arroyo Seco Parkway in Los Angeles County,
which, by no coincidence, ran the length of a municipal park
of the same name.[31] Knowing these circumstances, the visitor
to California should not be surprised when he hears that the
Highway Commission seriously considered running freeways
through the state's magnificent redwood parks, a decision that
would have meant an irrevocable loss for this and succeeding
generations. (In this connection, it is also important to note that
much of those lands had been given to the state as the result of
private subscriptions of individuals interested in preserving them
and were accepted by the state in that spirit.)

California is not at all unique in this respect. In community
after community, citizens who care about the environment in
which they live are attempting to rally their fellows against routes
chosen by the highway builders. Here, for example, is a typical
letter sent out by a group in Columbus, Ohio, in the spring of
1966: "Citizens of Columbus will determine on May 3rd one of
the most important questions that has recently faced the city.

"This question is—shall the sole remaining scenic valley within
the city be preserved for the welfare of the present and the future
generations, or shall it be turned over to become one more
stretch of concrete designed primarily to save a few seconds in
traveling time.

"If you vote *against* the ordinance, this beautiful valley will remain as an asset to our people. If the vote is otherwise, its beauty will, within a short time, be forever destroyed. One has only to look at what has happened during the past ten years to the part of this highway south of Henderson Road to visualize the future. The highway men destroyed forever an invaluable beauty spot." [32]

For a time, it appeared that the citizens' group might prevail and that the valley would be preserved for the present and future benefit of the people of Columbus. But the downtown merchants saw a threat to their cash registers in the absence of such a highway and launched a last-minute, but effective, campaign. On May 3, when the voters went to the polls, the ordinance permitting the construction passed by a majority of 180 votes out of the total cast of 51,170.[33] If only 91 of those 180 people had changed their minds, Columbus, ten years from now, would probably be a far better place in which to live and work.

In New Haven, Connecticut, the citizens were either more effective or more lucky; but only the most determined resistance prevented the State Highway Department from pushing an enormous expressway to Hartford through one of the city's two principal parks. The department was so certain of victory that it even started construction before the issue was settled; and today a section of roadway pointing in that direction and ending nowhere remains as a monument to wasted tax money and the citizens' concern, while the main route now veers to the right.

To cite one more instance of this attitude toward the environment in selecting routes—on May 2, 1968, I was called to testify before a special meeting of the Planning and Zoning Commission of Weston, Connecticut, a community that is striving to preserve its residential character in a rapidly developing corner of the state. The State Highway Department, the town had discovered, was studying possible routes for another east-west highway, and one of the four under consideration ran through the Devil's Den Sanctuary of the Nature Conservancy. This tract was the generous gift of Miss Katherine Ordway, who has also endowed a permanent scientific research station on it, and it represents one of the largest undeveloped areas dedicated to the public interest in that general region. The highway representative spoke most forcibly about the need for advance planning and pointed out that the growing popularity of water recreation made important the construction of more highways in that part of the state. He failed to mention that Connecticut has one of the most tightly closed coastlines of any state I know. Public access is extremely limited even to residents of most shoreline towns. If only some of the money the state has spent on highways had gone into coastland acquisition, Connecticut would have an extremely significant esthetic and recreational asset. Nor could the highway representative seem to understand that the preservation of open space in crowded areas is as much—if not more—a part of intelligent advance-planning as setting out highway routes.

This single-mindedness of purpose and concentration on low-cost land also attracts highway departments to historic sites like so many flies to a pot of honey. Like parks and other open space, historic sites are generally underdeveloped in the commercial sense and therefore, from the highway departments' point of view, can be acquired at less expense. Thus the Highway Department of Louisiana proposed building an expressway through the old French Quarter in New Orleans. This section of the city, which was once allowed to decay, has over the years been the subject of an extensive campaign of restoration and is now one of the most charming and historically interesting features of any American city. This made no difference to the highway builders, who would have destroyed its character with a throughway to be known by the romantic name of Riverfront-Elysian Fields Expressway. After a long battle, Secretary of Transportation Volpe vetoed the route.

Even the most venerable historic sites are not immune from the attack. No building in this country is more sacred historically than Independence Hall, where the Declaration of Independence, the Articles of Confederation, and the American Constitution were all signed. The Pennsylvania Highway Department did not quite envision tearing it down, but it did propose pushing the Delaware Expressway through the historic section of Philadelphia, thus cutting off Independence Hall from Penn's Landing and the Delaware River and leaving visitors to the building exposed to the roar of traffic. Two groups, the Philadelphia Architects Committee and the Committee to Preserve Philadelphia's Historic Gateway, joined in opposition to this display of poor taste. As a result of their efforts, the highway is out of sight.

The invasion of park lands and historic sites by highway departments is tragic. Even more tragic is the invasion of low-cost housing areas. In most of our cities, the least expensive land is obviously where the poorest families live. Therefore it is their homes and businesses that are demolished by the highway builders. In February, 1969, residents of North Tarrytown and of Ossining, both in New York State, filed suit to protect the buildings in which they live and work. The Hudson River Expressway was designed to pass through the black and Puerto Rican sections of both of those towns. The lawsuit pointed out there was no other place in the two communities where these groups could afford to live.

Or take, among many others, the sad case of Nashville, Tennessee. Although North Nashville had been declared a model city, is also lay in the way of a proposed expressway. According to one economist who studied the problem, construction of the highway would wipe out 80 percent of the black businesses in Davidson County either by actual demolition or by cutting them off from their regular customers. An organization of moderates, concerned over the human tragedy and anxious about the possibility of increased racial tension, asked the Supreme Court for an injunction. Although the Supreme Court did order the case heard on its merit by the District Court, it turned down the plea for an injunction. Within two hours after its decision, the bulldozers were out. As the Attorney General of Tennessee remarked to a newspaper reporter, it was the state's responsibility to take the cheapest land available.[34]

As the numerous ill-effects of our highway program are becoming more and more evident, efforts have been made to regain control of the highway builders. In his Natural Beauty Message of 1965, President Johnson summarized the problem by saying, "The roads themselves must reflect in location and design, increased respect for the natural and social integrity and unity of the landscape and communities through which they pass." [35] It is unfortunate that this point did not receive greater attention before; but although it is too late to repair much of the damage already done, it may be possible to prevent even more from taking place.

Congress has enacted various legislation like the Historic Sites Act of 1966, the Highway Beautification Act of 1965, and, in a major move, has created the Department of Transportation. This places the Bureau of Public Roads in a department and under a secretary who has responsibility for all forms of transportation. Against the vigorous protests of highway departments and state governors, the Department of Transportation has attempted to establish new rulings requiring more extensive hearings concerning proposed routes in order to provide more general discussion of the many factors to be considered.

Like the Johnson Administration, the Nixon Administration has also recognized the need for developing alternate forms of transportation; and on August 7, 1969, the President sent a message to Congress in which he stated: "We cannot meet future needs by concentrating development on just one means of transportation. We must have a truly balanced system. Only when automobile transportation is complemented by adequate public transportation can we meet these needs." He ended his message with the rather obvious remark that a nation that can send men to the moon should be able to provide better transportation within its cities.[36]

Unfortunately the President's goals were far short of the country's requirements. He proposed the expenditure of $10 billion out of the government's general funds over a period of twelve years to improve public transportation, with $500 million of this amount set aside for research. We would never have reached the moon with that size effort, and it represents approximately 10 percent of what we are spending on highways. With this sort of approach, not much hope exists for a successful reformation of our transportation system, but at least the message expressed realization that the problem does exist.

There have been other hopeful signs. In 1968, Secretary of Agriculture Freeman resisted the pressure of the Colorado Highway Department and refused them permission to build Interstate

NO STOPPING EXCEPT FOR EMERGENCY · 117

70 through the Gore Range-Eagle's Nest Primitive Area.[37] New York City, following the lead of San Francisco which has a long and enviable record of opposing expressways, has dropped plans for two major throughways.[38] It is especially significant that Mayor Lindsay took this action during a campaign year when he was desperately trying to retain his office. A federal judge has held that the Corps of Engineers exceeded its authority in constructing dikes for the Hudson River Expressway without the approval of Congress or the Secretary of Transportation.[39] When government is not acting of its own accord, citizens' groups are being formed and becoming more and more effective. But the struggle is far from over, and the highway lobby is strong. So much is at stake: the manufacture of trucks, automobiles, gasoline and construction materials, the sale of services at restaurants, motels, and service stations, and the labor required to build cars and highways. The amount of business generated by our highway program is so enormous that the lobby has been termed one of the most powerful, if not the most powerful, in the country.

There are, however, steps that can be taken to restrain this program and bring it back into some sort of national perspective. The first, and most important, of these is for the American people to realize what they are doing to themselves and to their land. They must understand that in the cities the cry against a white man's road in black men's bedrooms has real validity and that parks and historic areas are a heritage not to be squandered. They must recognize that in the country for each highway gained something else has to be surrendered, and they should be sure they comprehend the exchange of values. Once they have done this, they will have the strength to demand of their political leaders certain needed changes.

One of their most important demands should be the abolition of the Highway Trust Fund. User-related taxes appear logical, but they often have a pernicious effect because they provide an agency of government with its own source of funds. Although still subject to the control of Congress, the funds cannot be used for some other purpose. Thus their expenditure is not weighed against the nation's needs. Also the agency can blandly reply to its critics that it is self-supporting, when actually it is not. The money that goes into the Highway Trust Fund comes directly out of the public's pocket like any other taxes and reduces the public's ability to assume additional tax burdens; and as more highways are built, the public has less and less chance to resort to an alternate form of transportation. Thus the whole operation becomes a closed circuit, feeding on itself. Funds derived from highway-related taxes should go into the general fund of the government. Appropriations for highways should come out of the general fund, so they will be more visible. Furthermore, no state should be permitted federal highway aid that does not follow the same procedure.

The people should also insist on significantly greater research in the field of transportation. Because of our obsession with automobiles and airplanes, we have given little consideration to many possible alternatives. Our railroads are decrepit and in a decaying state. They should not be judged in their present condition, operating with out-of-date equipment and roadbeds, but as they could be with liberal infusions of money and new ideas. Some cities are establishing busways, lanes that can be used only by buses during rush hours. Because the buses will be able to move faster than the traffic-jammed automobiles, the planners hope to encourage greater use of public transportation and to make it more convenient.[40] Numerous ideas have been proposed, some of them envisioning monorails, others modern trolley systems, and still other pleasanter and more effective underground transportation. The possibilities are many; and if we diverted some of the funds we now spend on our highways, we could duplicate the effort that we have spent on space travel and perhaps come up with equally astonishing results. Certainly it should not be beyond American ingenuity to develop a fast, economical, safe, and fume-free transportation system, offering far greater convenience than what we have now.

Government should also be persuaded that more factors must be considered whenever a new highway is proposed. We have grown too sophisticated to ignore, as we have done in the past, the social, economic, cultural, historic, and esthetic impacts of a road. Many times these values should take precedence over the lesser one of moving people by a system that will probably be outdated before long.

Most of all, government must regard automobiles and trucks with broader perspective. Automobiles are not likely to disappear from the scene in the next few years. They have uses, mostly for short-haul, individual transportation in less densely populated areas and for long-haul trips at leisurely paces. But there are limits to their practical use. Within this context, a better transportation program could be planned.

And the American people, too, must make some decisions of their own. They must accept as a demonstrated fact that private automobiles are not practical within our major cities. New York City without them might just possibly become livable again, with less noise, less pollution, less congestion, and faster and more efficient transportation.

They must also content themselves with slightly slower driving speeds when they do use their automobiles on open highways. We cannot devote so much of our natural resources merely to decreasing our travel time a few hours here and there. In addition, they must accept somewhat smaller, rather than larger, cars. Because as the highways have grown more crowded, the cars have tended to become bigger and bigger (most of the extra space is not especially usable), and small roads can no longer accommodate them. This one step would do much to alleviate parking congestion, traffic jams, and the need for widening some of our existing streets and highways.

As a nation, we have become mesmerized by automobiles. They have dominated our lives in a way that their inventors could never have imagined. If we truly desire a higher quality of living, better use of our land, and purer air to breathe, the time has come to shake ourselves out of this trance.

Along many of our major highways appear standard signs reading NO STOPPING EXCEPT FOR EMERGENCY. Since 1956, that has been the slogan of the highway builders. Perhaps now the emergency has arrived.

5

The Affluent Deterioration

THE ugly landing strip that we saw from Ranger Miele's plane symbolized much that is poor about the quality of American living, even the lives of those with comparative wealth. In spite of our affluence—and in part because of it—none of us is protected from the rapid deterioration of our surroundings; and although an official of the Dade County Airport caustically dismissed the protesting conservationists as "butterfly chasers," [1] the reverse may be closer to the truth. Those who think only in terms of economic development through technological progress may be the persons chasing butterflies—and nonexistent ones at that. The better life (often spelled with capitals) they are constantly seeking may eventually evade them altogether and leave all of us sitting on a dump heap built from the remnants of their shattered dreams. In fact, this has almost happened already.

Practical people like this often oversimplify. Thoroughly pragmatic in their approach to problems, they usually take actions they believe will lead toward limited and practical objectives; but often those actions have far-reaching consequences that are overlooked or raise questions that are ignored. The proposal to convert a 38-square mile tract of the Big Cypress Swamp into an airport is typical. Only its size and dramatic location made it unique.

The problem of the airport—or the opportunity to construct one, whichever way you look at it—started back in New York, which did not have the capacity to handle the air traffic that it had generated. Long delays were frequently experienced by travelers taking off and landing there, and it was not unusual for overseas flights to be diverted far north to Bangor, Maine, for clearance by customs. The planes then went on their way to their domestic destinations in the United States, leaving space for a few more to squeeze themselves into New York.[2]

This overcrowding, combined with New York's failure to find a suitable site for a fourth major airport, provided Dade County with an opportunity for economic development. Its international airport was already becoming more and more popular. If it could accommodate the jumbo jets, it could take business away from New York and concentrate it in Florida. The amount of money at stake was large. Within a short time, according to one consulting firm, New York could lose flights having an economic value of about $53 million a year.[3] At least, that is what New York feared.

The plan developed by the Dade County Airport Authority was simplicity itself. Using $500,000 from the federal government, it would build the first landing strip and remove training flights from its existing airport. Since these accounted for 40 percent of its total traffic, this would leave it with surplus landing space, and it could start absorbing some of New York's traffic. If all went well, it could build additional facilities and become a major international airport with particular emphasis on planes from Central and South America, at the same time bidding for business from Europe. If all did not go that well, it had some smaller airports that could be enlarged to handle increased traffic, and it could sell off at a profit part of the 38 square miles it had bought. Nobody would be hurt except perhaps the people of New York, which did not have the space anyway, and the general taxpayer, who had put up the original money.

Underlying this approach was the commonly taken attitude that if air traffic exists, provision should be made to handle it.

This attitude was clearly reflected in a message sent to Congress by President Nixon in June, 1969: "The purpose of air transportation," he said, "is to save time. This purpose is not served when passengers must wait interminably in terminals; when modern jet aircraft creep at five miles per hour in a long line waiting for takeoff; when it takes longer to land than it takes to travel between cities; or when it takes longer for the air traveler to get to an airport than it does to fly to his destination. . . .

"The growth in the next decade must be made more orderly. It must be financed more fairly. It must be kept safe. And it must not permit congestion and inadequate facilities to defeat the basic purpose of transportation: to save time. . . .

"The ability to transport people and products by air—safely, surely and efficiently—is a national asset of great value and an international imperative for trade and travel. . . .

"That ability is being challenged today by insufficiencies in our nation's airports and airways. The demand for aviation services is threatening to exceed the capacity of our civil aviation system. . . . we simply do not have the capacity in our airways and airports ample to our present needs or reflective of the future." [4]

The President's proposed solution was as simple and direct as his statement of the problem. He pointed out that federal taxes were being levied on airplane tickets and aviation gasoline, but the revenues were not applied directly to airway expenditures. Therefore Congress should raise those taxes, levy some additional ones on air users, and place the money in a special fund to build more airports and make other improvements. In other words, do exactly what we have done with the highways—create special taxes to construct more facilities that will generate more taxes to build even more facilities.

The belief that we must without further question accommodate an apparent demand prevails throughout the country. In Raleigh, North Carolina, it led to a proposal to cut into a nearby state park to provide space for lengthening a runway; and at Martha's Vineyard, Massachusetts, it split the community in two. Some people wanted a larger airport to handle jets; others wished to retain the peaceful, remote character of the island. But it ignores two fundamental issues. How many airports can we afford, not only in terms of money but also in terms of our environment? And how many airports do we actually need?

The answer to the first issue is that we probably can afford as many airports as are necessary to provide a reasonably efficient and fast national transportation system. The answer to the second is more difficult to determine because we have, in effect, no national transportation policy. If we did, we might discover that our existing airports were quite sufficient.

For example, we have never adequately examined the problems posed by the increasing use of private planes and weighed them against the interests of the public as a whole. On July 3, 1968, Mohawk Airlines made a study of traffic at New York's La Guardia Airport. That day, 1,453 aircraft took off or landed. Of these, 899, or 62 percent, were commercial aircraft; the remainder, 38 percent, were privately owned. Of the 70,748 passengers arriving or leaving that day, the private planes carried only slightly more than 3,000, or about 5 percent of the total. Each of these planes, whether private or commercial, took the same amount of airspace and used the same amount of runway, taxiway, and ramp.[5] Our national policy (perhaps "non-policy" would be a better word) assumes that anyone has the right to operate a private plane even in the most congested metropolitan centers. Yet even setting aside considerations of safety—and they are great—does the public good justify this? Should the vast majority of New Yorkers, many of whom rarely or never take a plane at all, be forced to suffer from noisy, space-consuming airports to provide some slight additional convenience for the few, particularly when those few are selected without any rational reference to the social value of their work? It may well be that private planes should be excluded, not just from major airports, but from major areas and that passengers going to Chicago, New York, Los Angeles, and other large cities should use the commercial airlines just as everybody else does. To regain some 38 percent of the facilities of one of New York's three important airports would be a large saving.

We have also failed to study the airplane's role in the total transportation system. For much of the day, flights to and from

Washington and New York occur at least every half hour, taking up a large amount of the facilities of both cities. Yet the distance is not great and might better be traveled by some other form of transportation. The new train, the Metroliner, is certainly not the complete answer, but operating at higher speeds on a rebuilt roadbed, it might provide excellent and more dependable service and release some of our airway and landing space. We might also ask ourselves if first-class travel on airplanes, with all the room it occupies, is really necessary? On flights of eight hours or less, might it not be restricted to the old and the infirm?

Just as we should with our highway system, we must raise and answer these and other basic questions before we can even be certain that we are really short of airplane facilities. (In 1969, while the debate over the Dade County Airport was going on, the Civil Aeronautics Board granted two fare increases to the airlines. One reason for their poor earnings had been their purchase of more equipment than they needed.) It might well be that a realistic examination would show we have more than enough facilities already and that the scar on the face of southern Florida was not so much of a necessity as many people thought. And the last thing we should do is to continue to build more and more airports and consume more and more of the little remaining open space in the country without first making sure we really have to.

One of the objectionable by-products of airports—and of many other aspects of our affluence—is noise. To the casual traveler, in haste to be on his way, the sound of jets taking off or landing is something to be endured but only momentarily. The effect is unpleasant but not great. To those living or working nearby, however, the noise can be destructive.

We once lived in a community that was chosen as the site of a large airport. Fortunately, our house was so located that we heard the planes only on days when the wind was blowing in one special direction and certain runways were being used. But some of our friends were not so fortunate. It is no exaggeration to say that their houses were ruined as places to live. When a plane passed overhead, conversation came to a complete stop, their houses vibrated, and at night the landing lights blazed through the windows. People can exist under those conditions but not well. Many normal social activities, such as talking or listening to music, are practically impossible; and life without them becomes lower and lower in quality. Nor does continual exposure make the slightest difference. Noise is not something that a person can adjust to, as some federal officials have stated. If a conversation is interrupted once by the sound of a jet, no improvement occurs because it is interrupted ten times.

This also holds true of sonic booms. In 1964, the Federal Aviation Administration conducted tests at Oklahoma City, a favorable spot for such tests, because one-third of the population were making their living from the aviation industry. For six months, up to eight sonic booms rolled out over the city each day. At the end of the period, 27 percent of the residents said they could not have borne the experience if they had not known it was temporary; and the majority said that the noise was just as objectionable at the end of the test as it was in the beginning. Furthermore, a large number complained of damage to their houses, and one man won $10,000 in damages when he proved to the satisfaction of the courts that his house had been split in two.[6] Citizens near Kennedy Airport in New York threatened to shut it down by pushing baby carriages and shopping carts onto its runways or blocking them with automobiles.[7] And in Arizona, National Park Service engineers reported that 80 tons of rock cliff fell on an ancient cliff dwelling in Canyon del Muerto as a result of repeated sonic booms caused by military aircraft.[8]

Airplanes, of course, are not the only source of noise. The roar of automobiles and trucks has adversely affected the lives of thousands of homeowners living near major highways. Because of this, Connecticut has now entered into a contract with CBS Laboratories to develop equipment to permit the state to set up "noise traps" along the lines of speed traps.[9]

Air compressors, construction work, lawnmowers, chain saws, and even simple appliances like kitchen blenders all add to the total. Few communities are even prepared to meet the problem. Memphis, Tennessee, has won distinction as a town with strict

antinoise ordinances and strict enforcement. (In a year, the police department may give out as many as a thousand tickets for
illegal horn-blowing, and many cars fail to pass the municipal
inspection because of faulty mufflers.) [10] On the other hand,
New York City has been warned by an expert on ear ailments
that many of its noise levels are higher than those permitted in
factories; [11] and the community in which I am writing this, ordinarily a quiet, residential area, has been disturbed by a man
clearing a small tract of land for building lots. Having purchased
a rock outcropping, he has been blasting, hammering, and truck-
ing for some eight weeks. The resulting noise, even quite a distance off, sometimes makes ordinary conversation impossible at
a distance of more than five feet. The Municipal Health Department has no ordinances under which it can prevent such a person
from disrupting the lives of hundreds of people for personal gain.
For safety purposes, the community can regulate the size of the
charges used, but little else except the hours in which explosions
are permitted. That last restriction, while it helps many of us,
does not assist valuable citizens like nurses, doctors, policemen,
firemen, newsmen on morning newspapers, and others who work
much of the night and try to obtain some sleep during the noisy
days. Ironically, this community is now constructing a sewerage
system to help eliminate water pollution at the same time that
it permits noise pollution to continue unabated. This confused
situation is duplicated throughout the country.

Although we are doing so little to control noise pollution, the
Federal Council for Science and Technology said in 1968 that
it constitutes a major health hazard to the American people. The
danger to hearing has long been recognized, the council pointed
out in a report, but more and more investigators are beginning
to believe that the effects may be much broader—and more
serious—than previously recognized. Other functions of the body
may also be damaged.[12] In 1969 the American Medical Association held a two-day symposium on the subject. Most of the doctors agreed that, except for the effect on people's hearing, it was
difficult to determine what might happen to the rest of the body.
They warned that the damage might be far greater than previously supposed. Experts at the meeting spoke of the inadequacy

of present state and municipal legislation and pointed out that
the federal government was spending only a million dollars a
year on controlling noise. Most of that amount—compare it
with the cost of a single airplane runway—was being used on
occupational noise, which, although it should be controlled, affects relatively few people.[13]

Once more we come to the question of how much money are
we willing to spend on our environment and what else we are
willing to go without. Noise control costs money that no one
seems willing to spend. A leading acoustical research company
estimates that the noise of trucks could be greatly reduced—but
at $500 to $600 a truck.[14] Experts from the Department of Housing and Urban Development have concluded that it would require approximately $240 million to insulate properly the most
badly affected houses near Kennedy, Los Angeles, and O'Hare
airports—an amount that no one, including Congress, will advance.[15]

Yet the same Congress, expressing the will of the American
people, had authorized the expenditure of approximately $3
billion to develop the supersonic jet. (Probably the total cost
will end up greater than that.) The arrival of these planes,
spreading their booms across the country—because of protests
from more heavily populated areas, they will undoubtedly shat-
ter the silence of our few remaining quiet districts—will enable
the few of us who travel frequently to get there faster. But where
are all of us going? From worse to better? Or from better to
worse?

The early settlers in this country received from nature the gift
of quiet; we have destroyed it. They also received the gift of
clean, fresh water; we have destroyed that, too.

Each year some 30 inches of water fall on the United States,
either as rain or snow. Some 21 inches evaporate or are retained
by vegetation. The remaining 9 inches run over the surface or
underground toward the oceans and provide most of the water
that we use. Although it is unevenly distributed and although
some areas are troubled by cycles of surpluses and deficits, the
total amount is more than sufficient to meet our heavy demands.

According to an estimate made by the U.S. Geological Survey in 1958, we were not then using more than an inch. But, the survey pointed out, "much of the surface water, although available, is nearly or entirely unusable because it is polluted so heavily that it is expensive to treat." [16]

The extent of this pollution can be illustrated by a few examples. In 1940, an estimated 646,000 tons of sulphuric acid poured down the Monongahela River in Pennsylvania and into the Ohio River.[17] In 1966, the Merrimack, the beautiful river of Massachusetts and New Hampshire that Henry David Thoreau celebrated in his famous book, was dirty brown and dotted with bubbles of nauseating gases. Near Troy, New York, the once magnificent Hudson was so filled with raw sewage that only scavenger eels could live in its waters; the eels attacked the sanitary engineers who came to take samples. In places, the Missouri ran red with the blood from slaughterhouses, and down its surface floated large balls of grease.[18] By 1965, the gradual death of the Great Lakes from pollution—those lakes hold 20 percent of the world's fresh water—was being widely publicized; Detroit alone was pouring contaminants in them at the rate of 20 million pounds a day.[19] A final touch came in 1969, when Cleveland's Cuyahoga River, so polluted that it was often referred to as a fire hazard, actually did catch fire and caused some $50,000 worth of damage by partially burning two railroad bridges and melting their tracks.[20] As far as health was concerned, a task force established by the Department of Health, Education, and Welfare reported in 1967 that only slightly more than half America's population was drinking water that met federal standards; the remainder were drinking substandard water or water whose quality was unknown.[21]

The examples and dates that I have chosen seem to indicate that there has been no progress in cleansing America's waters. This is not entirely true. There has been some progress, but whether it has been commensurate with the accelerating size of the problem is uncertain.

Until 1948, as the nation's waters grew fouler and fouler, Congress left the question of water pollution up to the states and local communities just as it had left them to deal with flood control for so many years. This produced no solution for the obvious reason that the upstream communities had nothing to lose and everything to gain by allowing their sewage and industrial wastes to pour into the rivers and be carried away free of charge; and the downstream communities saw little reason to clean up a river that was already filthy by the time it had reached them and might by then be impractical to clean.

Realizing that water conditions were growing worse and worse, Congress passed the Water Pollution Control Act of 1948, an experimental measure limited to a trial period of five years.[22] Although the act was ultimately extended another three years, it did not in itself amount to much. The total appropriation to carry out its provisions in 1949 was only $125,000.[23] In subsequent years, various additional legislation was enacted, none of it adequate to solve what was becoming a more and more acute problem. In 1965, however, Congress took an important forward step. The Federal Water Quality Act passed that year provided that each state must establish quality standards for its interstate and coastal waters and draw up programs for reaching and enforcing those standards. These programs were to be submitted to the Secretary of the Interior by 1967. Should any state fail to do so, or should the standards established prove unsatisfactory, the secretary was empowered to establish standards of his own.[24] The act also provided for the Federal Water Pollution Control Administration in the Department of Health, Education, and Welfare, shortly thereafter transferred to the Department of the Interior. For the first time, the United States was really looking at its water pollution problem as a whole and attempting to set up uniform standards of control.

The following year, Congress passed another act, the Clean Waters Restoration Act of 1966, which provided financial grants for river-basin planning, liberalized federal grants for the construction of sewerage facilities, and contained other provisions to advance America's pure water program. Although these initial acts have since been amended, they have provided the basis for a comprehensive antipollution program.

Yet from the examples of pollution I have cited, it is obvious that the problem is still with us in spite of all the legislation enacted since 1948. Twenty-one years later, Lake Erie was still threatened. Lake Tahoe was filled with all sorts of undesirable growth and was turning from its original blue to green. Even the Potomac, flowing alongside the nation's capital and relatively free from industrial waste, was receiving a daily average of 240 million gallons of inadequately treated sewerage. Fish could not live in the 12-mile stretch of river between Georgetown and Mount Vernon. Government laboratory technicians reported to the American Health Association that the bacterial count was a hundred times too high to permit humans to swim in it, and an army microbiologist stated his opinion that there was potential danger in eating shellfish or fish taken downstream in the river.[25] Although everyone is talking about water pollution—there is as much talk about this as about any subject in conservation—the talk far outweighs the action.

The reason lies in economics. In 1966, James M. Quigley, then Commissioner of the Federal Water Pollution Control Administration, quoted Secretary Udall at a meeting of the Southern Governors' Conference. "The tragic condition of many of the waters of this country is a result of the economic fallacy that we cannot afford to control pollution," he reported the secretary as saying. "Today, there is a wide and growing realization that we cannot afford *not* to control pollution, that the effects of pollution are far more costly than its control.

"We will never know at what precise moment in history public opinion crosses that great divide—if, indeed, it has not already done so. Perhaps that moment comes when one too many kids finds no place to swim. Perhaps it comes when a hunter or conservationist sees one too many ducks lying helpless in a film of oil. Perhaps it comes with just one too many rationing orders for the people of a great city once richly endowed with clean water.

"The knowledge that water pollution is more costly than its control can be triggered in an endless number of ways. It can be triggered by the fact that an industry cannot locate where it would otherwise like to locate simply because there is not enough water of suitable quality for its purposes. Or it can be triggered by the fact that the trout have died in a favorite stream. The list can be stretched out almost indefinitely.

"However it has come about, there is no question in my mind that in ever increasing numbers the American people want the destruction of the Nation's waters to stop, and that given the facts, they will get behind any practicable means of doing so, regardless of cost." [26]

The divide about which Secretary Udall spoke in 1966 had not been crossed by 1969. Although everyone was talking against pollution, few were willing to pay the bill. One mining company on Lake Superior was still discharging 60,000 tons of ore waste into the lake every day and refusing to stop. The Federal Water Pollution Control Administration, handicapped by some of the limitations of the law, held abatement hearings but concluded that it would keep the situation under surveillance a while longer rather than attempt to go to court.[27] In October, 1969, four steel companies were charged with dumping an unwarranted amount of waste into Lake Erie, one of them by way of Cleveland's inflammable Cuyahoga River. One company arrogantly refused to provide information directly to the Federal Water Pollution Control Administration, claiming that it was conforming to an agreed-upon schedule and that the federal agency could obtain the information it wanted from the state authorities.[28] That same month, at a meeting held in Washington, 700 industrialists met with members of the Federal Water Control Administration. They made their point clear. Everyone of them was against water pollution—just as long as it did not cost too much. One company president, reaffirming his organization's interest in cleaner waters, said that it had to earn a profit first. An unidentified questioner challenged this statement by saying that antipollution measures should be considered an operating cost, not a deduction from profits. The president of the company admitted this was probably true, as it will most certainly be if the American people insist on it.[29] Too often the same industries that clog our airways with their private—and expensive planes—are the ones that lag behind in water pollution problems. They cannot find enough money to repair the damage they are doing.

In some respects, their case is a fair one because they are

simply following the example set over the years by the federal government. In the fall of 1969, the government announced a drive against polluters and scheduled a series of abatement proceedings. Using the sharpest terms, the Department of the Interior stated that it was weary of delays in the antipollution campaign and that from then on the polluters would have to act more quickly.[30] As it made this announcement, the government's own program was falling apart—and for the same reason, lack of funds.

In 1966, a subcommittee of the Senate Committee on Public Works reported: "A careful analysis of the various estimates in the hearings and information provided by experts in the Department of Health, Education, and Welfare indicates that the cost of meeting our treatment plant construction needs by 1972 would be at least $20 billion.

"The Federal grant program for sewerage treatment is nowhere near an appropriate level to help communities meet their needs." [31] To solve the $20-billion problem, Congress for that year had authorized the expenditure of $150 million (or approximately the estimated cost of the proposed high-speed transportation system from Miami to its airport). Then Congress appropriated $7 million less than that. For the following year, it had authorized another $150 million and actually, because of certain provisions then in the law, spent $23 million more than that amount. For 1968, the authorization stood at $450 million.[32] President Johnson, a vocal supporter of antipollution measures, thought this amount was too much. He asked for $200 million. Senator Edmund S. Muskie of Maine, who takes water pollution problems seriously and realistically, quickly replied that "many states would not receive a sufficient amount in fiscal year 1968 even if the full $450 million were to be appropriated. For example, the state of New York . . . which has an estimated cost of $1.7 billion to clean up their backlog, would only receive $37 million in 1968. In New York City alone, information . . . indicates $179,585,532 will be spent in 1968.

"Therefore, even if all New York's money were allocated to New York City, that city would receive a little over 20% of its cost." Under the law, it was entitled to 40 or perhaps 50 percent.

Congressman John A. Blatnik of Minnesota, chairman of the House subcommittee dealing with water pollution, was equally infuriated and disillusioned. He pointed out that the authorized figure had been decided after long work and represented the absolute minimum necessary. Now the administration was requesting that it be cut by more than a half.[33]

Congress rebelled against the President's request. It added all of $3 million to bring the total up to $203 million as against the authorization of $450 million.

For the fiscal year 1969, the authorization was $700 million. (The authorizations had been worked out to provide an orderly, although minimal, program for combatting pollution.) Congress appropriated a little more than in the preceding year—$214 million.[34] By then the federal government's program was floundering. According to the original schedule, the amounts appropriated for grants for the construction of treatment plants should have totaled $1.55 billion. But they had amounted to less than half that.

As authorized by Congress, the grants for building treatment facilities were to reach a high of a billion dollars for the fiscal year 1970. President Nixon had other ideas, however. His budget recommended that the amount remain the same as the previous year's—$214 million. This would have been the practical end of the federal government's program. By then the Federal Water Pollution Control Administration had a backlog of applications amounting to more than $2 billion. An appropriation amounting to approximately 9 percent of that sum was meaningless. Some of the members of the House made their sentiments known. After all the years they had spent trying to improve our rivers and lakes, they were not ready to abandon the effort. Under the pressure they created, the Nixon Administration began to negotiate. In Washington, various figures were rumored as being acceptable to the administration. The one that finally emerged was just 60 percent of the authorization. A bipartisan group of Congressmen rallied the support of conservationists in an attempt to secure the full billion dollars authorized. By hard work, they secured pledges from more than 200 representatives—a majority of the House—to stand with them. When the bill came to the floor, Representative William E. Minshall of Ohio offered an amendment to raise the appropriation to the full authorization. After debate, the House took a teller vote in which the members walk by the tellers to be counted but in which no record is kept of their names. Something had affected the members who had pledged to remain firm. The amendment was defeated by two votes. Another amendment to hold the amount at $750 million was also defeated,[35] although later the Senate raised the figure to $800 million, an amount still short of the authorization.

Representative Lowell Weicker, Jr., from Connecticut described the situation well when he reported to his constituents: "We lost in our efforts to provide the $1 billion for a total attack on the pollution that is destroying our rivers, streams, lakes, bays and oceans. But the real losers were the future generations who will inherit an unusable Long Island Sound.

"It is tragic," he continued, "that politicians find it easy to endorse conservation at election time, but when it comes to appropriating the large sums of money that are needed for an all out attack on pollution, they suddenly lose their voices. Merely paying lip service to clean water, clean air and conservation of our resources is not going to preserve our environment. Action programs backed by money must replace good intentions." [36] Connecticut is one of the states that had moved ahead with a comprehensive water program; but although it was investing liberal amounts of its own funds raised by a bond issue, it needed the federal grants. As the Director of the State Water Resources Commission wryly commented, "All you get from Washington is talk." [37]

No amount of harsh comments will remedy water pollution in the United States. Two days before the amendment to appropriate the full authorization was defeated in the House, an official of the Federal Water Pollution Control Administration was speaking to an audience at Dallas, Texas. He told them that the federal government intended to be stricter in the enforcement of the water quality regulations and said that complaints about delays in federal assistance were often merely excuses for inaction. One state, he said, did not even have the funds to match the federal grant.

An entirely different point of view was expressed to the Senate several years ago by Hugh Mields, Jr., of the U.S. Conference of Mayors. "Some communities," he said, "simply do not have the money nor the prospect of raising the money to install the expensive plants which are required to meet abatement schedules established under Federal enforcement proceedings. A city which has lost its taxpaying, job-producing industries lacks the tax base required to finance such construction. Court action against the mayor will not clean up pollution. A treatment plant will." [38] And treatment plants cost money that Americans are not willing to spend.

This parsimonious attitude still existed in 1970. Although Congress had finally raised the appropriation for water pollution abatement to $800 million, the President was not legally compelled to spend the full amount and was hesitant about doing so. Not until many weeks had passed and he had finally realized that conservation and the environment are major campaign issues did he announce his intention of abiding by the wishes of Congress. In addition, he produced his own program, which he proclaimed a $10-billion one. But as so often happens with conservation measures, the rhetoric was greater than the substance. Of the $10 billion, only $4 billion was to be spent by the federal government. The remainder was to be borne by the states, many of which were already overburdened financially. And the federal government's $4 billion was not to be spent right away. It was to be spread over such a long period of time that the actual appropriation for the fiscal year 1971 would amount to only $40 million, compared to almost $30 million requested by the Pentagon for a single year's public relations budget. In spite of all the words that accompanied the presentation of this program, the thinking of the administration was clear: Water pollution abatement held an extraordinarily low priority and the cost of it would be left for the future. Cash outlays for more highways, but not for clean water; the old distorted values of the past were not to be changed.

This measure was to be coupled with a continuance of piecemeal legal action against individual industrial polluters, action that has not proved especially effective in the past. No wonder that in early 1970 many members of Congress despaired of ever restoring to America the clean waters that were once this nation's heritage.

If we have failed so badly in our program to build sewerage treatment plants, it is not surprising to find that other aspects of our battle against water pollution, such as the construction of storm sewers, are not doing much better. Abatement of water pollution is a popular issue at election time (no one votes for foul water), and it has been the subject of many stirring presidential pronouncements; but the talk has been considerably greater than the action. Every time Congress is called upon to vote an actual appropriation for the control of pollution, it cannot bring itself to provide the necessary money. The original authorizations, although they represented what many thought was a minimum, have not been met; and the words "water pollution control" have become more of a politicians' phrase than a reality.

Our efforts to end air pollution have run a parallel course. Everyone knows about air pollution, and no one likes it. Even without dramatic incidents such as the tragic deaths of seventeen persons in Donora, Pennsylvania, within a single four-day period of intensive smog, everyone who lives in or near a big city—and many who live in rural areas—are aware of air pollution. There is nothing obscure about it. Daily they see it, feel it, and breathe it. And they do not like it.

They may be people living in New York City, where the normal cost of air pollution in lost working time because of pollution-related illness and in extra painting and cleaning averages $620 a family, according to a study made by the state.[39] They may be the residents near Garrison, Montana, who complained about the fluoride gases poured into the air from a phosphate plant.[40] They may be farmers whose crops have been ruined by air pollution. A symposium held by the American Association for the Advancement of Science in 1966 found that in some parts of the United States air pollution was a greater agricultural hazard than weather or insects.[41] They may be the citizens of the quiet Delaware town of Selbyville, who bitterly protested against the odors coming from a nearby processing plant. The smell was so bad it made some of them actually vomit.[42] Or they may be persons living in the northern portion of Staten Island, New York, where a study made by the U.S. Public Health Service in 1967 indicated a close relationship between air pollution and a high incidence of death from lung cancer.[43] The only beneficiaries of air pollution I have ever heard about are the moonshiners of Ohio. The official in charge of enforcing the state's liquor laws says the stills that used to operate in the country are now being set up in urban areas, where the odor of the smog helps to cover up the smell of fermenting mash.[44]

Setting aside economic and esthetic considerations, our health alone should give us great concern about air pollution. Much remains to be learned about the relationship between various diseases and the contaminants in the air, and the experts often disagree on what causes what and to how great a degree. Nevertheless, the Senate's Committee on Public Works minced no words when it reported on the problem in 1967. "From the standpoint of public health," the committee stated, "the information available concerning the acute air pollution episodes that have occurred and the laboratory evidence of the effects of exposure to various pollutants that are in the air puts an exclamation mark by the word 'urgency' in relation to this problem.

"In any given instance, there may be several reasons why a particular situation may result in chronic disease. But there is no question that the pollutants in the air are contributing factors to the chronic respiratory diseases, lung cancer, emphysema, bronchitis, and asthma. When considering mortality in this country, it is this group that is showing a rapid rise as a cause of death and disability. These subtler, less dramatic long-range effects of air pollution are of much more serious consequence to the population as a whole than the occasional major tragedy." [45]

Because air is not a static element of our environment but moves from community to community and has no respect for state lines, the control of air pollution must eventually lie in the hands of the federal government. Realizing this, Congress in

1955 finally enacted its first air pollution legislation. The act considered air pollution primarily a local and state problem, but it did recognize that the federal government, too, had a responsibility. This, rather than the weak provisions of the measure, represented its principal significance.

In 1963, Congress increased the federal government's role with the passage of the Clean Air Act. Although still expressing the view that air pollution was fundamentally a local and state problem, the bill authorized a "broad program" of research and training, grants toward the cost of developing, establishing, and improving air pollution control agencies, and other measures designed to encourage air pollution control. The bill was amended in 1965 to help control automotive exhausts, to provide abatement procedures in instances where air pollution adversely affected a foreign country, and to stimulate further research on gasoline- and diesel-powered engines. The following year, the act was amended again, largely to liberalize the grants program.[46]

But all this activity and debate by Congress did not produce much in the way of concrete results. In 1966, after eleven years of federal legislation, only fourteen states had even started to use their authority to set up air-quality standards. Air pollution control programs were in operation in fewer than a hundred local communities. Not a single effective interstate air pollution control program existed in the nation. And, as might have been expected, air pollution was not less; it was greater.[47]

After studying the deteriorating situation, the Congressional enemies of air pollution introduced further legislation to strengthen the federal government's part in the struggle for cleaner air. The Air Quality Act of 1967 empowered the Secretary of Health, Education, and Welfare to seek injunctions against polluters presenting an "imminent and substantial endangerment to the health of persons." It gave the secretary the authority to set air-quality standards for states that had not done so for themselves within the next fifteen months. It expanded the research program on pollution from fuels and motor vehicles, and it provided further control over automotive exhausts. The Senate version of the bill authorized expenditures of $700 million over the next three years to combat air pollution.[48] The House, however, thought this was too much to spend on giving America clean air, so the bill, as finally agreed upon by both Houses, contained an authorization of a much smaller amount, $428 million, too little to do the job effectively, although more than ever provided before.

Thus the three-year, supposedly intensive campaign against air pollution commenced, the campaign against the evil that the Senate Committee on Public Works had described as putting "an exclamation mark beside the word 'urgency.' " And then history began repeating itself. Modest as the original authorizations were, Congress appropriated much less money. For the fiscal year 1968, it appropriated $44 million less than the authorization. The following year, when it voted the appropriation, it cut the authorized amount and the Nixon Administration's budget provided for only $95 million against the $134 million authorized.

By 1969, the federal air pollution control program had joined the federal water pollution control campaign as another example of ineffective action in improving the environment in which Americans must live. The government had given up one of its major fights. In the antitrust suit it had brought against the four major automobile manufacturers, charging them with delay in developing and installing antipollution devices, it was only asking for a consent decree. The most serious result of such an action would be to seal the records of the grand jury investigations, thus preventing public access to the information that had been obtained.[49] In New York City, the Air Resources Commissioner was complaining about the lack of a federal laboratory in the city to assist it in studying its problems. As he pointed out, the city was suffering from poorer and poorer visibility resulting from haze, but no one even knew what caused the haze. The official in charge of the federal government's air pollution research replied by saying there was not enough money; the total amount allocated to research was a million dollars or one five-hundredth of the amount being spent on studying the upper atmosphere and the atmosphere of some of the planets.[50] With few exceptions across the country, the situation was deteriorating. In 1967, the government had estimated that we were pouring some 130 million tons of contaminants into our air. By 1969, the amount had risen by another 10 million tons. Many states had penalties that were so low as to be negligible, ten dollars being an example. Few states had either adequate budgets or staffs.[51] After all the talk and debate, Americans were still breathing dirty air and had shown no real determination to do anything about it.

In 1874, a German student, while working on his doctoral thesis, synthesized the substance that later became widely known as DDT. Because he was conducting a theoretical experiment, he had no thought of any practical use for what he had developed; and the unusual properties of DDT remained unknown until 1939 when a Swiss chemist, Paul Mueller, discovered them. (He later received the Nobel Prize for his work.) The United States Army made wide use of DDT during World War II and found it extraordinarily effective in controlling certain insects. It was cheap; it was persistent (the effects of a single spraying lasted a long time); and there is no question that it saved many, many lives—some estimates have run as high as 10 million—by eliminating diseases.[52] DDT seemed like a simple solution to many civilian problems also; and as soon as the war was over and it became easily available, farmers employed it to gain better crops, municipalities used it in an effort to save their elm trees from the Dutch elm disease, and backyard gardeners found it helped them win the continuous battle against destructive pests.

But gradually a few more perceptive people became concerned that all was not as well as it looked. DDT was beginning to appear in places where it had not been employed; it was starting to kill wildlife that it was not intended to kill; and its persistence was posing a problem. Once used it was not quickly removed from the environment. The general public, however, remained more aware of its blessings than its dangers, and its use grew ever more common. One of the few concerned persons was Paul Brooks, editor in chief of Houghton Mifflin Company, and he believed that the bad effects of DDT and other pesticides deserved greater attention than they had so far received. To achieve this, he needed a well-known writer whose name would command an audience and respect. The person he chose was

Rachel Carson, and she acceded to his request. The result was her nationally famous book *Silent Spring* that appeared in 1962 and that did more than any single work to stimulate interest in protecting our environment from manspread chemicals. People everywhere became conscious that while insects were being destroyed, our surroundings were being contaminated by dangerous substances that we did not fully understand.

As an official of the Department of the Interior reported in 1963, "If these pesticides stayed where we placed them until they became biologically innocuous, our problem would be considerable, but its solution relatively simple. In point of fact, they don't. An increasing body of evidence shows pesticide residues to be nearly ubiquitous. Recent studies reported to the Congress by the U.S. Public Health Service show at least traces of one or more of the chlorinated hydrocarbon pesticides in virtually every major river system in the United States. Sampling of air for pesticides has not been extensive, but residues of DDT were found in 15 of 15 samples examined from 9 different locations in the country. DDT residues are found in virtually all samples of human fat examined in the United States." [53]

So we have surrounded ourselves with poisons. No one understands with any degree of certainty the effects of small amounts of DDT and similar pesticides on human beings, but we do know their effects on other forms of life. Aside from death, they can produce thinness in eggshells, sterility, lack of resistance to starving, and other strange results. As one scientist has remarked, just because we have not been able to conduct controlled experiments on human beings is no reason for conducting an uncontrolled experiment on the entire human race.[54]

Yet that is precisely what we are doing. Regulation of pesticides in the United States, in spite of Miss Carson's book and other wide publicity, remained extremely lax. In 1947, Congress passed the Federal Insecticide, Fungicide and Rodenticide Act, which has since been amended. This act required that all pesticides must be registered with the Pesticides Regulation Division of the Department of Agriculture. The division also has authority to determine the labeling that appears on the container. This must show how the chemical should be used and against what, as well as carry any necessary warnings. If food might be affected, the Food and Drug Administration can veto approval, provided the pesticides are likely to leave a residue above the tolerance level. The Department of Health, Education, and Welfare can review applications with respect to their effects on drinking water and health, and the Department of the Interior can review them with respect to their effect on fish and wildlife. Neither of these departments, however, can veto the registrations. In practice, this did not work out too well. A study made by the General Accounting Office revealed that in thirteen years the Department of Agriculture had not recommended a single prosecution in spite of frequent violations of the act. The General Accounting Office also charged that many violators of the act paid little attention to the warnings they had received.[55]

The same report included a case history of the chemical thallium as an example of the inadequacy and slowness of enforcement. In 1960, some fifty-eight products containing thallium were being used in American households to control insects and rats. A number of deaths, principally among children, had been a direct result, so that year the Department of Agriculture took steps to limit the amount of thallium used. But the deaths continued. The U.S. Public Health Service reported approximately 400 of them in 1962 and 1963. In 1965, the Department of Agriculture finally withdrew from registration all products containing thallium. It had, however, no means of checking on products already in stores. It was therefore possible, according to the General Accounting Office, for the public to purchase products containing thallium as late as 1968.[56] Eight years after the original charges had been leveled against that chemical, it was still available to the public who had no way of knowing its inherent danger, and it was still being added to the other pollutants being poured into our environment.

In 1969, a special committee of the National Research Council reported to the Department of Agriculture that "in general, present regulations contain inadequate provisions for protecting the environment. . . . The Committee believes that attention must be given to the problem of controlling residues in the biosphere. It is doubtful that control of residues in the biosphere can be

achieved by the same methods that are effective in food production (the inspection of foods and their removal from the market
if the residues are above the permissible tolerances) because of
the impossibility of fixing individual responsibility for contamina-
tion. Regulations to achieve this type of control would be concerned with benefits in which few citizens would have a direct
interest. Special efforts, including educational efforts, are needed
to explain the benefits and promote public acceptance of the
regulations.

"Controlling residues in the biosphere is an international problem, and any effective control over the accumulation of long-
lived materials in the ecosystems of the world must be through
control of use in all nations. Clearly, the United States must do
something about its own problems before it can advise other
nations to change practices." [57]

Basically the problem comes down to what the committee
called "a loop of cause and effect" in our economy. "The organo-
chlorine insecticides are of relatively low cost; for many purposes, they are highly effective; from a restricted viewpoint, they
are relatively safe. Therefore, they are used in large quantities.
Substitute materials having less persistence would probably be
used if they were available at equal cost and if they were equally
effective. But such substitute materials will not be developed
while the present persistent materials are in their advantageous
position. Unless there is a change (possibly in the form of regu-
latory action) by which the persistent materials lose their advantage, they will probably continue in general use." [58]

Slowly the forces have mounted to make these pesticides either
unpopular or impossible to use. As a result of the committee's
report, the Department of Agriculture in 1969 placed restrictions
on the use of certain pesticides in spraying programs it spon-
sors.[59] The State of Michigan, shocked to find that many of its
coho salmon contained DDT in amounts well above a permissible
tolerance, cancelled all registrations for the sale of DDT. Next
to automobile manufacturing, tourism and recreation are Michigan's most important industry, and the state wished to protect
its fishing.[60]

In Wisconsin, the state held long hearings on the use of pesticides and the possibility of banning them. The hearings received wide attention, largely because the Environmental Defense Fund, a privately sponsored agency, presented a galaxy of expert witnesses (who served without fees) and conducted skillful cross-examinations of witnesses presented by the other side. In California, the State Department of Agriculture banned the use of DDT and one other persistent pesticide in raising certain crops and in spraying livestock. The measure was intended to reduce overall employment of the chemicals by 50 percent.[61] And Arizona had placed a twelve-month suspension on DDT's use on crops, the first state to take such action.[62] By 1969, production of DDT had declined approximately 20 percent from the level reached in 1960.[63]

But overall, there was not much cause for optimism, and what the scientist called the uncontrolled experiment on the human race, including the population of the United States, was still continuing. In 1968, six years after the publication of Miss Carson's book and four years after the intensive Senate hearings it inspired, American farmers were spending an estimated $800 million on pesticides. That figure was expected to rise to more than a billion in 1969, with another half billion being spent on pesticides used by American homes, industries, and institutions. The total of $1.7 billion represented 70 percent more than the total spent in 1965.[64] It also represented far more money than the American people, through their Congress, were willing to permit the federal government to spend on removing pollutants from the air and water of the United States. But at least by the end of 1969, the federal government was finally taking steps to restrict the interstate shipment of DDT.

In 1968, while scientists and conservationists across the country were continuing their struggle against pollutants in the air and water, 6,000 sheep in the Skull and Rush Valleys of Utah became mysteriously sick. The efforts of veterinarians to save them proved futile. The sheep died, and the disease remained undiagnosed. Because of the mysterious nature of the illness, suspicion pointed to the nearby Dugway Proving Grounds, a million-acre area where the United States Army tests the weapons it develops for chemical and biological warfare.

The military, with the dishonesty to which it sometimes resorts to cover up its mistakes, promptly denied any connection with the dead sheep. Eight days later, in a classified reply to an inquiry from Senator Frank E. Moss of Utah, it did admit having tested nerve gas; and the truth, in spite of repeated public denials, began to leak out.[65] The army finally paid the ranchers for their sheep but still insisted that its activities had nothing to do with the mysterious deaths. Fourteen months after the accident, a subcommittee of the House placed three high military officials under oath. "Do you swear to tell the truth, the whole truth, and nothing but the truth?" the subcommittee chairman asked, placing special emphasis on the word "nothing." Faced with potential perjury charges, the officials finally broke down and publicly admitted the army's guilt.[66] In the late afternoon of March 13, an air force jet had flown over the proving grounds, spraying out 320 gallons of lethal nerve gas in a test of a new type of dispenser. A high wind was blowing that day—the gusts reached 35 miles an hour—but the army had invested millions of dollars in meteorological equipment and believed that it knew exactly what it was doing.[67] One valve, however, opened more slowly than expected. The gas dribbled out and continued to dribble after the plane had completed the test and reached higher altitudes.[68] One slight mechanical failure, and the United States Army had achieved the incredible; it had spewed a lethal nerve gas into the air of America, a pollutant far more deadly than any pesticide being manufactured today.

This disclosure was followed by others that were equally horrifying. In 1967 and 1968, the army had disposed of 17,000 containers of nerve gas in the Atlantic Ocean off Long Island and Atlantic City, New Jersey. The material had been moved from the Rocky Mountain Arsenal near Denver and had been carried across the country by train. When Representative Cornelius E. Gallagher of New Jersey learned that another shipment was to cross his state and be transferred to ships in a New Jersey port, he objected strenuously. Once again, the army insisted that its practices were absolutely safe, but a committee of the National

Academy of Sciences did not agree and pointed out several un-
certainties in the army's disposal plan. The committee also
pointed out that the gas should not remain where it was. The
army had stored it near an approach to the Denver airport, and
what might happen in the event of an airplane accident? [69] Could
that gas, too, be released into our atmosphere? In 1969, reports
came out of Washington that the army had also manufactured
poisoned bullets and had a stockpile of some 20,000 of them
divided between two arsenals.[70]

Not content merely with poisons, it was also cultivating dangerous diseases such as anthrax, Q fever, tularemia (rabbit
fever), and psittacosis (parrot fever).[71] The danger in having
these materials around is revealed in a single figure: One fluid
ounce of tularemia is enough to infect approximately 700 million
people. The excuse, of course, is that the Russians are doing the
same thing, although some Congressmen and officials state that
they have never heard the army substantiate this claim.[72]

What was worst about this science-fiction program was the
army's dispersion of its knowledge. The American taxpayer, who
had been supporting the army, had heard little about this activity;
and in Washington, it had been discussed only in hushed tones.
But from 1951 to 1969, the army had trained the officers of
thirty-five foreign nations in the use of chemical and biological
warfare. These included some reliable allies like Canada and
Great Britain. They also included some less certain friends such
as Yugoslavia, Iran, Saudi Arabia, Greece, and even Egypt.[73]
It is difficult to imagine what our environment will be, if small,
unstable governments start wiping out their neighbors with chemical and biological warfare, for once the poisons and diseases
have been let loose, where will they stop? The possibility dwarfs
any other pollution problem that we have today, in spite of the
restrictions that President Nixon has imposed on such activity,
restrictions that some skeptics do not think will work.

Although this immoral and dangerous activity was kept a
closely guarded secret, the amount of the taxpayer's money that
was going into it was more closely kept. Even most members of
Congress did not know what it was because it was not placed in
the budget as a single item. Instead, bits and parts of it were

scattered here and there. (The lack of control that Congress exercises over some of the departments of government staggers the mind.) Under the growing pressure to learn more that was generated by Representative Richard D. McCarthy of New York, the army held a briefing in March, 1969, to which certain representatives and senators were invited. At that briefing, a figure finally came out.[74] It was 60 percent greater than the amount allocated in President Nixon's budget that year for sewerage plant construction; it was more than three times what President Nixon had recommended the federal government spend on combatting air pollution.

Growing alarm across the country caused the Nixon Administration to have second thoughts about chemical and biological warfare. Five departments and agencies were to prepare papers on the subject and submit them to the National Security Council by September 5, 1969. To provide for the broadest possible discussion, these papers were not intended to reflect the departments' and agencies' official positions and were not to be cleared by their heads. But suddenly in August the Department of Defense recalled all the papers written by its representatives and did subject them to official review. This meant that the other departments and agencies had to do the same. As a consequence, the September 5 deadline passed, and nothing was done. The Department of Defense had single-handedly delayed consideration of one of the most serious moral and environmental problems facing the United States.[75] But at least by October, the Secretary of Defense was said to have submitted a report to the National Security Council urging that the United States stop manufacturing agents for biological, although not chemical, warfare.[76] At least we had moved forward an inch in the direction of humanity, sanity, and concern for our environment.

But we had not done so well with nuclear explosions. It is not surprising that a nation that manufactures the dread disease anthrax and considers the possibility of releasing it on the world should also be a leader in setting off nuclear explosions, even though the effects are not fully understood and therefore not predictable.

In December, 1968, the Atomic Energy Commission set off a blast at the Las Vegas Bombing and Gunnery Range in Nevada. It triggered 10,000 tremors in the earth that were still continuing as late as April of the following year, some of them six miles deep. Although none of them caused damage and none of them were far from the location of the blast itself, they raised fears among some scientists that larger earthquakes might also be triggered and that radioactive material could be released through fissures.[77] The latter has already happened several times; and although the amounts of radioactive material that emerged did not constitute a danger to public health (according to the Atomic Energy Commission), this is not what the commission had intended in the first place. Like the slowly opening valve on the air force's jet plane with its load of poison gas, predictions in these experiments are not always accurate.

Between 1969 and the signing of the nuclear test ban treaty back in 1963 (one of the wiser actions in which we have engaged), the Atomic Energy Commission set off 188 underground explosions. Of these, 19 released substantial amounts of radioactive material, 5 of them on purpose. Researchers in the Uinta Mountains of Utah reported in 1969 that the level of radioactivity was steadily increasing. It was not yet dangerous; and the Uinta Mountains, because of their geography, present a special case. But further research will be necessary before scientists understand what the total effect of these explosions may be.[78]

Scientists of the stature of Dr. Kenneth S. Pitzer, president of Stanford University and former Director of Research for the Atomic Energy Commission, have called the commission's reports on safety considerations inadequate and have stated that much more substantial hearings should be held before engaging in further large-scale testing.[79] Such pleas, however, receive little attention. In 1969, the Atomic Energy Commission set off a blast under Battlement Mesa, forty miles from Grand Junction, Colorado. Among those opposing the test was Lieutenant Governor Mark Hogan, who took the reasonable position that absolute safety should first be assured by some organization other than the commission itself.[80] His stand was supported by many knowledgeable people, and the American Civil Liberties Union carried the question to the federal courts. In a ruling that belonged more to the nineteenth century than to the twentieth, the district court held that the burden of proving danger lay with the citizens. This decision was upheld by the circuit court, and Justice Thurgood Marshall of the Supreme Court refused to halt the explosion, pending appeal.[81] This was in line with an earlier opinion written in 1954 by Chief Justice Warren Burger, when he was on the circuit court in Washington. In response to a suit against nuclear testing brought by a two-time Nobel Prize winner, Chief Justice Burger ruled that such actions lay entirely within the province of the legislative and executive branches and could be checked only by the electorate.[82]

Such decisions are leading us in a dangerous direction and are not based on the realities of modern politics and technology. We know from sad experience that one-purpose agencies demonstrate a remarkable ability to perpetuate themselves; we know that they tend to slip out from under the control of even the most alert and aggressive Congresses; we also know that the increasing complexity of our technology makes it more and more difficult for private citizens to obtain information on which to base sound judgments. Moreover private citizens do not have the time or the ability to keep track of all the activities of government. Too often they become aware of a problem only after the damage has been done.

For Chief Justice Burger to say that the electorate is the only authority that can ultimately pass on the safety of nuclear explosions does not take these facts into account. Such an approach to the solution of environmental problems might have worked perhaps even as late as the 1930's, but it will not work today. We need a far more adequate review system than anything we have established so far.

At the risk of sounding like a heretic among conservationists, I seriously question the worth of many of our antipollution programs, because of the piecemeal basis on which we are going about them. I will go even further than that and admit that I sometimes wonder whether, in the long run, they may not result in more evil than good unless we drastically change our approach. This may seem like a radical statement, but I believe it has enough foundation to warrant its consideration.

First, none of our various antipollution programs today is sufficient to handle its particular problem. All of them are way behind schedule and dramatically underfinanced; and with an economy-minded administration, they are likely to get worse.

Second, we seem to have no sense of priorities. We are trying to use inadequate resources to get everything done at once, spreading them across the board instead of concentrating them on one objective at a time. For these two reasons, I am pessimistic about the ultimate success of what we are trying to do.

The reasons I believe that some of our programs may be positively harmful are more complex. But take the example of water. In spite of the heroic efforts of men like Senator Muskie, the federal water pollution abatement effort is badly in need of funds. Not nearly enough federal money has been allocated to get the job done. Yet the $800 million finally appropriated for the fiscal year 1970 represented an enormous slice out of the total amount that we were willing to spend on our environment. Furthermore, the program as constituted was already showing signs of developing its own opposition. States like Connecticut that were really trying to do something about water pollution were seriously upset by the delay in receiving the federal funds they had been led to expect. Other states, like Iowa, were actively resisting the federal government's dictates on water standards and were likely to continue doing so until the federal government demonstrated more willingness to absorb part of the cost.[83] No amount of tough talking on the part of the Department of the Interior can remedy the absence of money; and if it comes to a conflict between a number of states and the department (and the number of states was growing), the department is the one likely to lose. If that happens, the chances of resuscitating an adequate water pollution abatement program will be slight.

As for private industry, it can hardly be expected to show much enthusiasm for a program that is so unenthusiastically supported by the enforcing government. It is one thing to pour acid wastes into a crystal clear river and bear the entire onus for the fish kills and stenches downstream. It is quite another

THE AFFLUENT DETERIORATION · 151

to pour acid wastes into a river that is already filled with sludge and sewage and in which the acids are merely one more unpleasant ingredient. Such an industry, if forced to comply with a law that it considers overstrict in the circumstances, will fight back. And if it is joined by many other industries, it may succeed in upsetting the whole concept.

In spite of our efforts, our pollution is enormous and growing worse. We are living in a garbage can of our own making. (I have not written about garbage and other solid wastes. We are about to bury ourselves in them without any advanced technology for disposing of them, even if we can land men on the moon.) But I do not think that we are going to solve the problem the way we are trying to. Our overall program is far too confused and out of focus.

If we are to make real progress, we are going to have to decide what it is we really want and determine the price we are willing to pay. As a first step, we might initiate an antipollution campaign in reverse. Instead of spending so much time and energy attacking pollution that already exists, let us at least slow down the activities that will contribute more pollution. Half the savings, which would be an enormous amount, could be devoted to conservation and environment measures. The remainder could be spent on other projects.

For example, as an individual, I am more greatly concerned about living in a country where some people I do not know are running around with phials of anthrax in their hands or dribbling nerve gases into the air through faulty valves than I am about the smoke emerging from a power plant's chimney. I do not like the smoke, but if that other stuff gets loose, we are done for. The army has admitted spending $350 million annually on such materials, and the figure may be much higher than that. So conservatively, we could leave the military $50 million and still apply half the savings—$150 million—toward air pollution abatement. That is more than the federal government has been spending.

It makes no sense to me at all to set up a program that envisions spending $500 million over five years trying to make America's air cleaner and then, as a nation, spend somewhere in the neighborhood of $10 billion a year nationally on highways, thus making automotive transportation more convenient, and thus enlarging the principal source of air pollution. What we ought to be doing is making automobiles just as inconvenient as possible, so as to discourage their use. If we cut our national expenditures on highways by some 90 percent, we would do more to reduce air pollution than any positive measures we have taken so far. And if we spent half the remaining sum on our environment, we would have available an amount far greater than the total of the federal government's natural resources budget.

The possibilities are enormous. We could reduce the number of nuclear explosions set off by the Atomic Energy Commission. (It may take 200 in all to loosen gas in Colorado, as the commission is attempting to do.) This would accomplish more to reduce radioactive materials in our air and water than almost any step we could take. Certainly we should scuttle the supersonic jet transport. That would cost travelers to Europe a few extra hours of flying time on each trip, but it would save the rest of us several billion dollars and the sound of those shock waves bouncing across the country wherever the plane flew.

The next step would be to consider our environmental problems as a whole and assign priorities to their solution, something we have not done. Instead we pay a little attention to this one and a little to that without weighing the importance of one over the other.

For example, we have spent an extraordinary amount of energy on our effort to control water pollution. But the General Accounting Office, after careful study, issued a report in the fall of 1969 labeling the effort ineffective.[84] Perhaps at this time water pollution abatement should not be at the top of our list. I do not mean this to be defeatist, but the human resources available to work on conservation are almost as limited as the financial resources. When all those Congressmen were attempting to raise the appropriation for sewerage treatment plants, they were not able to do much else about conservation. Yet few of them, I am sure, had consciously asked themselves whether or not this was the most important conservation issue facing the country. Because we have not set any priorities, it is difficult to tell; but

I suspect that there may have been other issues that deserved equal or greater attention and received none at all.

This also applies to private conservationists as well. Pure water is so simple a catchword that it is bound to fire people. Not long ago, I was talking to a top officer in one of the large conservation agencies, and he was describing to me the work that was being done to prove that a coastline industrial plant was placing more pollutants into the water than it had admitted doing. The study was an interesting and exciting one and was handled with great imagination. But I myself seriously questioned the effort. When all was done, the best that could have been accomplished was to change one single plant in the United States, and the effect on overall water pollution would be minimal.

Certainly no one can be against the cleansing of our streams, but the issue may have been enlarged beyond its actual significance in view of some of our other needs. Studies by Resources for the Future have turned up some results that may surprise many Americans. For one thing, industry does not generally need high-quality water. Most of the water required by industry is used for purposes like cooling in which the quality of the water makes little difference. When it is used for truly sensitive purposes, almost all water has to be treated anyway.

Studies by Resources for the Future also show that high-quality water is not necessary for municipal water supplies. The water in the Hudson River may stink, but it is about the same quality as that at the Torresdale intake in Philadelphia which is eventually used for drinking; and the people of Düsseldorf, Germany, have been cheerfully and healthily drinking water taken from the Rhine at a point where its waters are far worse than those of either the Delaware or the Hudson.[85] Studies have also shown that the primary reasons for cleaning water are esthetics and recreation, both good reasons but perhaps not demanding the urgency that some of us have assigned to the solution of this particular problem. The $40 million proposed by the Nixon Administration for treatment plants will do little to clean our rivers and lakes. Yet it represents a large portion of the total amount that we are willing to spend on preserving and improving our environment. Perhaps, for example, we should make up our minds to live with dirty waters for several years longer and concentrate most of our available funds on the purchase of open space, which is so rapidly disappearing. I do not know. But when the General Accounting Office criticized our water program for its "shotgun approach," it might just as well have applied the criticism to our whole conservation effort.

Control of pollution in this nation will be difficult until we start making some clear choices. Do we want quiet or a supersonic jet transport? Do we want pure air or nuclear explosions? We cannot have opposites of everything. Above all, we must beware of the lures offered by the advocates of the Better Life, who see everything in such simple—and limited terms.

6

More People and Worse Cities

IN a technologically advanced society in which 90 percent of the population reaches the age at which it can reproduce, the population will remain stable only if each family restricts itself to having no more than 2.3 children. If that number creeps up slightly to 2.5 children, the population will rise by 10 percent each generation. If the number is further increased to three children, the population will soar by 31 percent each generation. In that case, approximately one out of every four women would have to remain childless to restore the balance.[1]

These statistics should give pause to every middle- or upper-class American family that thinks it is divorced from the question of overpopulation and that the problem only concerns underdeveloped areas like China, India, and Latin America. Nor can such a family rest comfortably on the assumption that its economic ability to support its children gives it the right to have them. The resources of the earth are finite, and that family, just because it is economically strong, is probably consuming more than its share already. Its additional children will tip the balance of disproportion even further.

Although the average American of this generation will prob-

155

ably never suffer directly the most dire consequences of over-population, the prospects for the rest of the world are not so bright. At the time of Christ, the estimated population of the earth was a quarter billion. By 1830, it had quadrupled and reached a billion. Only a hundred years later, it had reached two billion. Thirty-five years later, it had reached three billion. By 1980, it will be four billion; and by the year 2000, it will be six billion.[2] This incredibly fantastic growth is brought about by what seems to be a small figure—2 percent annually. But if this rate continues unchecked for the next 1,500 years, the weight of the earth's human population will be equal to the weight of the earth itself.

Such a condition, of course, will never develop. If man does not control the threat himself, nature will take care of it for him. But nature's ways are neither just nor kind. The instruments at its disposal for controlling populations include starvation and disease, each of them often preceded by horrible suffering. Or if man does not check himself rationally, he may do so irrationally. Perhaps it is not completely a coincidence that DDT, credited with saving so many lives, may now be exposing those lives to danger or that a generation that is expanding so rapidly is also the generation that invented nuclear warfare and has spent some of its resources on manufacturing poison gases. Man's own intemperance and lack of self-discipline may be the means by which his population growth is stopped. The outlook is not a happy one.

But to many American families, 1,500 years seems a long time off, the chances of starving appear remote, nuclear warfare is a horror that will somehow be avoided, and they go on having children with little or no thought to the effect that our increasing population is already having on our own surroundings. Although current figures show that our birth rate is flattening out, if we should return to the birth and death rates of the period between 1950 and 1960, it would take only 150 years for our population to equal the present population of the entire world; and in 650 years, there would be one square foot for each person in the United States.[3] These figures are not merely alarmist; they represent cold facts that we must start facing now. The day of the large family is over; it has to be. And it is not merely the extremely poor and uneducated, who also have too many children, that are causing the problem. There are, fortunately, relatively few of them and therefore their impact on the total problem is less than might be expected. Also the difference in their fecundity is not as great as some have imagined. The sharp postwar increase in the birth rate was greater among middle- and upper-income families than among the poor.[4] Indeed, some experts on population believe that in this country "wanted" babies are creating most of the problem, not those babies who arrive undesired and whose presence places even greater economic pressures on their already strained families.[5] This puts a major responsibility squarely on those families in America who consider themselves leaders. It is up to them to start acting like leaders and to stop thinking of themselves as noble exceptions. They have a personal part to play in checking our population growth that they can no longer avoid.

The moral and emotional questions involved in the control of childbirth are diverse and complex. Until only recently a larger population carried with it the hope of greater prosperity. In the individual family, as soon as the children became old enough to work, which was not very old, more bread-earners were added to the family's total; and as long as the children earned a little more than they consumed, they added to the family's net income. Thus the farmer with several strapping sons could cultivate more acreage (and the acres were there for him to cultivate); the lumberman had a few more hands to help him cut down America's trees; and even the factory worker had a little more in the way of wages to support the family unit. For the country as a whole, an increased population also meant greater prosperity. The small crossroads community in Kansas saw itself as a future metropolis; land values rose in any area that absorbed a slightly disproportionate share of the increasing population; railroads thrived under the impact of more passengers and more freight being transported to more people; many businesses grew merely because they were located in regions where the population was growing or were filling a market that served more and more people, largely because of the expansion of the population.

Childbearing, therefore, had economic approval. Even as late as the years immediately following World War II, when we should have known better, economists were happily predicting the prosperity that would inevitably follow now that the younger men were back from the war and making up for lost time by fathering more babies. Thus over the years, large families have had the economic approval, whether conscious or unconscious, of the rest of us. We not only smiled when we saw a mother with ten children buying produce at the grocery store (and so did the grocery store owner who was selling more goods), we went out of our way to accord them special benefits. Scholarships at schools and universities were based not merely on lack of income but the size of the family. The more children, the more the public was willing to come to support the family. This attitude is still reflected in our federal income tax laws. The greater the number of a man's dependents—which are primarily his children—the less tax he has to pay. This applies to the multimillionaire just as much as it does to the father without money. The man with ten children will start off his fiscal year with $7,000 of tax deductions, even though the community in which he is living has to bear the additional cost of educating that many children.

This attitude was augmented by our normal reaction to childbirth. No event of greater importance occurs within most families than the addition of a new member; nothing so binds together a man and woman as their mutual love for their children; fewer experiences bring deeper joy to most of us than the assumption of the responsibilities of parenthood; and nothing is more personal than the birth of a child that is related to us and who will carry the family forward into future generations. We may die, but the child and the child's children will be there. Thinking and knowing this, it is difficult for young parents, holding their newly born child in their arms, to realize that the birth of that child will have an effect on the lives and happiness of others and that in the world as we now know it that effect may not be good.

In addition, nature intended us, like every other species, to have offspring in considerable numbers, numbers large enough to permit us to survive in spite of the ravages we once had to endure. As this had to be a big number, the impulses behind motherhood are strong, ranging from the desire for sexual gratification to the pleasures and pride of parenthood. Although W. C. Fields derived laughs from his now-famous remark that a man cannot be all bad who hates dogs and children, the laughter came from the obvious ludicrousness of the comment. Almost everybody does love children.

Complicating the issue further has been the traditional approach of many religions. Since religion tends to reinforce what we believe we should do for the good of our society, our various faiths have further strengthened our respect for parenthood; and the combination of economics, natural impulses, and religion has kept alive attitudes that we now know may have disastrous consequences on our future. The individual birth that we herald today with so much joy and confidence is still as mystifying as ever and still as hopeful. It is the *births* that we must worry about.

How we can reverse the accumulated instincts and traditions of childbearing in order to start emphasizing the quality, rather than the quantity, of human life is a subject that baffles even the experts on this subject. We approach the revision of our abortion laws gingerly; we are touchy on the issue of disseminating information about contraceptives; we still recognize that the right to have children is not only a personal right, it is also a sacred right. But these attitudes will either change or the human race—including the United States, which can claim no immunity—will witness horrors and squalor and suffering such as it has never seen before. In the light of everything we know and can foresee, that is inevitable.

There is some indication that the younger generation understands this in a way their parents did not. In testimony before a joint committee of Congress, Former Secretary of the Interior Udall said: "... the Department of Commerce puts out the figures and they become gospel as to what growth is, although we now have three or four sets of figures, quite rightly. But there is one reputable demographer, Dr. Bogue of the University of Chicago, who predicts that these sharp trends of the last 5 or 6 years indicate that our population, if these trends continue, will level off within the next decade at about 225 million. Yet, all of our projections that we talk about are to the effect that population is going to double by the year 2000, 2010, you name it. But, what are the consequences of this?

"The truth of the matter is that [the rate of growth of] our population has dropped very sharply since 1960 or 1961. It is below the low point in the depression of 1935. It is going on down. You can watch it month by month, and this population policy is being set by the younger generations. They are marrying later. They are having fewer children. They have a different outlook, different values, apparently, with regard to life." [6]

Setting aside the broader issues, which are beyond the scope of this book, we can still consider some of the more immediate problems that our increased population has presented us with, for the effects are already being felt.

Our increased population has already had enormous impact on the problem of conserving our natural resources. Conservation can be divided into two parts: the wise commercial use of natural resources and the preservation of nature in itself. Unfortunately the two often come into conflict, and many major conservation battles are waged, not between conservationists against outsiders, but between the two types of conservationists. Earlier in our history, we looked upon our resources as though they came out of a bottomless well. When one mine was exhausted, the prospectors went out and found another, often a larger one. When the trees were cut down in one area, there were always more trees a little distance farther off. When the soil was exhausted from overcultivation in one agricultural region, the farmers moved to another, generally farther west. In fact, although it is not too pleasant a thought in view of today's knowledge, the unwise utilization of this country's resources played a large role in its development. Many people did not move West just because they wanted to escape to something new. They moved West because they had used up what they had left behind. But there was still enough to supply the nation; and we had, on the whole, no real worries. Our rising population has now changed that. A few figures show what is happening. Between 1947 and 1964, we almost doubled the amount of money we were spending on products using minerals. By the year 2000, the figure will have gone up almost six times. In 1900, we consumed 40 billion gallons of water annually. By 1965, our consumption had increased more than 800 percent. It will almost triple again by the year 2000.[7] Wood, which we once regarded as an inexpensive material for many types of construction, is coming into short supply. The demand has been exceeding the output, and prices have risen drastically over what they were only a few years ago. This has been instrumental in sending up the cost of housing. In most parts of the country, land is becoming less and less available. In part, this is because of our affluence. More people can afford vacation houses, thus utilizing two pieces of ground at once. But it is also in part a result of our larger population. In many areas of the country, we are finding it difficult to locate people physically. There is no longer room for them. This, in turn, has led to a dislocation of some of our traditional land-use patterns. Certain desirable, but limited, sites such as waterfront property have become so scarce that they are generally available only to the wealthy. Even anchorages are difficult to discover. The fisherman who once operated a marginal business may now be unable to find a place where he can afford to keep his boat. Our larger population with its growing interest in boating may be able to command all the moorings, because it can pay prices the fisherman cannot.

If the pressure is increasing on our commercial natural resources, it also is not sparing those areas that are of interest to the preservationists. Less and less land is left for the man or woman who wants the peace and quiet of the countryside, either on a permanent basis as a place to live or merely as a place to go for a needed vacation and relaxation from the strains of modern urban living. For a number of years after World War II, considerable $10- and $15-an-acre land existed in the United States. Little, if any, such land is for sale today. It was not even necessary to own open space to enjoy it then. There was still enough for everyone, and the owner often did not object to visitors. Today, his asset is more valuable and therefore demands greater protection. In addition to which, if he permits visitors, he may be swamped by them. What remains of privately held open space for passive or active recreation is becoming less and less accessible to the public. Even the areas that we have set aside for noncommercial uses have become more and more crowded and less adapted to their original use. In 1962, the National Park Service observed what it called the "Billionth-Visitor Day." In 1904, it began recording the number of visits each year. They then totaled 120,690. The Statistical Analysis Office of the National Park Service estimated that the billionth visit would take place during the afternoon of August 22, 1962; and the service seized the occasion to honor simultaneously one visitor at most of its many facilities. That visitor was to symbolize the growth and utilization of our national park system.[8] Today the growth in the number of visitors is no cause for celebration; it is rapidly becoming a nightmare for national park superintendents. Their gates are lined with cars and trucks and campers each morning, and they often have to put up signs saying there is no more room. The national forests and state parks are experiencing the same upsurge.

We have not yet run out of natural resources of all types, but for the first time in our history many of them, as a result of our increasing population, are being severely strained. It is therefore more and more important that we allocate and use them wisely. Fewer resources—including actual living and working space—have to go much further if we are to preserve the quality of our lives.

In 1968, a committee of the Senate met with a committee of the House to discuss a national policy for the environment. Population and its distribution were, of course, among the topics, and the comments made are illuminating.

Dr. Philip Lee, Assistant Secretary of the Department of Health, Education, and Welfare, stated: "I might just add a few words about the present policies of the Federal Government in the area of population and family planning, and these really date to President Johnson's State of the Union Message in 1965 in which we really opened up this whole area for policy consideration and program development.

"Since that time we have developed policies domestically that emphasize solely equality of opportunity and making access to information and services available so that individuals might have the freedom of choice to decide on both the spacing of their children and the size of their families. *This cannot be described as a population policy*. [Emphasis added.] It could be described really as a family planning policy and because there are estimates ranging up to 5 million women in this country, particularly in low-income areas, who at the present time, do not have adequate access . . . to services, this has been a priority area in terms of domestic program development. . . ."

Dr. Lee pointed out that we have no national population policy and do not even possess adequate information "on the health aspects, on the social aspects, on the economic and other aspects" of population to formulate one.

He then continued, "When we examine our problems domestically and we look at the world's problems, we see, of course, an even more serious immediate problem; but long-range, the world's population problem, of course, is our own, and we ultimately cannot escape the consequences of continuing rates of population growth throughout the world that exists today." [9]

Where we are going to place the additional people was also discussed at the same meeting, and the various points of view underlined the complexity of the problem and set forth some of the possible solutions. John A. Baker, Assistant Secretary of the Department of Agriculture, had this to say; "In addition to the family planning or birth control or population increase phase, I would like to [ask] . . . where in the space of the continental United States and Alaska and Hawaii is the population going to live?

"Secretary Weaver [of the Department of Health, Education, and Welfare] pointed out a recent Gallup poll said 57 percent said they wanted to live in small towns and the open countryside. Over the past years the Federal Government with many enactments by Congress has put special emphasis on this aspect. . . .

"Now, in areas such as Wyoming, for example, the population decreased, according to the census from 1960 to 1967, by almost 5 percent.

"If . . . population overcrowding is in itself a form of serious pollution, then it may be that the Nation ought to have done something to enable Wyoming to provide economic opportunities for its people so it wouldn't have to lose nearly 5 percent of its population in less than 7 years."

He then pointed out that "specific policies to locate government installations and big employing government installations in areas of less dense populations instead of more dense population" should be considered. "Population overcrowding itself," he continued, "is some form of pollution, and certainly new cities, new towns, new communities—as Secretary Weaver has just pointed out, located 30, 80 miles from already overcrowded population centers are part of the answer to eliminating that kind of pollution environment."

Secretary Weaver then spoke up to amplify his idea. "I think 'overcrowding' is a rather complex problem. Obviously it seems to me in a democracy any governmental policy which has to do with dispersal of population has to be based upon a basic principle and that is that people have freedom of choice and these choices are really viable choices."

He suggested that although much of the future growth will not be in the central cities, "they form such a very vital and very necessary part of modernization that we can't just wipe them off the books and forget them. This is not an either/or situation. It is a both situation, and just as there are problems from concentration, there are also problems from too much dispersal and failure to get services which are required in a modern society to people who don't have some degree of concentration.

"It is also a problem of getting the cultural institutions and the other types of institutions that have to be supported by concentrations of people so that it is not just a question of cutting out and getting rid of the concentration. It is trying to keep it from getting larger, and it is trying to make concentration more viable while creating new patterns that will respond to the needs of our people."

Secretary of the Interior Udall responded by agreeing with Secretary Weaver, but added that "we need to rehabilitate and we can rebuild and make much more livable even the worst of our cities." [10]

This testimony brought out a number of significant points

about the dispersal of our population. First, we do not know what overcrowding will do. Experiments on various animals have indicated that a healthy, normal existence is not possible at certain saturation levels, even though there is an abundance of food, water, and the other necessities of life. Research indicates that this may also be true of the human race, although surprising differences seem to exist between cultures and their attitudes toward space.[11] Much more work should be done in this field if we are to meet adequately the needs of people; and it also appears possible that at least in some instances, if we used space better, we could satisfy their needs with less of it.

A second point brought out by the testimony is the desire of a majority of Americans to live in small towns and the open countryside. I am certain this is what they think they want, but I am not at all sure it is what they actually do want. It may be like the dream held by many metropolitan newspapermen of some day owning a smalltown newspaper. It sounds idyllic, but they have not taken into account the problems, and they would soon be homesick for the greater excitement of the large city daily. Imbued in the American tradition is the picture of the small village with white picket fences and helpful neighbors, a place where men and women can exist side by side in peace and reasonable comfort without the more strenuous pace of the city. This picture was once so strong that I can remember when many advertisers used it to portray the real America. Suddenly they discovered that few Americans came from such backgrounds and that they were dealing with a symbol only, not a reality. From my own experience living in the countryside, I have found that, while it appeals to many and they love and truly enjoy it, a large number do not. In a short time, faced with the problems of country living, they either move back to a more settled area again or they do whatever they can to convert the country into the city. They form clubs and build clubhouses; they give cocktail parties; they construct tennis courts and golf courses and develop more sophisticated schools for their children. And they do not want to put up with the discomforts and the isolation of true country living. Although they may enjoy this sort of existence during their vacations and find it a welcome and needed contrast from their regular lives, they are not country people.

The solution advanced by Assistant Secretary Baker and by Secretary Weaver is the one that we are most often following, and it is the one that, in my opinion, is causing us the most trouble. We build up a population center in a city; then, as its conditions deteriorate, we move out farther and start another one. This is encouraged by the surrounding communities, which forget, as I have often said, that nobody ever planned a slum to be a slum. Light industry, those are the magic words that will solve every community difficulty. Light industry will pay larger taxes and thus reduce the burden on everyone else. Light industry will pick up the deficit in the school budget, which has probably been caused by too rapid growth, unrestrained by adequate zoning that might have kept the growth of the community's school population in proportion to its resources. The community forgets, however, that light industry also creates its own problems. It brings more people, which may be good for the stores and restaurants, but it is not so good for traffic congestion and the condition of the roads. The quiet residential or rural character of the community starts to vanish under the impact. Pressures develop for more zoning changes, which, by then, the town is unable to resist. If there is a light industry in one area that is zoned for it, and the light industry is successful and grows, it will want more space. As the community is now dependent on the industry's tax contribution, the space will be provided. (How many times in America have we gone through this cycle?) Soon it becomes difficult to draw the line between light industry and industry that is just slightly heavier. In time, the heavier industry will arrive; and although it may momentarily increase the tax list, it also begins to increase the problems. Most of our slums are clustered around industrial centers.

The thinking that leads town after town to commit the same mistake can be exemplified by a community in which my family and I once lived. It contained a housing project for which the federal government made an annual payment in place of paying taxes. It also contained a large estate, owned by a wealthy bachelor and his spinster sister and occupied by them generally only over weekends. This situation deeply irritated many of the local officials. If only they could attract more housing projects and develop the estate, they complained, revenues would skyrocket. Indeed, they would have but so also would have the expenses. Practically every dollar paid by the estate owner represented a net profit to the town; he and his sister asked for extremely little in the way of services. On the other hand, the payments by the federal government barely equalled the current operating cost of educating the children who lived in the housing project. They did nothing to cover the capital expense of building the classrooms they used. Actually an analysis showed the town's principal financial problems had been caused by the housing project and the capital expense involved in absorbing the sudden increase in school children.

An entirely different—and unusual—point of view was expressed by the first selectman of Weston, Connecticut, when a water company decided to sell an extraordinarily large tract of land that it had reserved as a watershed. A donor offered to buy the land and set up the Devil's Den Sanctuary of the Nature Conservancy, taking the land off the tax rolls entirely. The usual hue and cry was raised, but the first selectman quickly countered by showing the effect on Weston's school enrollment if the land were developed. It would have created a crisis of unmanageable proportions. Everyone's taxes would have gone up sharply in order to pay for the necessary school construction program. Few communities are this farsighted. Most of them do everything possible to attract new residents and businesses.

Business responds to the lure. The top executives, weary of the congestion of city life and certain that their employees are, too, swallow the enticements offered them and leave the city they may well have been a cause of damaging. Earlier I mentioned the industrialization of Long Island that followed the building of the superhighway and the confusion and traffic jams that have been the consequence. While this was happening, New York City, which was already a business center, experienced a decline in population. In 1968, according to the U.S. Bureau of the Census, the population of New York City had fallen for the second year in a row and was then lower than it had been in 1960.[12] It may be that 8 million people is more than a city like New York can support; we do not know the answer to that question. But if 8 million is not, it is sad to see the core of the area decline, while the outer fringes that might have been reserved for other uses made to resemble the city.

There is small comfort in the thought that once-rich farmlands between Washington, D.C., and Columbia, Maryland, are now covered with industrial sites, enough to draw 100,000 workers into the area from other parts of the country.[13] There is even less comfort in the thought of the increasing industrialization of the eastern slopes of the mountains in Colorado. In that area, bounded on one side by the plains and on the other by some of the finest recreational lands in America (much of it in public ownership) is located a rapidly growing plant complex, partly encouraged by the placement of many government facilities in the general locality and partly by the desire of business for more space and better living conditions. The tragedy would not be so great if the need for space were real and not merely apparent. There are many regions in this country that have already been industrialized and now are depressed areas. They could use more businesses. Yet they are passed over in favor of another area that offers to the American people qualities that cannot be found anywhere else. (One point is completely predictable. Much of Colorado's land is in government ownership, more than 42 percent in 1964.[14] The major portion of this is held by the U.S. Forest Service for the use of the general American public. Since this includes some of the best building sites around cities like Boulder, it is inevitable that pressures will soon build up to develop at least part of it.)

As every schoolboy quickly learns in the most elementary course in American history, our early farmers often abused their lands for two reasons: One, they did not know any better; Two, when the soil was ruined, they could always move somewhere else. We laugh now at their ignorance and lack of perception, but that is precisely what we are doing today with business and industry. We build heavily commercialized sites, ruin them, and then move on to another. We can afford to only because we have so much space available, but space is beginning to run out. Before we occupy it all with our urban and industrial sprawl, perhaps we should reconsider what we are doing. There can be a place in this country for everything we want, but only if we keep it in its place.

As former Secretary Udall said in his testimony before the joint committee of the House and the Senate, we "need to rehabilitate and we can rebuild and make much more livable even the worst of our cities." If we were to do this, if we were to restore dignity and amenity to city living, we would automatically reduce the pressure on the American land and help solve many of the conservation problems that plague us. I often wonder if conservationists might not perform a better service to the cause in which they work by thinking less about the countryside and more about making our cities what they should be.

The problems that plague our cities can neither be ignored nor isolated. They are endemic to our society. Even our suburbs, where the more fortunate have fled, often discover they are suffering from the same difficulties as the cities, although perhaps to a somewhat lesser degree. In 1969, a reporter for the New York *Times* interviewed many residents in a suburb outside New York City, and here is what she found. The district attorney's office had started an investigation of the local garbage hauling company; he had reason to believe it might be controlled by the Mafia. The state was investigating the construction of a school building that had cost 50 percent more than estimated; a possibility of fraud existed in the award of the contracts. Crime had risen sharply and was checked only by putting more policemen on the streets during the evening. The cost of housing was soaring. People in the middle-income brackets, just like their counterparts in the cities, were finding it difficult to locate houses they could afford to buy or apartments they could afford to rent. The sale and use of narcotics was on the rise, both among the poor and among the wealthy; the police department was unable to check it. Racial tensions between the blacks, the whites, and the Jews were on the increase. Two black students had been arrested for throwing Molotov cocktails into the school cafeteria, and a self-appointed vigilante committee of white Gentiles was appearing at school board meetings to protect the school board members against what the committee claimed were possible attacks by Jews and blacks. One resident wearily complained that she had carefully saved her money to flee from the Bronx in New York City. Now, she said, all the problems she had tried to escape were catching up with her again.[15]

Her experience is that of many suburbanites. A glance at the newspapers shows that drug abuse is not something that afflicts cities only. Suburbs are also not immune to worsening traffic conditions, garbage disposal problems, poor or nonexistent public transportation, rising crime rates, burgeoning taxes, and the other ills of the city. We know now that the escape route will not work. For the more privileged individuals and industries to move deeper into the country does not solve the basic evils. It simply spreads them farther and farther, until soon our countryside will be pockmarked with the decaying centers of past developments, each surrounded by a ring of newer developments that are beginning to decay, and beyond them additional developments that are at the beginning of the cycle. We cannot conserve much of America if we allow this process to continue unabated. And we will not check it as long as we turn our backs on it or continue to evade it. And that is what we have been doing for all too many years.

Some years ago, the work I was doing took me in search of some records at one of New York City's precinct stations. The records had been placed in dead storage in a building located behind the garage, and we had to walk through the garage in order to get at them. As we did so, I noticed the feet of a corpse protruding from a piece of canvas that had been thrown on the floor. Before I could make any comment, the detective accompanying me remarked in a casual voice, "It looks as though they have found another one." This aroused my curiosity, and I asked how many they ordinarily found. He replied an average of about one a week. Some were dragged out of the river, some were uncovered in vacant lots. Each died in one of two ways: by violence or alone. And that was only one precinct in the large city. Think of that, you executives, as you sip your second martini during your expense account lunch in the skyscraper restaurant and plan how you can leave early that afternoon for a game of golf. The sheets of glass that isolate you from the rain and the cold outside cannot isolate you forever from the misery in those streets below you. Sooner or later it will catch up with you.

Although I had thought I knew New York reasonably well, I began to see another side. Before then, as a former newsman, I had believed murders were newsworthy. In most areas they are, but not in New York. There they are too numerous. Unless one is surrounded by especially gruesome circumstances or unless someone relatively prominent is either the victim or the perpetrator, murder goes unnoticed in the news columns. In the largest city of what considers itself the most advanced nation in the world, I walked into tenements in which the pervading sense was one of water, water leaking from the cold water pipes (there was no hot water available in this civilized country of ours), water dripping down the walls, and the constant smell of escaping urine. These places belonged to the Middle Ages, not to twentieth-century America. They were completely unfit as dwelling places for human beings in a society such as ours. Harlem? New York had not yet discovered Harlem, although a few politicians were making use of the black vote to perpetuate their power. Rarely, if ever, did I enter a Harlem apartment (and I went into many of them) without noticing that it usually had three or four separate locks on the doors and that the frameworks were scarred from repeated jimmying attempts. They were occupied by people—some of whom were criminals, but most of whom were honest persons—living in a state of fear such as few people in America are cursed with having to endure. They did not walk their own streets at night. As soon as the sun dropped behind the buildings, they called their children in and barricaded their doors against a possible attack. They had to spend each night that way because for them there was no temporary escape to the suburbs. They were locked into this life. Many of them were resigned to it but hoped something better lay ahead for their children.

Crime? The average American knows what the word "mugging" means. Some thugs have jumped on a man or a woman, beaten him up, and taken any valuables he may have had with him. That is not what mugging meant in Harlem in the 1940's.

At that time, mugging was used to describe a much more vicious crime in which two or more men walked up alongside their victim, whipped out a knife, stabbed it into his abdomen, and then ripped it upward. The attackers took nothing. This was a crime for sport, not for money. Prostitution? I recall a white high school in which the principal noticed that some of the girls suddenly had more money than usual. Investigation revealed that they had organized their own ring of prostitution, servicing largely the husbands of pregnant women.

These brief comments are not intended to shock—but to provide a backdrop against which the complacency and indifference of the average intelligent city dweller or worker will stand out. Caught up in his own business or professional problems, sending his children to select and expensive private schools or moving to the suburbs, and engrossed in a social life in which he meets only his peers, he has completely isolated himself from the problems and the miseries that may exist only a few blocks away. Part of this may result from the tempo of city life. In order to avoid hyperexcitement, the city forces people to withdraw. They isolate themselves in a pattern of daily routine in which they travel the same route to work each day and the same route back at night. They see the same people who share the same ideas. To survive, they become islands of provincialism in the center of the masses. Intellectually and emotionally, they are doing what the blacks have to do. They barricade themselves in. Only when violence beats at their barricades, as the blacks finally did with their riots in Harlem or as the criminals have done by extending their activities into wealthier residential districts, do they suddenly come out of their lethargy and take an interest in the city and people around them. Then once the crisis has passed, they drift back into it again.

The result is a worsening of conditions in city after city across the country. The crime rate has not improved; instead it has risen. Drug abuse is far more rampant. In some areas, high-cost luxury housing has replaced substandard buildings. For the wealthy who can afford to live in them, this is an improvement, but it is no help to the poor. The best they receive are the sterile, low-rent housing that we sometimes provide in place of tenements.

Yet New York—and I use it only as an example—contains what is probably the world's largest supply of the talent needed to solve its problems. Finance? It is the world's financial center. Certainly among the many economists and financiers working for the large banks, the brokerage houses, and the investment firms, there are men who could come up with workable answers to the city's monetary difficulties. Government? Its universities contain experts on government. Management? There are numerous management consultant firms in New York whose capabilities are sufficiently great to enable them to command large fees. They might apply some of their skills, free, to the solution of the city's problems. The list is endless. And in the end, the skeptic asks, how do you sell the needed changes to the electorate? The answer is simple. New York is also headquarters for some of the largest and most successful advertising and public relations firms in the nation. Perhaps they could be called upon to help sell the constructive ideas that might emerge.

If some leader were to harness the talents already in New York, persuade them to offer their services on a part-time, but serious, basis and put them to work on the city's problems, the results might surprise even themselves. But next to complacency, the one quality that marks most New Yorkers—like many other city dwellers—is indifference. They have not yet learned to care in a world in which caring is important. I can remember at least one top executive who spent far more time talking to me about whether he should bring his yacht to the city to entertain his business guests than I could ever get him to spend in discussing the Puerto Ricans and their impact on both the city and on what he was trying to sell.

What is true of New York is also true of many other cities across the country. There is one that I visit at least once or twice a year, and as I sit in its principal club, I am reminded of nothing so much as a novel by Sinclair Lewis. The city is small enough, so its elite all know one another well; and their conversation is almost always the same. It deals with minor jokes, minor parties, minor fads, and what they are all doing on their several vaca-

tions. Rarely are the problems of the city—and it has many—
mentioned. Each time I enjoy its hospitality—I have good friends
there whom I like to see—I feel as though I were paying the same
visit as the year before. Such intellectual stability was admirable
years ago. But in an age when changes occur quickly and pressures accumulate fast, stability of this sort may only create a
greater instability. And I am afraid that is what it is doing.

That city, like New York, is no special exception for the disregard with which the intelligent, educated citizens of most communities hold for the basic problems faced by their city governments and by the large majority of less intelligent—because less
well-educated—people. But there are exceptions. There are communities where the elite do care, and I would like to describe one
and tell what it did to make itself livable again.

By 1946, Pittsburgh, Pennsylvania, had run its full cycle as
an American industrial center and had reached its nadir. Its
history, in many respects, had been typical.

Because of its superb location at the confluence of the Allegheny and Monongahela Rivers, where they join to form the
Ohio, the French, during the French and Indian Wars, had
chosen this spot in the wilderness for the construction of a fort.
Whoever occupied this location held the gateway to the vast
lands to the west and controlled traffic down the waterways. The
British colonies could not expand westward as long as Fort
Duquesne remained in French hands. With the objective of capturing the fort, the crown sent General Braddock on the ill-fated
mission that ended in his famous ambush and followed this with
the more successful venture of General Forbes, who hoisted the
British flag above the stockade.

In the following years, Pittsburgh played a dominant role in
the opening of the Dixie frontier. Trade goods were brought over
the Allegheny Mountains from the Northeast and loaded on keel-
boats, flatboats, and rafts. They were then floated down the rivers
to settlements like Wheeling and Louisville. Purchases made in
those communities were carried farther down the rivers and at
New Orleans were loaded onto ships. From there they often were
taken to the West Indies, where other goods were bought and

carried back to the Northeast, and the trade loop was completed. Geography had indeed favored Pittsburgh, and the city flourished.

Even when the nation's dependence on water transportation declined, Pittsburgh's prosperity continued, again largely because of its geography. Its proximity to vast supplies of soft coal and limestone made it an excellent location in which to manufacture steel, and the discovery of oil nearby gave its growth added impetus. Although Pennsylvania's oil reserves were not large by modern standards, they gave the citizens of Pittsburgh an early understanding of the business. Much of the development of the Texas fields was financed, not from large centers like Chicago or New York, but from Pittsburgh, where banks and other investors were quick to comprehend the opportunities that were offered. (Pittsburgh was also the headquarters of Gulf Oil, whose foundations were laid with the discovery of oil down the river from the city.) George Westinghouse also chose Pittsburgh as the place in which to manufacture his airbrakes and electrical devices, and the city attracted other businesses like the Koppers Company and United Engineering and Foundry, which basically served steel.

But as Pittsburgh grew, it was laying the seeds for its future decay. Steel was a great industry, but it tended to drive out smaller ones. The little businesses had difficulty surviving in the shadow of giants. The city was also dividing into two groups, those who owned or managed the mills and those who worked in them. There was little room for the middle-income class, who normally set the temper of a community. This was reflected in the absence, for example, of many specialty shops. The wealthy went on regular shopping trips to New York; the poor did not need sophisticated stores. Although it contained two universities and other cultural institutions, including Carnegie Museum and its excellent dinosaur collection, it could hardly have been called a cultural center, and it was not located near one. The depression of the 1930's struck it hard; steel is extremely sensitive to general business conditions. World War II set the mills roaring again, and prosperity momentarily returned. But with the conclusion of hostilities, Pittsburgh had only the bleakest of futures to look forward to. One of the most alarming signs of its condition was the difficulty experienced by industry in employing the middle-income group of scientists, engineers, and managers, whom the increased technology and size of business make so important. Young college graduates offered jobs in Pittsburgh and some other city often declined the Pittsburgh offer. They had heard of Pittsburgh's bad reputation; and if they visited it, they only found their thinking confirmed.

Smoke rose from the stacks of the mills, black, oily smoke that lay trapped in the rivers' valleys. Day after day went by, and the sun never emerged even at noon. The dirt was so terrible that booksellers wrapped each of their volumes in paper before putting them on the shelves. Left exposed, they soon became so filthy as to be unsalable. The downtown area was a shambles, much of it occupied by old buildings whose original owners had long since moved elsewhere to escape the dirt and confusion. The city had little or nothing to offer new industries. Even its geography was now working against it. Although it still provided excellent water transportation, particularly for bulk cargoes, the steep walls of its valleys severely limited the number of possible plant sites. Politically, too, it was badly handicapped. Greater Pittsburgh covers a large area and must be considered as a unit, but the city itself is a surprisingly small part of the entirety. It is ringed by one independent community after another. They are so close that it is often difficult for the stranger to know when he is leaving the limits of one and entering another. To further complicate the problem, Pittsburgh and Allegheny County, in which it is located, had for years been traditionally controlled by the Democrats, while the state, whose legislation also affects the area, was firmly in the hands of the Republicans. The outlook for any significant political action seemed remote.

Pittsburgh's condition was like that of many other cities. It had run the full cycle from a wilderness outpost to a prosperous industrial center where great fortunes were made to a wasteland that many were now willing to desert.[16]

But Pittsburgh had a hidden asset that is rare among American cities. It contained some people of influence who cared about its fate and were willing to work in order to better it. One of these was Richard King Mellon, the leader of those members of the Mellon family who had remained in western Pennsylvania. When he returned from his wartime service in the army, he looked around him and came to a conclusion: He should either try to improve the city or move away, and he was reluctant to do the latter, arguing that his family had made its fortune in Pittsburgh and therefore he had a debt to the city. There was no other reason for his remaining. By that time, Mr. Mellon's investments were sufficiently diversified so that he had no real economic stake in the region. He could either have buried himself in the beautiful countryside near Ligonier, Pennsylvania, where he maintained his residence, or he could have moved to an entirely different section of the country. Nothing restrained him but conscience.

But alone he could accomplish little. Many people shrug off Pittsburgh's redevelopment with the comment that after all it had the Mellon family behind it; their communities could do as well with that sort of support. But Pittsburgh's problems were far greater than anything that the Mellon family could solve by themselves. Mr. Mellon needed allies, and he found them. One was Benjamin Fairless, chairman of the board of the United States Steel Corporation. In many respects, the combination was an unlikely one. In spite of their common interest in business, their backgrounds were entirely different. Mr. Mellon had inherited a large fortune. Mr. Fairless, on the other hand, was entirely self-made. He had risen from the humblest of origins to become the head of a great industrial corporation, an experience that often makes a man become self-centered rather than interested in his community. But he, too, had a conscience.

The combination of these two was extremely important. Mr. Mellon represented finance, and Mr. Fairless, industry, two of the dominant forces in modern American life. But a third essential element was lacking. Except in the state capitol in Harrisburg, neither Mr. Mellon nor Mr. Fairless could exercise political influence. The mayor of Pittsburgh was David Lawrence, a powerful force in the Democratic Party, not only in the city but also throughout the country, the state, and the nation. An oldtime politician, he had spent his life running against the Mellons. Any union between him and them appeared outside the realm of possibility.

One day, however, Mr. Mellon called the mayor and asked for an appointment. What happened was told me later by a man who was extremely close to Mr. Lawrence and thought that that telephone call marked the beginning of the change in the two men's relationship. The mayor believed that Mr. Mellon was coming over to level a complaint against some aspect of the city's administration, the tax rate, for example. Instead Mr. Mellon wanted to offer the city some family property he thought could be used as a park. The idea that he would come to the mayor's office to make such a gift, instead of summoning the mayor to his, made a profound impression on Mr. Lawrence. When Mr. Mellon left, he turned to an aide and said, "I think I could work with that man."

He found that indeed he could, and he, too, joined the movement to resuscitate Pittsburgh, bringing his political power to bear on the city's problems. Later there were some cynics who maintained that both sides had so much to gain, the alliance was a natural one. But that was not so. Mayor Lawrence had first to fight a battle within his own ranks to convince the Democrats that there was a merit in cooperating with the city's leading Republican family, and Mr. Mellon was subject to considerable criticism from many of his peers at Pittsburgh's Duquesne Club. That they weathered the storm among their own friends and supporters was a credit to both men.

An initial policy decision of the triumvirate proved a wise one. Instead of creating a mammoth new agency to oversee the task of Pittsburgh's redevelopment, thus adding to the city's bureaucracy, they determined to use existing agencies whenever possible. But they also decided that priorities must be established and the work of the agencies coordinated. (In other words, they did precisely what the American conservation movement has not done.) To carry out this job, they formed the Allegheny Conference on Community Development, with an extremely small staff of highly capable people and a board that was composed of people of influence who were accustomed to accomplishing things.

The conference gave first priority to smoke control. It represented a major problem, one that might well have been postponed until the new effort had enjoyed some smaller successes, but they thought that if they could clean the air of Pittsburgh, they would gain a great psychological advantage. If that problem could be solved, anything else would appear possible.

The program was divided into four steps. First, industrial, then domestic furnaces (which actually accounted for more smoke than industry did); and, geographically, first, Pittsburgh, and then Allegheny County. The pressure brought to bear on industry was enormous, because of the prestige of the Allegheny Conference. It could not be resisted, especially since the conference demonstrated a willingness to engage in realistic compromise. Mills that were unable to meet the standards by the deadline set for them were not summarily punished as long as they were making a real effort. One such mill, even after spending approximately a million dollars on smoke control, found that it was still not complying, but everyone looked the other way as it continued trying. Labor also had to be considered. Soft coal was Pittsburgh's principal fuel and also the principal source of its heaviest smogs. To convert to another fuel would mean the loss of a substantial market and perhaps jobs. Fortunately times were prosperous, so no objections came from the miners.

Passage of the enabling legislation by the state would have posed no great problem with the combination of the Mellon Republicans and the Lawrence Democrats backing it except for one of the most powerful elements in Pennsylvania—the Pennsylvania Railroad. It had made no serious objection to smoke abatement within the city limits of Pittsburgh; it simply stoked its engines before entering them and built up enough steam to last until the engines left. But it could not apply this simple expedient to the whole of Allegheny County. The distances were too great, and the only way the railroad could avoid violating the proposed legislation was to convert to diesels, something it had no desire to do. It began to lobby vigorously against the bill, and the day before it came up for vote, a tally showed that the measure was likely to be defeated. Mr. Mellon, however, saved it. In a telephone call to a top official of the Pennsylvania Railroad, he pointed out that he and his family were among the railroad's largest stockholders and that they favored the legislation. The bill passed.

The major obstacle had yet to be overcome. That was the reaction of the individual houseowners, who were the principal cause of the polluted air. As the program moved through its various stages, a strange and unexpected emotionalism became uncovered. To many of Pittsburgh's workers, clear skies were synonymous with a depression, for the only time the sky was blue was when the mills were closed down. Anyone who has lived in a community that is largely dependent on a single industry will know what this means. Everything else—stores, movie theaters, restaurants, automobile dealerships—feels the impact almost at once. It was not that Pittsburghers wanted dirty skies, but a form of superstition seemed to grip part of the city's population.

The real test, however, lay in the willingness of the people to spend the money necessary to comply with the law. As I have mentioned, the most commonly used fuel was soft coal because of its cheapness and ready availability. Pittsburghers had used it since the early half of the previous century, but it is virtually impossible to place soft coal on a furnace fire without sending out clouds of black smoke. Every houseowner was therefore faced with a practical choice: Install an automatic stoker that would feed the coal in small amounts over a period of time or convert their furnaces to gas. Many an improvement program has been wrecked on the shoals of individual action. For it is one thing to shake a fist at a large corporation and denounce it for ruining our environment, and quite another to dig down into one's own pocket to correct what seems, when taken by itself, only a minor contribution to the total problem. Although there were grumblings here and there, the people as a whole were beginning to be excited about what was happening to their surroundings and made the change gladly.

Just as the leaders of the movement had expected, the conquest of smog had an enormous psychological impact on the community. Granted that the problem was not entirely solved and years later still is not, nevertheless the change was dramatic and great. The booksellers were able to remove the wrappings from their volumes and place them on the shelves unprotected. Housewives no longer had to launder their curtains with appalling frequency or wipe the oily soot from their desks each time they sat down to write a letter. On many mornings, the mists still rose from Pittsburgh's rivers, but they no longer hung over the city all day long. The sun could disperse them.

As Pittsburghers looked around themselves, they liked what they saw, and a constructive civic pride began to take hold of the community. Talk of abandoning the city became less and less. The United States Steel Corporation, which had considered moving its headquarters elsewhere, was persuaded to remain. Redevelopment started on the downtown area. Where once there were slum-type buildings, there now stands a state park, revealing again the site of Fort Duquesne and the magnificent view of the rivers. New office buildings began to rise. Each of them required a major investment, but the combination of political forces and industrial and financial influence were sufficient to meet each challenge. The state, for example, took responsibility for the park. Industry and finance made certain that the buildings would be rented before they were erected. Each step was thoroughly coordinated.

Nor was the effort limited solely to physical improvement. Pittsburgh was one of the earliest cities to adopt a United Fund for its charitable giving. It refurbished its outstanding museum, creating new displays that would attract more visitors as well as stepping up its scientific work. It poured money into its symphony. Each of these actions was related to the other. As one of the planners said, to cite a single instance, "If we build up the universities, we are also creating an audience for the orchestra." Nor was the effort restricted to the city. In a surprisingly farsighted move, a private foundation, with the knowledge of the county commissioners, quietly bought up land that might be needed for future county parks. It then resold it at cost to the county, which did not attempt to immediately develop it but rather banked it to meet future demands for open space and recreational areas. The Western Pennsylvania Conservancy, under the leadership of the Allegheny Conference, went even further afield. Privately supported but working closely with the state, it helped the state park system substantially to increase its holdings within reasonably short driving distances from the center of the city. Pittsburgh, unlike many other American cities, will not in the future be tightly ringed by industrial and residential areas. Its citizens will always have somewhere to go when they want to be in the countryside.

The results of Pittsburgh's efforts have been far from perfect, as the most ardent supporter of the movement would readily admit. The insurgent Democrat, who won the mayorality campaign of 1969, ran against the regular party chiefs who had been instrumental in the redevelopment. One of the defects to which he pointed was the sharp decline in the population of the city itself. More attention should have been paid, he said, to refurbishing the older residential centers rather than concentrating so much effort on the downtown district. Many of the criticisms leveled against Pittsburgh's program are valid, but the fact remains that the city did save itself. Those who deride what it has accomplished forget what it used to be.

But the key to its salvation did not lie with a handful of men. They initiated the effort, but their enthusiasm and concern was so great that it soon spread to others. A larger and larger proportion of Pittsburgh's executives and professional men became interested in improving their city. To broaden the base of participation, the planners, when they could, created authorities rather than city agencies to carry out certain tasks. Nonresidents could then be appointed to the boards of authorities, and so a suburban dweller would come face to face with inner-city problems and be given direct responsibility for solving them. Others were drawn to the boards of private agencies, and in no other city that I know about was working for the community so fashionable among the elite. Membership on the board of the Allegheny Conference was almost as prestigious as memberships on the boards of the largest corporations.

One high executive, a new arrival in the city, admitted his surprise in a news magazine. When he had first come to Pittsburgh and was asked to serve in several community positions, he had thought the people talking to him were joking. It was something that he had never done before and could hardly imagine doing. Then he learned that they were deadly serious, that this was expected of him. Merely running his company was not sufficient to earn him Pittsburgh's plaudits or the respect of his local directors. Once he had reached this startling conclusion, he got to work and found civic problems both interesting and challenging, as well as broadening.

Many executives and professional men in other cities would, too, if they would only look more closely at the places where they live and work and realize that as people who have been favored by our society, they have a responsibility toward their surroundings. They could become like their counterparts in Pittsburgh— men of conscience and men who care.

Many books have been written on the fate of our cities and what can be done to redeem them. The proposed solutions are not always the same because the problems are not easy ones. But certainly this country has the financial and human resources needed to bring our cities back to life and make them what they should be—comfortable, livable centers of population, where we can carry on activities that are not compatible with the country. If we can do this—and do it fast—we will also reduce some of the enormous pressures that are creating many of our greatest conservation problems. But this will never occur until more leaders recognize that the responsibility for their communities cannot be shifted off to someone else. They themselves, like the leaders of Pittsburgh, must start caring enough to be willing to contribute their own skills and abilities and join in the struggle.

Regardless of what happens to the world's population—and if we ignore our obligation to help solve that problem, we may reap serious consequences—and regardless of whether our own levels out as it has been tending to do, we are going to be living in a country that has more human beings in it than ever before, and we will experience an unfamiliar crowding. Space, just physical space, will be more at a premium than ever before. The only solutions are to reduce our population through personal restraint and to learn to use space more wisely than we have. In this respect, we cannot afford to destroy our cities and then abandon them. There is just not that much room in the United States. Instead we must learn to rebuild and improve what we have already started and bring it up to date with our needs. This will happen when the residents of more of our major cities develop the same civic conscience and sense of responsibility as the leading citizens of Pittsburgh. The difference between Pittsburgh and other communities can be summed up in two words: "caring enough." If sufficient people cared enough, we could remake our cities.

7

The Tale of Three Parks

T HERE are few simple answers to most conservation
issues, and we complicate them even further by taking each one
up individually without first adopting a basic policy. It is not
surprising, therefore, to discover that we have difficulties making
decisions about the use of our land. I am not speaking now of
choices as complex as the nationwide location of industry but
of problems that should be relatively easy to solve, such as the
preservation of some of our outstanding open areas. As examples
of our confusion and lack of determination, I would like to cite
the histories of three parks.

Although far less well known to Easterners than such dramatic
and familiar sites as the Grand Canyon and the Yosemite, few
places in the United States surpass the Cascade Mountains of
Washington for magnificence and splendor. No matter which
way the traveler approaches them, whether he comes from the
east and journeys up Lake Chelan—a miracle of beauty in itself
—or enters them from the west, he will find himself deeply
moved. A few words cannot describe the Cascades. They are a
land of glaciers and rocks, heavily timbered valleys, and deposits

of ore with occasional ruins of an old mineshaft or the now-deserted buildings of a mining town. One of their most striking features is the numerous waterfalls from which they get their name. I have stood in a small valley and seen as many as seven of them from the same spot, each plummeting in a plume of clear water over the sheer sides of the surrounding mountain. At least a part of such a range deserves preservation, not only for the benefit of our own generation, but for the benefit of those coming after us. It has finally won it, but the steps were long and complicated.

The land became the property of the federal government in 1846 with the establishment of the Oregon Territory. It was first placed in the public domain (land that is owned by the government but not designated for a special use like a national forest or national park). In 1893, the government set up the Pacific Forest Reserve, composed of the lower portion of the North Cascade Mountains; and in 1897, the year William McKinley became President, the government created the Washington Forest Reserve, which included the northern section of the mountains. (Forest reserves were the forerunners of our national forests.) That same year additional acreage was placed in the Washington Forest Reserve, which was renamed the Mount Rainier Forest Preserve. Two years later, part of the forest reserve was used to make Mount Rainier National Park.

Subsequently the forest reserves, with numerous boundary and other changes, became the Mount Baker, Snoqualmie, Wenatchee, Okanogan, and Gifford Pinchot National Forests. But many people thought more land should be given national park status; and as early as 1908, a conservation group proposed that a park be created in the Lake Chelan area. Nothing came of the idea or of the suggestion made the following year, that a national park be established that would include Mount Baker. In 1916— and I mention these dates only to show how slowly the mills of government grind—three bills were introduced with the objective of making Mount Baker a national park. Only one bill survived as long as the following year. During the next three years, six more bills were introduced. They also quickly died. From 1919 to 1921, three more bills were introduced, calling for the formation of a Yakima National Park. They suffered the same fate as the preceding legislation; Congress took no action on them.

The U.S. Forest Service, which is alert to changes in the times, became aware of the growing interest in recreation in the Cascades and between 1925 and 1933 developed recreation plans for the mountains and also designated several areas as "limited," limited, that is, to the degree that they might neither be developed nor exploited. Nevertheless many were afraid these safeguards were not enough, for part of the function of the U.S. Forest Service is to make lumber available to the nation; and also the national forests, unlike the national parks, are open to entry for mining. These fears were accentuated by the increased cutting of the forests. As the quantity of timber declined on private lands, more and more lumbermen in the Northwest were turning to the national forests for additional timber; and in many places they were doing clear cutting, which leaves ugly scars. In 1937, the National Park Service made a study of the area and how best to preserve it. Although this study was cited frequently in subsequent years, it did not result in any positive action. World War II passed and still nothing happened. In 1960 and 1961, bills were introduced in Congress that provided for another overall study of the area. These, too, produced no results, so in 1963, the Secretaries of Agriculture and the Interior, both of them sensitive to growing public concern, established a joint study team to look at the problem. The report they made was published in 1965.[1]

By 1967, time was running out in the North Cascades. A large mining corporation owned some 3,000 acres in the Glacier Peak Wilderness. This area was protected by the provisions of the National Wilderness Act, a constructive measure that permits the federal government to set aside certain areas as wilderness in which development and commercial exploitation is severely restricted. Unfortunately the act contains a provision that was made as a concession to industrial interests; it provides that mineral claims in designated wilderness areas could be mined until 1984. The very act designed to protect wildernesses was putting a premium on their fast exploitation, and the mining corporation that owned the land in the Glacier Peak area announced

plans to take advantage of this loophole. It was going to determine the feasibility of creating an open pit mine.[2]

Secretary of Agriculture Orville L. Freeman gave a speech in
April of that year in which he summarized the situation well:
"The Cascades are an ocean of mountains, frozen in space and
time . . . wave after cresting wave of stone, dotted with the deep
blue-green of alpine lakes . . . laced with the glacial remnants of
another age.

"If you have been down the San Juans, or the East Face of
the Tetons, you have an appreciation of the Cascades—but only
a partial appreciation. To call them 'America's Alps' understates
the case. They are uniquely American—and if Americans destroy
their character they will not see their like again . . . really to
know these mountains, one must experience them with all the
senses . . . hear the wind above timberline, a voice like all the
rivers in the world, flowing over a thousand miles of granite and
green . . . smell the pine . . . feel a pebble polished by eons of
time.

"If everyone could do this, even for a day, I am confident that
most of the controversy over invasion of wilderness would rapidly disappear. But unfortunately it hasn't."

He then went on to describe in precise terms the issues and
the choices. "Within this vastness is Miners Ridge and Image
Lake," he continued. "This ridge is also the site of a valuable
copper deposit, placed there, perhaps, by a wise Creator to test
whether man could forego material riches for the fullness of the
spirit.

"We may face this test in the very near future, when and if
the application is made to begin open pit mining operations
within the Wilderness.

*"The reasons given for this mine are not so very different from
the reasons given for other resource development.* [Emphasis
added.] The copper deposit is valuable; companies are being encouraged to increase domestic production; and, as we all know,
there's a war going on. The company owns, or has mineral rights
on, some 3,000 acres of land. Many of these claims were patented years ago.

"Perhaps some of the same reasons were given many years ago when a mine was opened on the rim of the Grand Canyon.

"But, in balance, it can also be pointed out:

"1. Our present war effort will not suffer if Miners Ridge is left undeveloped. Neither will our civilian standard of living suffer.

"2. This is not the only undeveloped copper deposit in the United States. Others exist, perhaps less valuable, perhaps more costly to develop. Some are in the Upper Lake States—in areas of high unemployment—where development could both decrease the jobless rate and leave wilderness values unimpaired." Here the secretary brought out our constant tendency to industrialize new areas rather than fully utilize our older ones.

"It is not," he continued, "a case, in short, of 'either-or.' It is rather a case of economics, of choosing alternatives; of balancing a priceless, yet intangible, national treasure, against ledger sheets and profits.

"The decision in this case lies almost totally with the Kennecott Copper Corporation, and not with the Secretary of Agriculture. They own, or have claims on, the land on which the deposit is located. The language of the Wilderness Act and the intent of Congress is clear. They have the right to develop it, if they insist. . . .

"I further urge that the Sierra Club [which he was addressing] take every possible opportunity to inform the officers and shareholders of the company, and the American public, of the issues at stake on Miners Ridge.

"These issues are not simple. But if they are presented fairly and completely, I am confident that the public interest will prevail.

"The issue in the North Cascades presents, in microcosm, some of the larger conservation issues we face across the continent. Ours is a nation of exploding population and expanding standards of living. There is near-infinite demand on very finite natural resources.

"This means pressure for consumptive use of resources such as the copper deposit at Miners Ridge—and it also means 'people' pressure on wilderness. . . ." [3]

Secretary Freeman was correct when he said the North Cascades presented in microcosm the larger national conservation issues that we face. Here was one industry making studies to determine the economics of conducting an operation that would leave an irreparable scar in the middle of one of the nation's most beautiful areas. And the only considerations were economic, not esthetic, not even the economy of the country as a whole and the help that might be given centers of unemployment. This is not so much the fault of the company as it is the fault of the system. Wiser land-use planning earlier might have prevented the company from acquiring those lands in the first place and thus gaining an economic stake in their development.

But settling the case of the corporation was not the only issue involved or obstacle to be overcome. The lumber industry, with its increasing dependence on logging federal lands, wanted no national park at all, or if there had to be one, it wanted it to be as small as possible. Logging is not permitted in national parks. The sportsmen, too, were not unified in their views, and wide differences existed between them. Hunting, for example, is not permitted in most national parks except under certain extremely restricted conditions; it is permitted in national forests. So those who liked to hunt and those who made their livings supplying hunters also opposed the formation of too large a park. They were joined by other active sportsmen, for the National Park Service does not do as much to encourage active sports as the U.S. Forest Service. At the other extreme from the industrialists stood the preservationists, those who wanted to keep as much of the area as possible in its natural state and with a minimum of easy access by highway or other forms of motorized transportation.

The controversy was further heightened by competition between the National Park Service and the U.S. Forest Service. No agency of government likes to surrender part of its holdings to another, and the U.S. Forest Service was no exception. Having managed the North Cascades for many years and having done what it considered a good job, the service was not willing to turn over the property to the National Park Service without a struggle. The National Park Service, on the other hand, was anxious to

enlarge its responsibilities. So even after the joint report of the
Departments of Agriculture and the Interior was finally issued,
there was still disagreement. A member of the study group, who
represented the Department of the Interior (this department contains the National Park Service), filed a dissent. "There is no
doubt, I suppose, in anyone's mind," he wrote, "that Mt. Baker
and the area surrounding it are of national park caliber. . . . In
addition, in my opinion, the Mt. Baker area would benefit from
Park Service administration. The Park Service can operate winter sports facilities as well as anyone else [meaning, of course,
the U.S. Forest Service]. . . ." [4] A dissenting report filed by a
representative of the Department of Agriculture, which contains
the U.S. Forest Service, included this statement: "It is difficult
for me to see the justification for proposals to make a national
park out of Mt. Baker. Mt. Baker does not compare with Mt.
Rainier in geologic and scenic attractiveness as a mountain mass.
Mt. Baker is now a well-known, popular winter sports area. It
has an international reputation. The present pattern of management has been highly satisfactory to the residents of the State
of Washington." [5] If representatives of the two agencies most
closely involved with the problem could not agree even after the
report was completed, it is not surprising that the legislation
passed by the House and Senate did not follow the recommendations of the study team. Instead of creating a single national park,
it established the North Cascades National Park, divided by a
national recreation area with another national recreation area
at the southern end. (National recreation areas are also administered by the National Park Service, but less restrictive standards
are maintained.) In the national park, further logging was prohibited, and entry by mining was eliminated. But many of those
who worked for the passage of the bill were still concerned about
the area's future. The measure stated that the National Park
Service was to administer it in accordance with the service's basic
policies, but at least one powerful member of the House made it
clear that he counted on the National Park Service to develop it
extensively. He spoke in terms of an investment of $35 million
in physical development over the coming years, far more than
Congress appropriated for the purchase of the private lands

within the park boundaries.[6] His plans hardly seemed in harmony
with the stated purpose of preserving the mountains.

Of course, the final bill did not please everyone. No compromise could. But what is disturbing is that it took us so long to
make even that. Here was one of the most magnificent regions
in the country. Yet we could not make up our minds whether to
mine it, lumber it, open it up to intensive recreation, or conserve
it. At the same time, however, we had been making dramatic
and influential decisions about the future of the State of Washington. On December 13, 1935, actual construction began on
the Grand Coulee Dam, which would bring water to the farms
and electric power to the cities. This began an era of development and growth, fostered by the federal government. It was
followed by other federal spending in the area, including large
contracts awarded to the Boeing Aircraft Corporation and the
construction of the first big reactors for the production of plu-
tonium. These factors helped the rapid increase in Washington's
population. From 1940 to 1960, it rose by approximately 70
percent, while that of the United States as a whole increased
about 34 percent. Furthermore, projections indicated that Washington's growth would continue to exceed the United States's
through the year 2000.[7] This growth, stimulated by federal projects, contributed to the pressure on the North Cascades. As the
study team reported, there were now about 3.5 million people
within a short distance of the mountains; and by the year 2000,
there might be 8.6 million.[8]

And yet only at this date, after years of delay, had we really
started formulating a policy for the use of the federally owned
lands that were affected by this increase in population. The
absence of a basic land policy, even concerning lands already
owned by the federal government, can be seen in our handling
of the North Cascades over the years. And they constitute only
one area in one state.

(The situation in Washington was not unique. Again and
again, the government through the establishment of federal facilities, the development of natural resources, or the letting of
federal appropriations has heavily influenced the growth of an
area without any overall plan. Often the states, in an attempt to

get what they consider their share of the federal dollar, encourage the process. Thus, for example, in the summer of 1970, Arizona was pleading for federally financed water to relieve its desperate shortage at the same time that it was begging the government to enlarge the military bases already within the state. Most particularly, it hoped for the transfer of a large contingent of men from Maryland, a transfer that could only aggravate the water shortage. If it follows the patterns of the past, the federal government will most likely accede to both requests.)

Perhaps wise planning for the use of a mountain range and the coordination of that planning with other federal activities that were affecting the surrounding areas was beyond our capabilities. But certainly we should be able to take advantage of a surprising opportunity to preserve a notable section of our vanishing shoreline.

Although Americans have long emphasized the importance of the freedom of the seas, they have been considerably less emphatic about freedom of access to those seas. Over the years, more and more of the nation's coastlines have gone into highly developed private ownership; and in many regions today, only the wealthy can easily enter America's waters or walk its beaches. This is apparent to any traveler. For miles and miles, he finds himself barred from the water by lines of private developments, broken only occasionally by a state park, a national seashore, or other public lands that he may enter. This situation is so well known it barely needs restating, and it lends urgency to our efforts to preserve what coastline remains.

One of the most unusual of opportunities existed at Point Reyes in northern California. This is a remarkable peninsula. It contains many miles of coast. Southward it faces on Drakes Bay, a spot where Sir Francis Drake is reputed to have anchored and which was used as a harbor by the early Spanish explorers. Westward it faces the Pacific Ocean, and to the northeast, it is separated from the mainland by Tomales Bay.

It is a large area—approximately 64,000 acres—but its size alone does not account for the wide variety that it offers. A combination of climatic conditions and geology have provided it with unusual diversity. The visitor can leave the beaches and the pounding waves and, in a short time, be wandering through the bishop pines that grow on Inverness Ridge. Or he can walk on the brushy slopes and look at the live oaks and California laurel. If he likes marshes and marsh birds, Point Reyes offers these too, both fresh water and salt water marshes. And there are also the grassy lowlands, the sand dunes, and the white cliffs that remind many travelers of the White Cliffs of Dover. Anyone who has walked the beaches of Point Reyes, seen the waters of the Pacific rolling against its coastline, or stood in the shade of its small grove of coastal redwoods, will agree that this is a place that deserves to be preserved for the benefit of the American people, not merely of a handful of persons with the ability to pay the prices currently demanded for waterfront property. This is especially true, as real estate developers within the last few years have been making serious inroads on even some of the most remote parts of the northern California coast.

If the topography and diversity of Point Reyes is remarkable, so is its history. Settlement first began in the early 1820's under the Mexican colonization laws. Because it was difficult to reach the peninsula, it was not suitable for small farming and instead became the site of a number of large ranches. The Treaty of Guadalupe Hidalgo, signed by the United States and Mexico in 1848, guaranteed the personal and property rights of Mexican citizens living on what then became American territory. For various reasons, including the expense of complying with the American laws, the Mexicans began to sell their lands to Americans, but the tradition of large-scale ranching continued. Most of the peninsula remained in the hands of a few families. In time, these turned from producing hides and meat to dairying, a business that proved profitable but still required large acreage in individual holdings.

Point Reyes was still remote. Although it is only about 30 or 35 miles north of San Francisco, the Golden Gate Bridge had not been built, so there was no quick and easy way to cross the bay into Marin County, in which Point Reyes is located. Most of the commercial traffic between the peninsula and the large metropolitan center so close to it was by schooner. For dairy ranches, this was sufficient, but not for people who had to be in San Francisco frequently. So the years passed Point Reyes by. Farther to the south, San Francisco and its environs continued to grow into large cities, but Point Reyes remained an area of rural calm and scenic grandeur.

This condition prevailed even after World War II, but few people could enjoy it. As the National Park Service reported in 1960, "on the Point Reyes Peninsula less than five miles [of beach access] are publicly owned and thus accessible for public enjoyment. With the exception of these beaches, the lighthouse, the State Park [which contained three small beaches], and about 30 miles of public road, all of the Peninsula is off-limits to the public. South of the road from Inverness to Point Reyes the land is all privately owned and public access is prohibited." [9]

With traffic pouring across the Golden Gate Bridge and more and more of San Francisco's population moving into Marin County, the future of Point Reyes became apparent. It was going to go one of two ways. Either the land would be taken up by private ownership and subdivided, or it could be purchased by a government agency and held as open space for the use of the public. In any case, dairy ranching that close to the city would eventually disappear.

Common sense dictated the latter course for Point Reyes rather than the former. The number of people who could be accommodated on Point Reyes in a profitable real estate development would do little to relieve congestion. On the other hand, held in public ownership and kept open to the public, the peninsula could provide recreational facilities from which millions would benefit, not only millions from San Francisco and its environs but others from farther away, who were finding it increasingly difficult to get to the waters of the Pacific Ocean. As a consequence, the National Park Service commenced an investigation of the feasibility of purchasing property on the point and creating a national seashore.

In 1957, George Collins of Conservation Associates in San Francisco, but then employed by the service, wrote a preliminary report in which he said: "The usually crowded conditions prevailing at existing public seashore areas on the Pacific Coast demonstrates that the demand for seashore recreation is growing more rapidly than areas are being established to supply it. Americans by the millions are discovering the value of their limited seashores. . . . But in the meantime, more and more of this precious heritage is going beyond reach for purposes of public recreation. That is true of the Point Reyes region as it is of other undeveloped recreation resource areas.

"If there exists the possibility of this coastal area for public ownership, positive action should be initiated immediately, and cooperatively to that end, by the County, State, and Federal Governments." [10] Mr. Collins stated the case succinctly, outlining not only the opportunity but also the need to act quickly. The chance was there, but it would not last long.

By 1961, almost four years after the preliminary report, the National Park Service produced another and more detailed report entitled *Land Use Survey—Proposed Point Reyes National Seashore.* This was a thoughtful analysis of what could be done, but—and here the taxpayer might take notice—the National Park Service did not have the funds to make it. The expense of conducting and printing the study had to come from private sources. Billions for highways, dams, and airports, but not one cent for a land-use survey of a priceless asset. This is what Congress seems to be choosing for us again and again.

The study proposed that the federal government acquire about 53,000 acres out of the total of 64,000 that make up the peninsula. Excluded from the project were to be Tomales Bay State Park and the private lands within it, villages on the peninsula, sufficient lands for their future expansion, two radio receiving installations used in international communications, the oyster beds, and the oyster cannery. Twenty thousand acres in the center of the peninsula, although to be acquired by the federal government, were not to be included in the public use area. Instead they were to be leased for dairy farming or, if the renters preferred, for raising beef cattle. This imaginative idea was designed to preserve the rural character of the area, and at the same time it ensured that the land would not be threatened by future suburban development that might overwhelm the national seashore. The public use area, the report said, "would make available for public enjoyment a 70-mile coastal area with many miles of sandy beaches, interspersed between steep bluffs containing marine caves and flanked by offshore rocks. Inland from the bluffs and beaches are grassy terraces, sand dunes, or rolling uplands covered with coastal brush, and wind-pruned trees." The report then described other aspects of the peninsula, including the 14,000-foot-high Inverness Ridge with its slopes on which grow broadleaf trees and Douglas firs, and it concluded: "The varied character of the PUBLIC USE ZONE, its natural condition and proximity to a large urban center, make the area one of the five most outstanding segments of unspoiled seashore remaining along the Pacific Coast." [11]

The feasibility of acquiring the land also looked excellent. The federal government already owned 115 acres. (This included the lighthouse and a lifeboat station.) The remainder was in the hands of only fifty individuals and corporations.[12] In parts of the United States, land has in the past been divided and sold and resold so many times that it becomes difficult to locate and negotiate with the owners. Point Reyes presented no such problem. Fifty transactions would complete the entire acquisition.

The economic impact of the national seashore on Marin County also looked extremely favorable. As the report stated, "Marin County has fewer industrial properties in proportion to residential properties than other counties in the Bay Area—over 67 percent of the tax base is in improved residential property. This fact, in turn, has resulted in a property tax burden on households which is greater than for any other Bay Area county. A national seashore would serve in the same role as industrial property in that it would attract taxable commerce and facilities beyond what would otherwise be required to serve the visiting public. Such expansion would add to the property, sales, gasoline and other tax bases of the county." [13]

In addition, the local tax officials, who often oppose the transfer of land into public ownership, were well disposed toward the plan. The same report said, "On the basis of research to date the question of whether subdivision developments, which might occur if a national seashore were not established, would increase or decrease the tax burdens of other residents would depend largely upon the types of developments. However," the report continued, "according to Marin County fiscal officials, the addition of the average tract home to the tax base does not react favorably to the tax position of property owners in general. This is so because the added tax revenue realized from the new home is less than the costs of education and other governmental functions needed to service that home." [14] The wise officials of Marin County recognized what so many officials fail to see, that new developments often increase taxes rather than lower them.

Of course, not everyone was for the proposed national seashore. The fifty property owners certainly would have wished to keep their lands and dispose of them in any way they wanted. And there were those in Marin County who preferred the more usual process of residential development for the peninsula. But probably few conservation land-use possibilities had more support than this. Logic was behind it in view of the increasing demand for waterside recreation and the rapidly growing population of the nearby communities. Added to this was the desire of people from other areas and from outside the State of California to get to the water. Many local and national groups understood this and campaigned vigorously in support of the national seashore. It all seemed simple. Congress had only to provide the rather small amount of money needed, and the National Park Service could start making the actual purchases.

In 1962, Congress authorized the park; the first park superintendent was appointed in 1963, and in 1966, with appropriate ceremonies, Mrs. Lyndon B. Johnson dedicated the park. A superb area near a large metropolitan center had been preserved for the enjoyment of the millions instead of the thousands, and everyone concerned had cause to congratulate himself. Or did he?

In 1968, visitors to the Point Reyes National Seashore received one of the typically attractive folders that the National Park Service puts out for the facilities it administers. The centerfold contained a handsome map of Point Reyes, showing the national seashore, Tomales State Park, and the principal roads and towns, along with an inset map showing the seashore in relation to San Francisco. But printed in the center of the map were these sad words: "Most land within boundary is privately owned. Respect property rights."

The text of the folder, after extolling the merits of the peninsula and explaining the meaning of a national seashore, went on to say: *"Today*. Much of the land to be included in Point Reyes National Seashore is still in private ownership and is not open to the public. However, there are several points of interest that can be visited and enjoyed now. . . . One of the principal attractions is the lighthouse, constructed in 1870 at the tip of Point Reyes. It is operated and managed by the U.S. Coast Guard. Visitors are welcome from 1 to 4 p.m. on Saturdays, Sundays, and holidays. A large herd of sea lions may be seen on the rocky beach at the end of the point by walking a short distance off the road. While watching the sea lions, take care to stand back from the edge of the cliff." Over this paragraph was imprinted with a rubber stamp: "LIGHTHOUSE CLOSED TO VISITORS." Being one of the few attractions open to the public, so many people had come to see it that the Coast Guard could not handle the influx. At the end of the paragraph entitled "Today" was this sentence in capital letters: "PLEASE RESPECT THE PROPERTY RIGHTS OF PRIVATE LANDOWNERS." No other comments in the entire folder were given the emphasis of capitals.[15] In spite of all the hearings in Congress, in spite of the dedication ceremonies conducted by Mrs. Johnson, in spite of all the publicity given the project, the American people still did not have a Point Reyes National Seashore.

In 1957, Mr. Collins had written, "If there exists the possibility of this coastal area for public ownership, positive action should be initiated immediately. . . ." Eleven years later, here was the actual status of the Point Reyes National Seashore. Excluding marshlands that had been owned by the State of California and deeded to the federal government by the state, only about one-third of the total acreage authorized for the national seashore had actually been purchased, and all the appropriations had been committed. The remaining two-thirds of the land was still in private ownership. Meanwhile, the prospect of the national seashore and the publicity it had created had helped to escalate the price of the other property. The developers were already trying to move in. In the summer of 1968, one developer had offered a plan to the county to subdivide 82 acres into 64 lots. If he succeeded, others were ready to follow his lead. Without funds, the National Park Service was powerless to block them. The only government capable of doing that was Marin County itself through its zoning laws. If the county maintained sufficiently tight zoning restrictions, it could perhaps make development economically unfeasible. But the county was already facing one lawsuit from a property owner who charged that county limitations on the widths of roads had adversely affected his property values. Although some beaches had been opened and some trails constructed, the original concept of the Point Reyes National Seashore was more a dream than a reality. And many feared that was how it would remain.

It would take a detective to unravel everything that went wrong with the Point Reyes National Seashore, but here is the story—and the factors involved—as best as I am able to determine them. And they point up some considerations that we should take into account in future transactions of this sort.

In the first place, the National Park Service's original estimates of the value of the lands to be acquired were too low. It has been severely criticized for this error, which probably arose from two causes. In the first place, like every other agency of government, the National Park Service has a tendency to underestimate the costs of a proposed project. The agencies do this in an effort to persuade Congress to embark on a particular course of action. In this instance, the tendency to underestimate was aggravated by an unusual circumstance. When the National Park Service first discussed the seashore informally with the appropriate members of Congress, it was considering a smaller area. When it started making the on-the-spot land survey and recognized the enormous potential of the region, it decided to enlarge it. There is reason to think that at this point the service was reluctant to increase greatly its original rough estimate out of concern that Congress would then be scared off and fail to act at all. Therefore when serious discussion of the bill started, the price mentioned was not a realistic one.[16] This became apparent shortly afterward, when the actual purchases started. Congress could then easily have done what it does with practically every agency, increased the appropriation and completed the seashore. It might even have reprimanded the National Park Service, something it does not often do with other agencies that commit the same offense. The amount involved was minuscule compared with the total federal budget. It was tiny even when compared to the underestimates often made by other government agencies and quickly forgiven by Congress. But the committees that handle the establishment of new parks and similar matters are, to put it bluntly, among the nickel-and-dime committees of the House and Senate. Other committees talk in billions, and the armed services budget is so large they can hide $350 million for chemical and biological warfare, so the average congressman cannot even find it. But the committees dealing with the conservation of our natural resources have to haggle over every dollar. It was true in this case, and while they haggled, the price of the land on Point Reyes continued to rise. The price was like the automatic rabbit at a dog racetrack; Congress could never quite catch up with it.

The lessons to be learned from this are obvious. If we are to accomplish much in the way of preserving our environment, we must assign more of our budget to this purpose. If that had been the case, the National Park Service need not have been so wary about raising its original estimate. And even if it had made a mistake, Congress could have quickly corrected the appropriation and brought it into line with the realities of the situation.

Another complicating factor resulted from a further effort by Congress to save money. In the bill was included a provision that, if the landowners were agreeable, they could be paid, not in cash, but by receiving acreage of equal value taken from the public domain. This brought into the negotiations another agency, the Bureau of Land Management, which administers the public domain. Although the bureau is also contained in the Department of the Interior, the procedure proposed by Congress was almost certain not to work effectively, for Congress was asking one agency to give up some of its assets in favor of another without receiving anything in return. This is something no agency likes to do. Moreover, the process was extremely complicated. In each transaction, the federal government and the seller would have to agree on two sets of values, the value of the land being sold on Point Reyes and the value of the land being exchanged for it. This provided a broad area for disagreement and delay, often augmented by another complicating element. For the Point Reyes landowner might not want land elsewhere. Therefore, he might bring in a third party to whom he planned to sell the exchanged lands, and the third party also had to agree on the values.

Much controversy was also aroused within the Bureau of Land Management and outside it over the lands to be chosen for exchange. One tract was in Oregon, and this aroused the smaller lumbermen in that state. The big companies were not greatly concerned, but the smaller lumbermen are more often dependent on public lands for their cutting operations. They did not want to see them pass into private ownership. Because of some past land scandals in the state, it was easy to stir up the press; and before long, hearings were being conducted by the Oregon Legislature, tempers were at an all-time high, the Secretary of the Interior had to intervene, and two high officials of the Bureau of Land Management lost their jobs.[17] As one conservationist remarked to me, "This dispute is a classic example of a great many special interests all pressuring the central issue. At the time it occurs, the various interests are not all aware that they are vying with each other to attain their preferred position."[18] The principle of land exchange seems so simple; the execution, as with so many ideas in government, is actually so complex. And it will remain complex as long as we do not have an overall policy toward the use of our land.

Even as I sit writing at my desk on the opposite side of the continent, I can easily conjure up the sight of Point Reyes, that remarkably lonely peninsula of northern California with the waves beating against the long beaches, the seagulls circling and screaming, and the winds rustling the grasses of the lowlands or whispering in the Douglas firs of Inverness Ridge. For such an area to remain virtually unspoiled so long in spite of its proximity to a major metropolitan center was one of the small miracles of this half of the century. It presented us with opportunity that is not likely to recur.

But we have risked losing it forever because of our lack of a basic policy of land use. If it is our fundamental decision that we want to preserve in federal ownership the few remaining large tracts of seashore, then we should have purchased Point Reyes years ago. At the very least, we should stop further procrastination and do so now. But the truth is that we do not know what we want. We seem unable to come squarely to grips with the choices—and the chances—facing us. By the time we do, it may be too late.

Redwood trees are a tradition in the United States. Most Americans, even if they have not actually seen one, are familiar with them. Like Paul Revere's ride or the signing of the Declaration of Independence, they form part of our heritage.

There are two types of redwoods. The giant sequoias are famous for their enormous girth. These are the trees through which, in earlier and less enlightened days, men carved tunnels large enough to permit the passage of an automobile. Fortunately for their own protection, they are difficult to lumber. Although a single tree could sometimes supply the wood for fifty six-room houses, a considerable amount of breakage is likely to occur during the felling. In addition, the wood, except for its resistance to decay, is not particularly desirable.[19] Therefore they have been spared extensive lumbering in recent times, and large stands of them remain in Yosemite, Kings Canyon, and Sequoia National Parks and elsewhere on the western slopes of the Sierra Nevada.

Their relative, the *sequoia sempervirens,* or coastal redwood, has not fared nearly so well. These trees, which grow farther north and closer to the Pacific Ocean, do not attain the girth of the giant sequoias, but they grow much taller. Also their wood is superior, and so they have suffered from continuous cutting. It started about 1820, reached a peak in the first half of the twentieth century, declined during the depression and World War II, and then rose rapidly to a new high in the years following the end of the war.[20] The original stands of redwoods covered almost 2 million acres. By the 1960's, the virgin forest had been reduced to about 300,000 acres.[21]

Except for a few of the persons who have been economically dependent on the redwood industry, most people have agreed that representative portions of the virgin forests should be preserved. They are one of the great wonders of America, and the privilege of walking among the giant trees, a truly emotional experience, is a privilege we should pass on to our children. This is not a new idea. As early as 1852, a resolution was introduced in the California Assembly that urged the passage of legislation prohibiting settlement on public lands containing redwoods and the lumbering of the trees. The resolution did not pass, but the idea of saving at least some of the trees did not die.

In 1902, a group of conservationists in San Jose, California, formed the Sempervirens Club, which was successful in establishing the Big Basin Redwoods State Park. (As I write, a group of conservationists are working hard to enlarge this park and attach to it another sizable tract that has been preserved by private funds.) A further step was taken in 1908, when William Kent, whose family is still active in California conservation, made a generous gift to the federal government of what is now Muir Woods National Monument.[22] These trees are especially significant because they are only a short drive from San Francisco. Even a hurried visitor to that city has an opportunity to see them. During the San Francisco Conference that set up the United Nations, I am told, cars with diplomatic license plates could often be seen in the parking lot. Weary of the long negotiations, many of the diplomats would quietly slip away and find rest and solace wandering among the giant trees. Dag Hammarskjöld was one of the statesmen who especially admired the redwoods. He rarely, if ever, went near redwood country without taking time to look at them, and I have heard that he always wanted to spend a night under them, an ambition that he had not realized at the time of his death.

In 1918, as concern for the remaining redwoods grew, a group of California citizens formed the Save-the-Redwoods League; and a year later, when Newton Drury and his brother, Aubrey, founded their own public relations firm, the league became one of their first clients. Soon Newton Drury was appointed secretary; and later, when he went to Washington to serve as Director of the National Park Service, Aubrey took his place. Newton later became head of the California park system but never lost his deep interest in the league and, on Aubrey's death, once more became its head.

The story of the Save-the-Redwoods League is one of the great success stories of American conservation. By 1921, only a few years after its establishment, it had acquired the 2,000 acres of redwoods that formed the first unit of what, with many later additions, became the magnificent Humboldt Redwoods State Park. Even more important than the actual land preserved was the mood set by the Save-the-Redwoods League. It had a single objective, saving redwoods, and it went about doing just that in such an orderly and effective fashion that it soon began to attract new friends who might be thought at first to have no interest in the league's efforts. After the league had successfully acquired those first 2,000 acres, both Humboldt and Del Norte Counties, in the heart of the redwood country and economically reliant on lumbering, appropriated money for additional acquisitions, and four lumber companies gave land. In 1927, the California Legislature passed a park act that provided an agency to look after the redwoods once they had been acquired and in the same year passed a bond act that made it possible for the state to offer matching funds in state park land purchases. A few years later, the league, with the help of the state, had largely completed the Del Norte Redwoods State Park; and in 1931 alone, it acquired almost 20,000 acres, including the outstanding Rockefeller Forest.[23] What had started as the effort of a handful of people was now a vigorous, energetic movement that was drawing support from across the nation. Much of this was because of the spirit of the league. Although it worked hard for the passage of the park act and for the preservation of redwoods, it was able to do so without making many enemies. When it wished to buy a tract of redwoods, it would cruise the land and rarely was the difference between the asking and offering price greater than 10 percent. This difference was always negotiated out. Furthermore it maintained a good working relationship with the lumber companies.

Obviously the two groups were not always in accord; obviously there were disagreements among them. But the fact remains that the lumber companies did make substantial contributions; and when the widow of one of the lumbermen decided to give a costly grove of redwoods, she insisted it be named the Newton B. Drury Grove and that this be done during his lifetime as a token of her respect for him. It is not often that this sort of thing happens.

The league was also working closely with the State of California. Realizing that private funds could not do the job alone, it persuaded the state to assume some of the expense. This meant that the state park system was tightly involved with the league in every aspect of its operation, including its plans for the future and for the administration of the areas.

Not all was well, however, in the redwood country, for two disaster-creating forces were at work. One of these was natural, and it came in the form of flooding. Redwoods are curious trees, and much remains to be learned about them. They have incredible endurance and can even survive forest fires that would destroy other trees. Many of the finest redwoods bear the blackened scars of past fires. They can survive flooding, too. At the Founders Tree—364 feet high and once believed to be the tallest tree in the world—a marker shows that the floodwaters of December, 1964, were 28 feet high. This would have destroyed many lesser trees, but the Founders Tree still stands unharmed. But for all their size, redwoods have extraordinarily shallow roots, so shallow that the trees can be adversely affected even by large crowds walking near them and compacting the dirt. This root system—there is no central taproot plunging deep into the earth—can be clearly seen in overturned trees or in some of the displays set up by the state at various parks, and it constitutes the redwoods' Achilles heel. They simply cannot withstand flooding that cuts away the soil beneath them. Once that happens, they go down like ninepins.

One day we were walking through the Rockefeller Forest on our first visit there. The woods were almost entirely still, except for the sound of trees creaking in the light wind. Occasionally we came across a fallen giant. In time, a fern garden often forms in the roots, adding mystery and a sense of life's power of re-

THE TALE OF THREE PARKS · 207

generation. Then we emerged from the forest's shade into an area where there was not a single tree standing. They lay piled on top of one another like great matchsticks dropped wantonly on the ground. Before that, I had heard that the preservation of redwoods required control of the watersheds above them to prevent floods. That one sight convinced me. For what we were looking at was the aftermath of the 1955 flood, when Bull Creek eroded its banks and brought the redwoods tumbling. From that year on, the Save-the-Redwoods League, the state, and other interested groups began emphasizing the acquisition of watersheds as well as the actual groves of trees. This, of course, makes the preservation effort far more expensive because larger tracts of outlying land need to be obtained.

The other disaster was a manmade one and serves as another in the endless examples of how we counteract our own efforts to maintain our environment. The California Highway Department is a powerful force in the state, one of the most powerful; and it has a strong propensity to take park land whenever it can as being cheaper than purchasing privately held areas. So the redwoods, which had been given to the state by private contributors and had also been purchased by state funds, proved a perfect target. Here is what a National Park Service study said about one such construction project: "Humboldt Redwoods State Park . . . contains what are generally recognized as outstanding forests, perhaps the finest from the standpoint of pure climax stands and concentration of dense timber.

"The heart of the area lies in the magnificent groves and flats along the South Fork of the Eel River and Bull Creek, a main tributary.

"Here just a few years ago U.S. Highway 101 was re-routed and upgraded to freeway standards. While a compromise solution avoided the world famous Avenue of the Giants [this compromise was only reached because of the strenuous objections of the league and others], it did slice a wide swath through this most important heart of the Park along its east edge, and generally paralleling the Avenue and the River. This results in serious damage to park values and a shocking scar, not only in the loss of thousands of trees but also in the sight and sound intrusions which extend well beyond the actual cutting.

"Furthermore this freeway location isolated a strip of redwood forested lands along the east boundary so effectively that it ceases almost to make a contribution to the Park either for public use or as needed background or buffer zone. In addition, for some miles the freeway has destroyed the beautiful forest edge along the river replacing it with rip-rap and cut and fill slopes." [24] Once again, we spent money to preserve something and then spent more money to destroy it. Sometimes I wonder if we have any sense of proportion at all.

In spite of such handicaps, the Save-the-Redwoods League, in cooperation with the state, continued to acquire areas containing the giant trees. By January, 1964, there were almost 30 of them with a total of more than 100,000 acres. Of those acres, more than 48,000 contained virgin stands. This represented about 2½ percent of the original forest.[25] Although this may seem like a small proportion, the accomplishment was significant.

Yet no one was completely happy about what they had done. In a study issued in 1964, the National Park Service said: "The Save-the-Redwoods League and the State Division of Beaches and Parks, which jointly have accomplished so much, now find themselves in an increasing dilemma. The dramatic growth of population in central and southern California is pulling more of the park and recreation dollar in that direction [for the purchase and maintenance of land and facilities]. At the same time, the price of virgin redwood has increased many fold since the 1920's and 30's when most of the acquisition for parks took place. The program of the League and the State in recent years has been designed to fill in and round out existing Redwood State Parks. Since the disastrous Bull Creek flood in 1955, it has further concentrated on acquisition of that particular upper watershed. The net result of these several factors and trends, naturally, has been a greatly reduced program in terms of acquiring additional acreage of virgin redwood, even important tracts.

"Compounding this picture even further are two subtle trends, often little understood or ignored completely. One is the dramatic and continuing increase in park visitor use; the other a relentless eating away of existing virgin growth in the parks, both in actual acreage and its effectiveness for full public enjoyment and inspiration. The fact is that in a very real sense, there is less in effective acreage 'preserved' today than a decade ago.

"At the same time, remaining opportunities are fast being lost —betimes a cliché, but in this case all too true. Since the Second World War, the harvest rate of redwood has risen sharply to an average for the last five years just short of a billion board feet. Remaining old-growth has already been reduced to the point where the major lumber companies locally, have now moved to re-evaluate their positions. Most are converting to relatively short-term sustained yield management (partly in the face of the present tax structure) and look towards a fuller utilization of their harvest including, notably, pulp products to sustain their operations. The days of old-growth redwood lumber in quantity are numbered.

"Remaining virgin growth has dwindled even more drastically. Opportunities to set aside complete watersheds still untouched no longer exist except in terms of a few small sub-drainages. . . .

"To add bits and pieces here and there will not do the job. A major addition is required and one preferably which would add not merely size, but high quality redwood groves and forests in a situation where, so far as possible, they can be preserved, interpreted, and made available, to the public as outstanding examples in an outstanding manner. . . .

"That does not mean that all remaining virgin growth should be so reserved. That would not be either reasonable or feasible." [26]

The Save-the-Redwoods League, the State of California, and other interested groups and individuals had done a superb job of preserving an important asset, but times were unfortunately catching up with them. A more massive effort was needed to finish what they had started. The best way to accomplish this would be to take one or more of the existing state parks as a nucleus and, by additional purchases, build it into a national park.

The idea of national park status for some of the redwoods was not new. It had been advanced before the turn of the century;

but nothing was done about it, although intermittently the federal government had shown an interest in the future of the trees. In 1899, Gifford Pinchot had conducted a study of the redwoods and made recommendations for their preservation, but no action resulted.[27] In the 1920's and 1930's, the federal government conducted further studies. Some of these recommended the creation of a Redwoods National Park, but again nothing happened. In 1946, a bill was introduced into Congress calling for the creation of a Memorial National Forest, comprising 2.5 million acres with about 180,000 acres to be preserved according to park principles. This bill was introduced into Congress several times, but it, too, died.[28] Although by that time, large numbers of people were aware of the magnificence of the redwoods and the threats to them, we could not as a nation look far enough ahead to take the steps necessary to save this significant part of our heritage. Meanwhile the stands of redwoods were growing smaller every year, and the cost of acquiring them was soaring.

In 1963, the National Park Service received a grant from private funds to undertake yet another study of the redwoods. Note again that the federal government could not afford this comparatively modest conservation expense. To initiate the study, President Johnson held an appropriate ceremony in the White House. Representatives from a number of conservation organizations were invited to attend. One organization, however, was conspicuously absent, because it had not received an invitation. That organization was the Save-the-Redwoods League, the one group that knew more about the preservation of redwoods than any other and that had already provided the nucleus around which any national park would be built.[29] This may have been an oversight, in which case it is incredible. It may have been the result of interprofessional jealousies, in which case it is even more incredible. But it did not augur well for the planning of a future Redwoods National Park.

In 1964, the National Park Service completed and published its report; and as might have been expected, it had done an excellent job. But one complicating factor had already been introduced. The basic concept was to take one or more of the existing state parks and expand the acreage to include more vir-

gin redwoods and to gain better watershed control to prevent
a recurrence of the disaster that took place on Bull Creek. The
complicating factor was what came to be known as the Tall
Trees.

This is a stand of redwoods that contains some of the tallest
trees in the world, and therefore it is certainly worth preserving.
But it also presents certain difficulties. It has no true relationship
to the existing parks, and the watershed of Redwood Creek on
whose banks it stands is enormous. Furthermore the trees are not
high up on the slopes; they are close to the river itself; and when
I was there in 1968, one of the two slopes rising above the
riverbed had recently been lumbered, in part to get the timber out
before a park could be created and in part because tempers had
worn thin. If ever the stage was set for a replay of the Bull Creek
flood and the resulting loss of redwoods, this was it, unless the
entire watershed could be acquired and controlled. It is quite
probable that if the National Park Service had been left to its own
devices, it might have ignored the Tall Trees in favor of the fundamental objectives of acquiring virgin stands, tying them into a
state park, and gaining ownership of a geographical entity. But
the National Park Service was not left to its own devices. Considerable publicity had been given the Tall Trees, and the donor
of the funds for the study was interested in them. Therefore they
had to be included in the proposal one way or another. And this
is where much of the subsequent controversy started.

Some conservationists wanted to purchase the Redwood Creek
watershed and thus protect the Tall Trees. This was a practical
impossibility. It would have meant buying some 200,000 acres
of land and would have driven the cost of the project far above
anything that Congress would have been at all willing to pay.
That expenditure would have exhausted any possibility of making other acquisitions to help protect and enlarge the excellent
stands already in public ownership.

The Tall Trees were somewhat like Eris' apple in the discord
they introduced. By presenting a situation that made it possible
to argue for a practical impossibility, they opened the way for
proposals and counterproposals. The relative calm that had been
the hallmark of the Save-the-Redwoods League's operations soon

vanished. Conservationists were arguing among themselves and calling the lumbermen names. Some of the lumbermen were retaliating in any way they could. There were wide differences in Congress between the House and the Senate. It is much to the credit of the National Park Service that the bill that finally emerged, although not as good as it might have been, was also not as bad as it could have become.

The original report had been issued in 1964. In the fall of 1968, a conference of the Senate and the House finally agreed on a bill that authorized a $92 million national park of 58,000 acres. Capitalizing on the work already done by the state and by the Save-the-Redwoods League, the park was to include three state parks—Jedediah Smith, Del Norte, and Prairie Creek.

It also contained two provisions of unusual interest. In the 1930's, the timber industry had been in serious trouble. Declining demand for lumber and higher real estate taxes were combining to make it impossible for landowners to hang on to their acreage. Because of this situation, the federal government then adopted a plan calling for the establishment of two national forests of redwoods in northern California with a total area of 863,000 acres. This proposal met with the approval of the California State Legislature, which, in 1934, passed legislation giving the federal government permission to do so. In view of the record of the federal government on conservation measures, it is not surprising that this plan was not carried out. Of the 863,000 acres originally designated for the national forests, the government actually bought only 14,567.[30] This became known by the unromantic name of the Purchase Unit because it had been purchased and not taken from the public domain. The Redwoods National Park bill gave the Secretary of the Interior discretionary power to trade some of this land in exchange for land within the park. This provision gave many conservationists and many conservation-minded members of Congress great concern. It opened the door, they said, to a wholesale intrusion into the national forests. When the measure came to the floor, Representative Sikes of Florida said: "I consider it a dangerous principle that can lead to serious impacts on our Federal land systems. Specifically if this trade off idea is extended it could put our great national forest system in grave and imminent danger." And Representative Kenneth J. Gray of Illinois said that he hoped the provision would be regarded "as an exception and that our action will not be construed as having established a precedent for subsequent proposals." [31]

In this instance, the idea of trading land in one place for land in another was designed, not so much to save money, as to relieve the economic strain on the counties. During debate on the bill, Representative Don H. Clausen of California pointed out that if one lumber company in his district had to liquidate, the county would lose a $3-million-a-year payroll, and he hoped that Congress, in the next year, would help him with legislation that would alleviate this.[32] Over the longer term, a Redwoods National Park would probably prove to be of greater economic benefit than the timber industry, particularly now that the vast tracts of virgin trees were gone and the companies would have to start operating on a sustained yield basis. But in the meanwhile, there could well be a temporarily adverse effect.

At least one company, the Georgia-Pacific Corporation, during negotiations with the government, voluntarily relinquished its interest in the Purchase Unit, thus gaining the praise of the Acting Director of the Bureau of Outdoor Recreation, which was handling the payments. "We deeply appreciate the wholehearted cooperation and assistance given us by the Company and its representatives," he said.[33]

But the fears of the conservationists were warranted. Within a few months after the President had signed the Redwoods National Park Bill, one company was exerting pressure to obtain lands, not in the Purchase Unit, but in Georgia.[34] The door had been opened; and by 1969, both the House and the Senate were considering several bills dealing with a National Timber Supply Act. The various versions of this act were all designed to accomplish the same purpose: greatly increase the cutting permitted on national forest land. A number of elements played a part in this movement—the rising cost of lumber, the large demand for timber abroad, particularly in Japan. But there is also little question that the formation of the Redwoods National Park, with its provision for exchanging lands, and the formation of the park in the North Cascades gave it impetus.

A second provision in the Redwoods National Park was also of unusual interest. Because Congress rarely, if ever, appropriates the amount of money needed to make a complete purchase but instead buys over a period of time, it inevitably faces a problem of land-price escalation just as it has at Point Reyes. In the case of the redwoods, however, it adopted a new technique. The bill provided for the legislative taking of the lands at the time the President signed the measure. This set October 2, 1968, as the date on which values were to be based. During the course of the subsequent negotiations with each owner and until final payment had been made, the government would pay interest at 6 percent on the unpaid balance. This was a wise provision, for the 6 percent is probably not as great an amount as the lands would increase in value.

In the fall of 1968, Mrs. Lyndon B. Johnson made a final conservation tour of the United States; and on November 29, 1968, she went to a grove of trees northeast of Orick, California, and there she dedicated the park. Almost a year later, we had another dedication ceremony. This time President Richard M. Nixon arranged it. (Dedication ceremonies seem to be the joy of politicians.) He invited former President Johnson and Mrs. Johnson to his estate in San Clemente, California, to celebrate former President Johnson's birthday. During the visit, they all traveled back to Orick; and there in the same spot at which Mrs. Johnson had dedicated the park, President Nixon dedicated the surrounding grove to Mrs. Johnson.[35] This was a very pretty thing to have done, and it permitted the erection of a nice plaque with Mrs. Johnson's name on it along with Mr. Nixon's. They both could now get credit for being associated with the new park.

The ceremonies also underscored one of the dramatic failings of American conservation. For at the time both ceremonies were held and the politicians were basking in public approbation, there was no park. And there was even some doubt as to whether there ever would be one.

Forgotten at the dedication ceremonies were the three state parks, saved mostly by the efforts of California and the Save-the-

Redwoods League. These parks were to form the nucleus of the Redwoods National Park, and contained almost half its total acreage and some of its finest redwoods. Everyone had been assuming all along that the state would cede these valuable lands to the federal government without any particular compensation. But Governor Ronald Reagan, who had come into office after the original planning had started, was having second thoughts. He saw no reason to give the federal government millions of dollars worth of property without receiving something in return. He had appointed a commission to look into the problem and decide whether California would be better off with the continued operation of the state parks or with a single national park. The commission was also charged with looking into some of the unanswered legal questions.[36]

Some optimists claimed that even if the price he might ask proved to be too high, the redwoods were saved and that was all that truly mattered. To an extent that was correct, but the lands are so laid out that cohesive management and development would be difficult under two separate authorities. What strengthened Governor Reagan's bargaining position was the new technique the federal government had developed to combat land-price escalation: the declaration of taking and the payment of interest on the balances that would be due the lumber companies. While the governor was making up his mind whether he would ask a price for the state lands, the federal government had no choice but to go ahead with its purchases. If it did not, the accumulated interest charges might become too great. Governor Reagan knew this and realized that, whatever he now did, the federal government was committed to proceed with its purchase plan.

In view of these considerations, the two dedication celebrations were ridiculous delusions. Even as late as the second one, the entire personnel of the "Redwoods National Park" consisted of ten persons, headed by a superintendent. And they were cautious about erecting national park signs for fear of confusing the public.[37]

In essence, the three case histories I have described were simple. In the first, the fundamental issue was the transfer of some federally owned property from one agency to another, thus effecting its reclassification. Part of the reason for doing this was the population pressure generated nearby by the expenditures of other federal agencies. In the second, the issue was simply the purchase of a large tract of seashore—something almost every planner is agreed we need—close to a heavily populated metropolitan center and to do so at reasonably low prices because of lack of development. In the third, the issue was merely enlarging several excellent state parks to assure the preservation of an American heritage.

Yet in each case, we allowed the necessary procedures to drag on and on for years; and the costs mounted, as we fumblingly tried to make up our minds. We permitted special interests to influence deeply what should have been national questions. Even when we finally decided what we wanted to do, we failed to provide the necessary funds to do it. And in handling each issue, we swamped ourselves in emotionalism instead of dealing with the problems realistically and with considerations for the nation as a whole.

In our conservation activities, we lack a basic purpose and attitude, and we certainly have no fundamental policy toward the use of our land. If it takes us more than a century to decide whether we should preserve some virgin redwoods for future generations, if we cannot vote the small amount of money needed to purchase an outstanding seashore tract, if it takes years of debate to determine the classification of some federal lands in one state, it is small wonder that we cannot move on to broader problems of land use, such as the location of industry, the placement of residential areas, the preservation of unique areas for scientific research, or the acquisition of open space and recreational areas for growing centers of population.

Yet we know from experience that when we do occasionally look at a land-use problem as a whole, the results can be surprising. Even though the case histories in the next chapter are limited in scope, they indicate what might be accomplished with a different approach.

8

Toward Better Use of Our Land

ALTHOUGH the Commonwealth of Virginia is a large Atlantic coastline state, it has extremely little ocean front; and as a consequence an interesting pattern has built up in the southeastern portion of the state near Norfolk. It contains examples of poor overall planning with an isolated example of excellent planning in the middle of it. So within a distance of a few miles it demonstrates both what can be done and what often is not.

The region is heavily populated. Portsmouth, Newport News, Hampton, Norfolk, Virginia Beach, and other communities are clustered together in a small area. Of the major towns, Virginia Beach occupies the prime location for esthetics and recreation. It faces squarely onto the Atlantic Ocean, and a visitor can stand on its shore and watch the ships entering and leaving the entrance to Chesapeake Bay. It also has a magnificent stretch of beach that attracts thousands of people and greatly enhances the city's real estate values. Since the beach is under city control and is a major financial resource, the city intends to keep it that way. Through the careful use of parking regulations and other such restrictions, the inhabitants have made it all but impossible for a visitor to reach it without using commercial facilities such as rental houses or motel rooms. This is not said in criticism. Virginia Beach is a pleasant place, and it is merely doing what thousands of communities in the United States are doing, reserving natural resources for its own benefit.

Continuing up the coast a short way, the traveler comes to an anachronism, Fort Story, a large army installation that occupies the finest portion of the state's shoreline. It stands on the point at the entrance to Chesapeake Bay and, of course, its lands are not available to the public. In long-gone days, the location of Fort Story was strategic. With proper gunnery, the fort could prevent an enemy from sailing up the Chesapeake and taking Washington, Annapolis, or Baltimore. Today its site, with the possible exception of its use for training in amphibious defense and offense, hardly seems pertinent to the nation's safety. It is an incongruous use of land in view of what we know and need.

Traveling through this part of Virginia, I had seen two classic forms of land use in a highly congested area: the natural asset reserved by a fortunate community for its own exclusive benefit and the publicly owned property held for a highly specialized use that has no real relation to the value of its location. (There are other examples of army seaside property that could probably be converted to more general purposes. Fort Ord, just above the Monterey Peninsula in California, is one.)

Continuing along the shore of Virginia, I came to Seashore State Park; and although I knew the fine reputation of the Virginia park system, I expected to find a third classic pattern: the rather forlorn, overcrowded state park, with rows and rows of picnic tables standing on heavily trampled, almost barren ground. For wedged in between the cluster of towns and the reserved beaches of the fort and the city of Virginia Beach, it carries a heavy burden of use.

In 1968, for example, it had a total of 610,000 visitors. Of these, more than 173,000 were overnight campers, more than 7,000 rented the cabins owned by the state, and the rest were day visitors. The land itself has an interesting history and reflects America's early interest in conservation. The first permanent settlers in the United States, heading toward Jamestown, landed at

Point Henry, the site of the fort's installations, and there the commander opened the royal box containing the charter and the rules of the London Company. Later, with the wisdom that the earliest settlers often displayed, they declared the beach a "common" for use by all the people of Virginia. Unfortunately in this case, the state sold the land after the conclusion of the Civil War, but in the 1930's, the mistake of the past was rectified, and the land reclaimed for the public's use.[1]

It is not a large park. Its beach front is only three-quarters of a mile long and is insignificant in size compared with Fort Story. The total acreage of the park, which runs inland and also borders on Broad Bay, is under 3,000 acres. Yet because of excellent land planning, the Virginia Division of Parks has been able to combine in harmony a remarkable number of activities. The boat ramp is located back on a bay. This is just as convenient for the boat owners but keeps this activity, including the necessary parking places, from the fragile sand dunes and the limited beach area, leaving that section virtually unspoiled for those who want to swim, walk along the shore, or camp. Inland is a well-preserved natural area. Here is located a museum that interprets the surrounding countryside. Behind the museum are miles of trails that take the visitor through the Bald Cypress Swamp, a fascinating place where Spanish moss, rarely seen this far north, hangs from the trees, and where the knees of the cypresses protrude from the dark water.

The most impressive aspect of the Seashore State Park compared with many other areas is the well-defined priorities of those charged with its administration. Other park departments might have given way under the various pressures that are always exerted in such a populated area, but the Virginia Division of Parks has not. The division seems to know exactly what it is trying to do, and it is succeeding.

Seashore State Park reminded me of another area in which uses that might be incompatible have been skillfully combined through careful planning, an area that also demonstrates, even though on a limited scale, what can be accomplished when priorities are clearly determined. This is Point Lobos in California, the peninsula made famous by the sensitive photographs of Edward Weston. This point, which runs along the southern edge of Carmel Bay, remained in private hands until 1933, when the state acquired it with the help of the Save-the-Redwoods League. At the time, according to the state, "Residents of Carmel, a quaint and leisurely village which had long been a refuge for votaries of the arts, held up their hands in horror at the prospect of a state park. They visioned formal paths and artificial masonry, networks of roads and the frantic rush of automobile traffic, the din of crowds, the nondescript structures of catchpenny concessions and tourist camps. All, they feared, to the loss of more precious, but more fragile things—the spell, the mystery, the beauty of this site.

"The Carmelites sighed with relief, therefore, and so did most everyone throughout the nation, when the State Park Commission pledged that Point Lobos would be a 'reserve'—a property held in trust as nature had designed it." [2]

Personally, I doubt if the Carmelites sighed with relief. I believe they thought this designation of "reserve" gave them ground for some slight hope, but that was all. Actually they need not have worried. California's Division of Parks and Beaches has, like Virginia's Division of Parks, resisted outside pressures and maintained the point in its original beauty by careful land use and by the strict enforcement of well-thought-out restrictions. For example, no camping is permitted; the place is not suitable. Also no trailers are allowed within its boundaries. Just outside the gate is a parking lot, where trailers can be left until the visitor leaves. The reason for this rule is simple. Trailers block the view of other travelers, and they also often require larger roads. Both of these factors would adversely affect the spirit of Point Lobos. While I was standing by the gate, I saw a tourist drive up with a trailer behind his car and ask for admittance in spite of the sign that set forth this regulation. Although he pleaded vigorously in his own behalf, the rangers were polite but adamant. No trailers were admitted under any circumstances. In the end, he gave up. He did not have the time or the energy, I am sure, with which to unhitch the trailer, and so off he drove without seeing Point Lobos. The loss was his, but the incident made an impression on me.

For California has done what so few governments or individuals do—differentiate between pieces of land and keep their uses separate. To the north and south of Point Lobos, it maintains parks in which campers can stay; and although these parks are crowded—often campers have to be turned away—it has not allowed that pressure to destroy the high quality and extremely fragile character of Point Lobos.

On the other hand, its attitude toward the small peninsula is not rigidly preservationist and antirecreationist. The rules about staying on the trails are strictly enforced, as strictly as in any place I have ever been. But where the terrain can stand the traffic, visitors are permitted off the trails, and some of the beaches, again where recreation will not damage them, are open to swimming.

Point Lobos and Seashore State Park stand out, in my opinion, as examples of wise land use. Both areas have unique qualities not to be found anywhere else nearby. The agencies administering them have recognized this and have protected their unusual characteristics by fairly severe restrictions, so they can continue to be enjoyed in the future. Yet wherever possible, without incurring damage to the land, the agencies have permitted broader and more intensive use. They have followed the principle of looking at the tracts as a whole, utilizing the best each section has to offer, and not trying to do everything everywhere at once. The problem is to expand this principle to include much larger areas, including whole regions of this country.

In 1969, as I moved north from Virginia's Seashore State Park I was again struck by the discordant use of the Atlantic Coast. Leaving behind the superb, but restricted, area occupied by Fort Story and crossing the Chesapeake Bay Bridge, I came to Fishermans Island with its excellent sweeps of beach facing both the bay and the ocean. Here the traveler finds himself greeted by fences and large signs saying GOVERNMENT PROPERTY, NO TRESPASSING. This is a wildlife refuge, administered by the U.S. Fish and Wildlife Service. This service, with its long and honorable history, has as its primary purpose the preservation of our wildlife, most notably our migratory birds. These, too, are part of our heritage and deserve protection just as much as the redwoods or the beaches of Point Reyes. But as I drove by those uninviting fences and signs, backed by the implicit threat contained in the words "government property," I wondered if this was the way to do it. If Virginia and California could, in two outstanding instances, intermingle uses and still maintain basic objectives, could not the U.S. Fish and Wildlife Service do the same or something similar? Could not the beaches of Fishermans Island be made available to the general public under certain restrictions and at certain times of year? It is much simpler administratively to hold the tract for a single purpose than to make it play a part in a comprehensive master plan, but in view of the limited coastline left to us, this may not be practicable. We may have to adopt a broader outlook without, at the same time, surrendering to the tendency to homogenize our land uses.

Continuing north on the main highway, I could see signs pointing to the next federal oceanside facility, a launching site operated by the National Aeronautics and Space Agency. Once again, the thought occurred to me. Was this the best purpose that the area could serve? If we needed another launching site, was there any possibility that it, too, could be included in a master plan for the most effective utilization of our precious coastline?

Farther north, I turned toward Ocean City, Maryland. Ocean City is seashore tourism gone wild. It is solid with restaurants, motels, and even a roller coaster. Its development led a speculator to look south to Assateague Island, which is a bar separated from the mainland of Maryland and Virginia by Chincoteague Bay, and it, too, has superb oceanfront beaches. In the mid 1950's, the developer was able to get possession of a large tract on the island. He built a central road named Baltimore Boulevard, brought in power, and carved the island up into citylike blocks. Each block was composed of eight lots, measuring 100 by 200 feet. There was a total of 8,000 of them; and by 1962, he had sold more than 3,000. In March of that year, however, a violent storm raged on the coast. It destroyed most of Baltimore Boulevard, carried away some buildings, and greatly dampened enthusiasm for the further development of Assateague Island as a seashore resort.[3] This provided an opportunity for creating the

Assateague Island National Seashore, the bill for which President
Johnson signed in September, 1965.

Considerable controversy has centered on the National Park
Service's plans for the development of the seashore. Approximately 36 million people live within 250 miles of the island, and
75 percent of them are within a three-hour drive.[4] This has
obviously influenced the National Park Service, whose plans call
for intensive development, including massive parking areas, some
motels, and other facilities, which many people do not want to
see on the island.

But the National Park Service deserves special credit for the
efficient manner in which it conducted the land acquisition program. Unlike the programs at Point Reyes and other localities,
this one moved ahead comparatively smoothly. Between the fall
of 1965, when the bill was signed by the President, and the spring
of 1969, approximately 80 percent of the designated area was
put in actual federal ownership despite the difficulty of com-
pleting transactions with more than 3,000 landowners. In some
respects, the relatively unimaginative subdivision of the island
was a help. Once a value was established for a particular lot, it
was possible to apply that same value to every similar lot, so that
thousands of individual prices did not have to be established. But
the key to the success of the land acquisition program lay in the
manner in which the National Park Service went about it. Instead of buying here and there as opportunities offered themselves, the service divided the island into tracts and established
priorities for each one. Thus it knew at all times precisely where
it wanted to concentrate its available funds. It also took another
unusual step. Because the majority of the owners lived in either
Baltimore or Washington, D.C., the National Park Service established field offices in both those cities, which meant that their
agents could reach the owners more quickly and easily. Whatever
the controversy over the development of Assateague, at least the
acquisition aspect of the program moved more smoothly and
efficiently than most.

The distance, as the crow flies, from Virginia Beach, Virginia,
to Ocean City, Maryland, is approximately a hundred miles; and
it encompasses the variety of what we have tried to compress

into our vanishing shoreline, starting at one end with a municipality determined to preserve its beaches for its own use and
then a fortification occupying one of the primest sections. It also
includes an excellent state park (there is also a state park on
Assateague), a rocket launching site, one wildlife refuge closed to
the public, another south of the national seashore through which
visitors can walk, a national seashore that, bearing as it does
the burden of the recreational requirements, may well become
overdeveloped, and ends with another tourist resort. Although
there is cooperation between the Maryland state parks and the
National Park Service and between the National Park Service
and the U.S. Fish and Wildlife Service, one cannot look at this
small, but typical, stretch of the Atlantic coastline and gain the
impression that anyone has drawn up a master plan for its best
use. Certainly the principles so successfully followed within the
smaller areas of Seashore State Beach or Point Lobos have not
been applied here.

This is significant. If we cannot plan wisely for the use of our
coastline, which almost everyone is agreed represents one of our
great assets, how can we plan wisely for the use of the rest of our
land? How can we deal with such problems as selecting on a
nationwide basis the areas that we wish to reserve as wilderness,
those that should be national parks, those in which we should
concentrate more industry, and those that should be comfortable,
attractive places in which to live? If we proliferate our activities
along our limited coastline, it is not surprising that we do so all
over the country.

The future of our coastline is a particularly urgent problem
because there is so little of it left. A further examination of what
we have done there—and what we have not done—should provide insight into what could be better planning, not only for the
coastline, but for the rest of our land as well.

In 1954, a private donor gave the National Park Service the
funds to make a survey of the eastern and southern coasts. (Once
again the money had to come from private sources, not from the
government itself.) The results of the study were astounding. Of
the 3,700 miles of shoreline along the Atlantic Ocean and the

Gulf of Mexico, only 240 miles—about 6½ percent—were in federal or state ownership and open to the general public for recreational uses. Worse than that, more than half of the 240 miles were concentrated in three federally owned areas, Cape Hatteras National Seashore in North Carolina, Acadia National Park in Maine, and Everglades National Park in Florida. Although there are some excellent beaches in the Everglades, they are generally accessible only by boat, and most of the shorefront of the two national parks is not beach. On the entire eastern and southern coasts of the United States, there were only thirty-six state seashores; and included in the 240 miles were eight national wildlife refuges that were not truly open to public use.[5] Americans, traditionally a seagoing people, could barely reach their own waters. Access to the oceans had fallen into private ownership or specialized agencies of the government. As a result, we have doomed many of our children to do their sunning and swimming only at concrete pools, and we have prevented many of them from hearing the sea gulls scream above the breaking waves, or from seeing the water lap along the shore. Thus we have limited the scope of their lives.

This tragic situation was completely unnecessary and resulted from one cause—lack of foresight. In 1935, the National Park Service had also conducted a survey of those same coasts and found plenty of unspoiled seashore areas and recommended that twelve major strips, with 437 miles of beach, be preserved. It also located many other sites that would have been suitable for state acquisition. In the intervening twenty years, Congress had gotten around to acquiring one out of the twelve locations recommended for purchase.

Meanwhile, the 1954 report went on to say, the market for seashore property has become so active that inaccessibility was no longer a serious deterrent to its sale. Isolated islands were being subdivided, roads and streets constructed, and buyers found even while the islands were still accessible only by boat. Most of the 5,000 lots in one large island development 150 miles from the nearest population center had been sold at constantly increasing prices although all attempts to secure a bridge had failed.

"Under such pressure," the report said, "beachfront holdings respond to the inevitable law of supply and demand. The supply of such land is fast dwindling; the number of persons seeking to acquire property is skyrocketing—and so is the price.

"An undeveloped area 30 miles long recommended as a national seashore in 1935 could have been purchased then for $260,000, or about $9,000 a mile. Today only nine miles remain undeveloped, and they would bring $110,000 a mile—an increase of 1100 percent in 20 years." [6]

A great opportunity was lost—forever. Even in 1935, when federal expenditures were lower, $260,000 for that one beach was not a large sum of money; over the years it would have brought enjoyment and refreshment to millions of Americans. Based on our experience with attendance at other seashore areas, if we had bought that tract and if each visitor had contributed an amount equal to the present federal tax on a single gallon of gasoline, the purchase would have resulted in an enormous profit. It would not only have been an investment in America's environment; it would have been an excellent financial investment as well.

In the 1950's and 1960's, we finally took some remedial steps to preserve our shoreline, mostly cautious ones like the underappropriation for Point Reyes. But perhaps even more important than the actual expenditure of money is the need for a change in our basic attitude toward the coastline. As a result of the National Park Service's study and the slow awakening of the public, government has acquired more land; but at today's prices and with diminishing opportunities, it probably will not be adequate. So we should take a fresh look and try to develop new methods for giving Americans access to the water.

In his remarks on the signing of the bill creating the Assateague National Seashore, President Johnson said, "Sometimes I think we must learn to move faster. Our population is growing every year, but our shoreline is not. . . . What the Good Lord once gave in greatest abundance have now become rare and very precious possessions. Clear water, warm sandy beaches are a nation's real treasure." Later in his remarks, he described one of the steps he was taking. "I have asked the conservation and park and seashore people," he said, "to put under the microscope every acre that has been declared surplus by our great Defense Department to see if somehow, somewhere the little people of America might not be able to enjoy this in the few hours of relaxation that is theirs on a weekend." [7]

If the case is as urgent as he said it is—and I believe this is so —then waiting until the Department of Defense declares a piece of shoreside property surplus is taking an old-fashioned attitude toward a modern problem. The Department of Defense has no responsibility for—or real interest in—our land-use problems. It is not likely that it will declare any land surplus as long as it has a use for it, although there might be a better and higher one. Instead just the opposite approach should be used. Wherever along the coastline the military has holdings, these should be examined for their potential recreational value or suitability for wildlife. Then the military should be compelled to give good reasons for retaining the land and to explain why that particular tract is essential to the nation's security rather than another piece elsewhere with less recreational or esthetic worth. If it should prove possible to open up all, or most, of Fort Story's beaches to the public, for example, it would have an effect on the entire strip of coast between Virginia Beach and Ocean City. Being the nearest location to a metropolitan center, it could be devoted to reasonably active recreation and drain off much of the pressure on the shorefront generated by the Norfolk region. This, in turn, might make it possible to have Assateague less developed.

To carry this thinking further, perhaps the National Aeronautics and Space Agency does not need exclusive use of a launching pad area in Virginia; it is already occupying an enormous tract in Florida. This would provide one more access to the water. Certainly the restrictions placed on national wildlife refuges along the coast should be reviewed. Not for one minute should their basic purpose be forgotten, but it might well be possible to combine wildlife protection with somewhat greater accessibility for passive recreation. This, too, could help relieve the pressures on Assateague and at the same time provide many persons with the more wilderness-like experience that they would like to have. I am not sure that signs saying, government property, no trespassing, are any more the answer to our seashore problem than signs saying, private property, no trespassing.

This point was well made by former Secretary of Agriculture Orville Freeman in his speech about the Cascades. "It seems to me," he said, "that one of the things we can do to relieve such pressures [of people] on wilderness is to make sure that resources and recreation are plentifully available in non-wilderness areas. ... The demand for outdoor recreation is increasing at a rate about four times as great as population increases. Shorter working hours, higher incomes, a desire to escape increasing urbanization—all these contribute to this trend. This is a demand that will be met, one way or another. ... Perhaps this kind of recreation isn't your cup of tea. But many people do enjoy camping in improved areas, or skiing with the help of a chair lift or T-bar, spending a day at a National Seashore area, or a week on a farm.

"Leaving aside the merits of one particular kind of recreation over another, it seems to me that we wilderness supporters have a real stake in providing other kinds of recreation for those who wish it, if for no other reason than to take the population pressure off the wilderness and primitive areas." [8]

This sort of thinking should be applied to some of our coastal wildlife refuges. The U.S. Fish and Wildlife Service enjoys a favored position among government agencies in the acquisition of lands because it has its own source of revenue for this purpose —the sale of the duck stamps required of every hunter of migratory waterfowl. It is, therefore, less dependent on the current whims of Congress. But although it accomplishes its fundamental purpose well, it has a tendency to hold itself aloof from the general problems of our coastline. Many wildlife refuges, which would not be damaged by restricted human use, are barely accessible even to the most dedicated of bird lovers. This only increases the pressure on the remaining areas and accentuates an already great problem.

There are other possibilities, too, for the more effective utilization of our coastline. In some fortunate states like Connecticut, the entire shore below mean high tide belongs to the public. Where such laws already exist or could be enacted, a major opportunity presents itself. The problem then becomes, not ownership of the beaches, but access to them through the private lands that block the public from taking advantage of what is legally theirs. In states like those, public rights-of-way to the water could be acquired within comparatively modest natural resource budgets, for all that is needed are small strips of land, sufficiently wide for a family to walk on.

Two obstacles to this approach can be raised. First is the difficulty of providing parking space for the visitors. This could be done on less expensive land back from the shore. It would be better to walk a mile to the beach than not be able to reach the beach at all. In summertime, perhaps school parking lots could be used, with bus service to the beach.

The second obstacle would be the objections raised by the adjoining shorefront property owners. Their screams would be heard in the capitols of any state that attempted this. But this begs the issue. They never have owned the beach in front of their houses beyond the mean high tide mark. Just because they do control access to it, they have not acquired squatter's rights to it. To take an extreme example, if the Yellowstone National Park were completely ringed by private landowners who denied access to the park and reserved it for their own private use, the American people would rise up in indignation and do something about it. The parallel is not as wide as it might appear. The waters and shoreline of America belong to all the people; nobody ever intended that they be reserved for the wealthy few.

In selecting the strip of coastline in Virginia, Delaware, and Maryland that I have described, I was guided by the consideration, not that it is unusual, but that it is so typical. Although we can handle certain areas like Point Lobos or Seashore State Park so well, we have difficulty extending the same approach to larger regions and larger problems. On those occasions when we do, the results are often exciting.

The coast of Oregon has more variety than most, with great beaches, steep cliffs, and strange rock formations that must have been horrors to early mariners caught on a lee shore but which are today a sight that thousands of people enjoy. Like every other shoreline in America, Oregon's, too, has come under pressure; and as I drove through what is called the 20-mile miracle— a term coined by some local promoter—I felt as though I could be in any of a hundred other places near the shores of America. On both sides, the road was lined with gasoline stations, shops of all varieties, motels, restaurants, and all the many other enterprises that we build up along our waterfronts. In other locations, on the Oregon coast, just as has happened elsewhere, the development is far more tasteful; but in those instances, it requires comparative wealth for people to acquire property and get to the water. But the development of Oregon's coast has a distinguishing feature that makes it outstanding. The private ownership of land is constantly broken by publicly owned areas to which the public does have access. No one has to go far in Oregon in order to be able to reach the Pacific Ocean, and Oregon's law is similar to Connecticut's; the beaches, once reached, belong to the public. Some of the access areas are owned by the federal government, some are large state parks with camping facilities, some are little more than parking lots, where a visitor can leave his car and wander on the beach. Taken together, they represent an astounding achievement.

Earlier I cited the National Park Service's figures for the Atlantic and Gulf of Mexico coasts. Of the 3,700 miles, only 240, or about 6½ percent, were in federal or state ownership and open to the public, using the words "open to the public" most liberally. If the words "and moderately easy of access" had been added, the total amount would probably have been cut in half. Contrast this with Oregon, whose total coastline is slightly more than 355 miles long. In 1968, federal agencies held 63.4 miles; state agencies held 108.9 miles; local agencies, 18.3 miles. The total of more than 190 miles represented 53 percent. Nor were these by any means second-rate lands. For the agencies owned more than half of the state's usable beaches.[9]

How this came about is an interesting and revealing conservation story; and it starts, in part, back in 1903, when a young engineer named Samuel H. Boardman moved to Oregon. The following year, he took up a homestead in eastern Oregon, where the present town of Boardman bears his name. Becoming concerned about the treeless portions of the Columbia River Highway and the Old Oregon Trail, he requested permission from the highway department to inaugurate a massive tree-planting program. Using seedlings he obtained from the Union County Experimental Station, he started his undertaking; and soon trees that Mr. Boardman had planted could be seen from The Dalles on the Columbia River all the way east to the border of Idaho.[10]

It is not surprising that Mr. Boardman received the encouragement he did from the highway department, for the people of Oregon have long regarded their roads in a different light than most states do. Curiously enough, even state ownership of the beaches is based on a highway decision. In 1913, in his message to the legislature the governor stated that "the ocean beach from the Columbia River on the north to the California State line on the south should be declared a public highway." [11] This was hardly what we would think of as a modern use for a beach, but the message expressed the opinion that the beach should be open to everyone.

Oregon was also interested in keeping the borders of its highways as handsome as possible. In the early 1920's, long before the federal highway beautification program, Oregon's state highway attorney said: "It often develops that state highways could be made more convenient and more beautiful and their scenic features improved if the State Highway Commission or some other department of state government had the authority to acquire by purchase, agreement, or by the exercise of the right of eminent domain, additional land for parking privileges and purposes. . . .

"Closely related to the subject just mentioned is the matter of preserving the trees along the highways for a certain distance back from the right of way . . . such legislation would, of course, necessitate the appropriation of private property for the purpose of beautifying . . . public highways." [12] In 1921, the Governor of Oregon addressed these remarkable words to the legislature: "No other state in the Union has been blessed with so many natural glories as is the State of Oregon. Crowning all these glories are our forest growths. Without them our mountains would be rocky, forbidding eminences; our streams would dwindle into rivulets; our lakes be shorn of the sylvan fringes which make them entrancing to the nature lover, and our valleys would be monotonous stretches. This heritage has been too long neglected. . . .

"The public realizes the importance of these things now, and is fully awake to the fact that, while we have lost many things, there are many things we cling to and preserve for all posterity. . . .

"All the things we have been striving for, the development of tourist travel; the urge to make and keep our state the most livable in the Union; the desire to keep our children in God's own environment, surrounded by the beauties to which they are the true heirs, all of these will be surrendered and lost unless we act and act promptly." [13]

Even today, we have all too few governors who speak like this, and in 1921, it was exceptional for one to state such views. Furthermore, the governor was already, within the limited scope of his authority, taking steps to preserve Oregon. Although recognizing the economic importance of the lumber industry, he had persuaded one company to cease cutting near a highway; and he had reached an agreement with the Bureau of Indian Affairs to leave standing a belt of trees along the highways that passed through Indian reservations.[14]

Indicative of the unusual support such steps were receiving is a resolution passed by the Oregon Chamber of Commerce in 1926. It urged the public to refrain from picking flowers along the highways and encouraged the planting of more trees and shrubs.[15]

Although Oregon had no state park department, it was slowly acquiring parks through its highway department, partly to make the highways more attractive and partly to provide camping sites for the tourists it was attempting to draw to the state. Earlier, in 1919, Mr. Boardman had gone to work for the department as an engineer. When the office of State Park Commissioner was created in 1929, it was only natural, because of his long interest in tree planting and other conservation activities, that he should be the first appointee. And because parks and highways had now become interrelated in the minds of most Oregonians, the new state park system remained a part of the highway department. To most conservationists, who have come to regard highway departments as among their deepest enemies, this may seem an anomaly. In actual practice—and in proper hands—the arrangement has had its advantages.

The year 1929 was not a propitious time for starting to develop a statewide park system. The stock market crash and the subsequent depression reduced the state's income and yet placed many demands on it. There was little money for the acquisition of park lands. Mr. Boardman, however, was a man of imagination. Instead of staying around Salem and lamenting to the legislators over the small amounts they allocated to his work, he was determined to use any device he could to obtain the needed acres. Sometimes he cajoled land from the federal government, sometimes from the state forester. Often he was able to persuade individual citizens to give either funds or land.

He was a truly remarkable man, both in his ingenuity and his patience. A picture of some of the vicissitudes he encountered and how he overcame them can be gained by reviewing the history of a single park, one of the many he created in much the same way. In 1951, he described some of the steps he had taken to put together what had then become a park of more than 2,400 acres. He started his account by going back twenty years. "The park," he wrote, "had its original conception through the desire of E. S. Collins, a wealthy timber man of Portland, to give the state a fine stand of matured timber for park purposes. I spent the better part of 1931, off and on, on trips through western Oregon with Mr. Collins looking for timbered tracts that met his approval. He finally decided to buy a 160-acre tract on Short Sand Creek fronting the ocean [but he kept title to 42 acres, which he intended to give other organizations for summer camps]. . . .

"Then came the purchase of the George E. Huntley property consisting of 354 acres for the sum of $18,000.00 The commission tied a string to this purchase. I had to sell enough timber off the 354 acres to meet the $18,000.00 payment.

"The timber was advertised for bids. The terrain of the park is very rough for logging purposes. The bids were low and unacceptable to the commission. One other try was made and failed and the timber was saved for the park.

"The next purchase was Cape Falcon proper. I was given the choice of one of the two parks I had planned for the consideration of the commission. . . . I took the Cape. . . .

"The history of the acquisition of the Preston Timber Company property," he went on, "consisting of 9.29 acres should be recorded. Due to a high bluff on the west side of the highway I decided to acquire only a narrow wayside strip through the property to cut down the cost. The 9.29 acres cost $365.00. Later this company failed and the County took over [its] property for delinquent taxes. The County Court promised to turn the property over to the state as a unit of the park. Something went wrong and one day I was notified that the property had been turned over to the State Forester. Then began a campaign to get the State Forester to turn the property over to the Parks Department. A ruling controlled the State Forester wherein he could only exchange acre for acre. A trade solution was worked out wherein excess wayside lands bordering the Wilson and Sunset Highways were exchanged for the State Forest property. This acquisition was started in 1943. The exchange deeds will be signed by the Commission at the August 20th, 1951, meeting."

In 1932, Mr. Boardman persuaded a man from the State of Washington to give the park another tract of 40 acres, after which, he obtained a still further gift of 336 acres. In another instance he commenced negotiations for 112 acres in 1941. Eight years later, the park commission finally gave him permission to purchase the land—at a much higher price—but only on the promise that he would not bring any more land acquisition proposals before them for this particular park.

All this time, he had been worried about the 42 acres the original donor had held back to give to other organizations. "This division of the property," Mr. Boardman said, "complicated the development of the park as the 42 acres took in most of the beach. It is unethical to switch the tail of a gift horse at the very start. From time to time I did present my views of the difficulties the division of the property presented in the development of a state park." Mr. Boardman's efforts to obtain the tract failed, but he raised enough doubts in the donor's mind so that he never gave it to anyone else. In 1946, fifteen years after the original gift of land to the park, the state was able to purchase the 42 acres from the donor's heir.[16]

This description of some of the problems involved in assembling one 2,400-acre park reveals certain things about Mr. Boardman and also about conservation generally. It should certainly serve as an object lesson to those conservationists who want to do everything at once and, when they find that they cannot, grow discouraged, and abandon their effort. It also underscores the importance of several elements in Mr. Boardman's success. In the first place, he always had in mind an overall objective that he never forgot. Starting with less than 160 acres, he could envision an important and significant park; and in the following twenty years, he never lost sight of this goal, even when he was dealing with tracts of less than 10 acres. In the second place, he was patiently persistent. Instead of losing his temper when he met with rebuff after rebuff, he simply tried to devise a new means of attaining his objective. He did, however, say that "a proposed park should be set up in its entirety to begin with, and its completion made at the earliest possible date. To delay its acquisition is to multiply its cost." [17]

The third point that this case history illustrates is the ingenuity exercised by Mr. Boardman. From the beginning, he knew that he could not obtain from the state all the money he needed, so he resorted to every other device he could think of, whether it was attempting to wheedle tax delinquent property out of a county, persuading donors to give him land, or arranging a complicated land exchange with the state forester. When one approach failed, he thought up and tried another. This tradition of farsightedness and ingenuity prevails in the Oregon State Park Department today and explains why the state's citizens now have such frequent access to their ocean.

In 1961, Oregon made a statewide study of its parks and projected its needs through 1975. One of the areas it looked at closely was its shoreline. It had every reason to be complacent about what it had done. Thanks to the excellent work of Mr. Boardman and the staffs that had helped and succeeded him, Oregon had a number of good oceanside parks, and the U.S. Forest Service also owned property on the water. And at that time pressure had not built up on the coastline. For one thing, Oregon's population had not suddenly increased like California's. For another, fogs are frequent on the shore, and this had tended to discourage developers. But Oregon was wise enough to know that this condition could not last and that its coast would not prove an exception to what was taking place elsewhere in America. It was also wise enough to foresee that easy access to the Pacific would benefit every citizen of the state as well as provide an attraction for the tourists who are important to the state's economy.

The goal the state set for itself was to have public access every three miles, and by 1968, Oregon had almost accomplished this. They had a good start toward this objective, because of the work already done by Mr. Boardman and because of the Sinuslaw National Forest, which touches the ocean front at several points. But to complete the program, when they built Route 101 in the south, they acquired all the land between the highway and the ocean as part of the highway program. As one official of the park department explained to me, it often costs only a little more to purchase the additional land, if it is done at the time of the highway acquisition. I had never thought of this possibility before, but it is one that deserves consideration by other states.

The U.S. Forest Service put in an excellent interpretative program at Cape Perpetua in Sinuslaw National Forest along with trails that provided magnificent views of the ocean as well as direct access to it. In the area where the famous Oregon sand dunes are located, the state hoped to persuade the federal government to establish a national park. (How contrary this is to some of our other states where the resistance to the creation of national parks can be great.) The proposal drawn up by the National Park Service, which is governed by rather strict standards of quality, encountered local opposition. Some thought it would be too expensive because it encompassed lands that had already been developed; and the timber companies were concerned by the restrictions it placed on their operations. So in the spirit of

Mr. Boardman, when the state realized the bill would have difficulty passing Congress, they approached the U.S. Forest Service
to determine whether they would create a recreation area that
would accomplish much the same purpose but be more acceptable to more people.

A study showed that it would also be desirable for the state
to acquire twenty-five specific additional pieces of land in order
to round out the program of access to the ocean. Some of these
were large and some were small. By 1968, nine of them had
already been purchased, and most of the others were in negotia-
tion.[18]

But this was not the end of Oregon's activity, for this was an
overall program, not merely the preservation of particular tracts
of land. For many years, the state had claimed title to the
beaches. In the winter of 1967–68, the legislature passed a
"statement of policy and legislative intent," which stated in part
that "the Legislative Assembly hereby declares it is the public
policy of the State of Oregon to forever preserve and maintain
the sovereignty of the state heretofore existing over the seashore
and ocean beaches of the state from the Columbia River on the
North to the Oregon-California line on the south so that the
public may have the free and uninterrupted use thereof." Another bill encouraged the highway commission to acquire any
additional lands near the "Oregon seashore and beaches as may
be appropriate for recreational purposes where such lands are
held in private ownership." Further farsighted legislation forbade
the construction of buildings along the seashore below the sixteen-foot contour line, thus providing more sense of open space
for those on the beaches. There are some carefully defined exceptions in the law. For example, the law changes at the mouths
of rivers and other places where the sixteen-foot contour line
might be at an excessive distance from the ocean. But the purpose is clear: To prevent building close to the waterfront. This
law provided a final touch to an amazing program.

To me, the experience of Oregon is impressive. While other
states have temporized in confusion about the preservation of
their coastlines, Oregon has acted, not in a piecemeal fashion,
but by establishing a basic policy and following a concrete prac-

tical plan for carrying out that policy. And the state utilized every resource available to it—the National Park Service, the U.S. Forest Service, even the highway department, in striving to reach its goal, again not in a hit-or-miss fashion but as part of a coordinated whole. The results show what can be accomplished when Americans really make up their minds what it is they want to do with their magnificent land and are willing to pay the price to do it.

The skeptic might argue that while the attainment of a limited, although praiseworthy, objective within a single state represents a substantial achievement, it does not prove that land planning in America can be more extensive. If so, he might consider our national forests.

The lands controlled by the U.S. Forest Service are vast. They amount to more than 186 million acres, an area about the size of France and the United Kingdom combined, and they range from forests in the South to the crests of the Cascades in the Northwest and to two mountain ranges in New England. In the early days, the purpose of the national forests was simple: to preserve an adequate supply of commercial timber for the United States. The ranger's job, as the U.S. Forest Service says, "was primarily one of protection. Distances and vast areas made it difficult for the Ranger to do little more than protect the resources. He used horse and mules for transportation and travel. There were few roads. He rode and hiked long distances across Ranger Districts larger than some eastern states. On a $60-a-month salary, he had to provide his own horse. Often the Ranger built his own log home which also served as the Ranger Station. Equipment was limited to little more than an ax, a string of mules, a saw, his horse and a rifle. Physical stamina and woodsmanship were more important than knowledge of timber, forage, soils, or wildlife management. Even in Europe resource management—as we know it today—was still in its infancy. There was little resource management in the National Forests. Rangers kept a weather eye out for poachers and struggled unceasingly to protect vital watersheds from overgrazing and illegal timber cutting. Most of the time the Ranger worked alone. Fire was the big threat to his district. Sometimes forest fires burned for days before they were detected. Once detected, it often took several days for the Ranger to reach the fire with a firefighting crew." [19] In that time, the only conflict in the use of the national forests was between those who wanted to overutilize them and those who wanted to use them for the same purposes but less wantonly.

For many years, the role of the U.S. Forest Service personnel did not basically change. As one man said to me, "They were loggers all the way," for a knowledge of lumbering was the primary skill required. Even the maintenance of the watersheds within the national forests was regarded largely as a matter of controlled cutting. This does not mean that the U.S. Forest Service neglected recreation or that its personnel were not interested in the outdoors for the sake of the outdoors. Among conservationists lumbermen have a bad name, and some of them have deserved it. But many have entered the business in an effort to make a living by providing a useful commodity and still enjoy being in the woods. They are ardent fishermen, hunters, campers, hikers, and mountain climbers. So it was with the men working for the U.S. Forest Service. In spite of their economic interest in the timber industry, they did not join the service just to cut down trees. They were fundamentally outdoorsmen, or they would have found easier work to do. It is not surprising, therefore, that in time they began to look at the national forests as more than reservoirs of potential timber and sites that contained good grazing. In fact, they pioneered the concept of federal wilderness areas. Rather proudly, the U.S. Forest Service states, "The Wilderness Act is new, but the idea behind it is not. In effect, the act confirms 40 years of wilderness protection within the National Forests. The Forest Service, U.S. Department of Agriculture, pioneered this concept of land management, and its efforts are now reflected in national legislation.

"The first step toward this wilderness system was made back in 1924, when the Forest Service set aside a special area of the Gila National Forest in New Mexico to protect its wilderness values." [20]

But even this foresight—this realization that different types of land designations could be useful—was insufficient to prophesy what was going to take place in the 1950's. In that decade, the number of visitors using the national forests for recreational purposes suddenly spurted, rising at a far faster rate than either the population or the gross national product. In the ten-year period the number of visits tripled to reach a total of 92.5 million in 1960,[21] with the expectation there would be 195 million visits annually by 1972, and 635 million by the year 2000.[22] This influx of visitors made it necessary for the U.S. Forest Service to take a new look at the management of the lands under its control.

No problems would have been caused by this increase in visitors if it had been accompanied by a lessening in commercial use, but quite the contrary occurred. In the same decade, the timber harvest from the national forests more than doubled, and the cash receipts rose almost four times. By 1960, more than a hundred different kinds of permits for special uses were issued by the U.S. Forest Service. These included permits for telephone and powerline rights-of-way, cabins, churches, resorts, schools, landing fields, and other uses. More than 58,000 such permits were being administered as well as more than 11,000 oil, gas, and other mineral leases and permits.[23] The acceleration in the commercial use of the national forests is dramatically underscored by the sudden rise in the U.S. Forest Service's receipts. From the time the national forests were established until 1958, they grossed one billion dollars; they grossed the second billion between 1958 and 1965.[24]

Those who are surprised by the diversity of activity in the national forests have probably confused them to a degree with the national parks. The National Park Service's mandate, written into the original law that set up the service, is clear. "The service thus established," says the act, "shall promote and regulate the use of the Federal areas known as national parks, monuments, and reservations . . . [so as] to conserve the scenery and the natural and historic objects and the wildlife therein and to provide for the enjoyment of the same in such manner and by such means as will leave them unimpaired for the enjoyment of future generations." [25]

In 1918, a year after the establishment of the service, Secretary of the Interior Lane addressed a letter to Stephen Mather, then the director. "For the information of the public," Lane wrote, "an outline of the administrative policy to which the new Service will adhere may now be announced. This policy is based on three broad principles: First, that the national parks must be maintained in absolutely unimpaired form for the use of future generations as well as those of our own time; second, that they are set apart for the use, observation, health, and pleasure of the people, and third, that the national interest must dictate all decisions affecting public or private enterprise in the parks." [26] Over the course of years, these statements of basic policy have to an extent been modified and amended, but they still outline the fundamental purposes of the national park system.

The U.S. Forest Service, on the other hand, has quite a different mandate, and its responsibilities are often conflicting. It must preserve its watersheds (numerous city reservoirs and the headwaters of many of our great rivers are in the national forests); it must permit the commercial use of its resources through lumbering and grazing; it is charged with responsibility for the wildlife in its areas (hunting is allowed in the national forests, but not—with certain special exceptions—in the national parks); and it must provide recreation and esthetic enjoyment, as well as protecting the designated wilderness areas within the system of forests. It also administers the national grasslands. These, to the surprise of many people, are not samples of outstanding prairie; they are lands of such poor quality they have been withdrawn from private ownership. Only under direct federal control can the grass sod be reestablished to help prevent the recurrence of more dust storms. To a large extent, this multiple use of the national forests came about because of their size, their diversity, and the flexible provisions of the U.S. Forest Service's original directives. But the principle of multiple use was formally affirmed by Congress in 1960 with the passage of an act that stated in part "that it is the policy of the Congress that the national forests are established and shall be administered for outdoor recreation, range, timber, watershed, and wildlife and fish purposes." [27]

With a broad assignment such as this, the potential for conflict is enormous. For many aspects of the multiple-use concept are not compatible. Cattle cannot graze in freshly reforested lands;

lumbermen can hardly cut down trees in lands that are open grazing areas; recreationalists cannot derive pleasure from driving or hiking through cut-over lands, no matter how carefully replanted. On the face of it, the problem seems almost unresolvable, because of the wide gaps between the various demands on the land. The temptation in such circumstances would be to resort to compromise, bending a little here and giving a little there, according to the pressures applied on each tract. Instead, the U.S. Forest Service launched the largest land-use-zoning program ever undertaken, as far as I know, in the United States. While local communities across the country were arguing whether the commercial district on Main Street should be extended another block or whether a school might be permitted in a residential district, the U.S. Forest Service was drawing up land-use plans for the more than 186 million acres under its supervision. Granted that this zoning did not require legal action and does not have the force of law, its accomplishment nevertheless represents a substantial achievement and sets a pattern that might well be copied in the solution of other land management problems. For it provides a good example of an agency's weighing its total land resources and the demands made on them and then assigning use priorities to what is available.

Because the types of areas included in the national forests vary so widely, separate management plans are drawn up for each Forest Service Region. This process begins with the designation of major management zones. In the Northern Region, for example, which supervises forests and grasslands in Washington, Idaho, Montana, and both Dakotas, there are seven such zones: high area, general forest, lower-slope-foothill, water influence, riverbreak, travel influence, and special. (Additional zones may be created to cover unique situations.) The high area zone is generally above the timberline or in the alpine and subalpine forests. It is a place of wildflowers during the short spring and summer, but the trees are usually slow to grow and are often deformed by the winds and severe weather. Such areas, while magnificently beautiful, are not good for lumbering. They also have limited recreational use because the soil is generally thin and the plant-life delicate. Consequently, "the manager," according to the U.S.

Forest Service, "seeks to protect and maintain vegetative cover by spreading use over a larger area."

On the other hand, in the general forest zone, a much hardier region, lumbering is permitted along with more intensive recreational and tourist use. The travel influence zone, which centers on the highways, is the most heavily used of all. Here, according to the U.S. Forest Service, "Recreational facilities are provided to handle large numbers of forest visitors. Opportunities are utilized at selected sites to explain local human and natural history and to demonstrate forest resource management. Timber, grazing, wildlife, and other resources are managed to protect or enhance recreational values." In this zone, lumbering gives way to tourism. Cutting is generally limited to diseased, insect-infected, or overcrowded trees. Even on the distant mountain slopes that can be seen from the travel influence zone, the U.S. Forest Service attempts to make the lumbering operations as esthetically inoffensive as possible by leaving a protecting screen of trees or by insisting that the area be cut in an irregular shape that conforms to the terrain, thus making it look like a natural opening in the forest.[28]

Once general zones like these have been established, criteria are set up for the management of each one. These are set forth in a handbook that is given each district ranger. It then becomes his responsibility to divide his district into the appropriate zones and to state specifically how he intends to meet the criteria of management for each one. The district rangers' plans are then approved by the forest supervisor, who puts them together into a total plan for the entire national forest.

Such planning, however, is remarkably flexible. Charles A. Connaughton, Regional Forester for the Pacific Northwest Region, said to a meeting of lumbermen, "We're inclined to take our own relation to the forest for granted. We have convinced ourselves that the forest use of the past with few changes would stand the tests of the future. And we readily assume a defensive position when our policies, actions, and methods of the past are challenged. Actually we may be correct but are we very realistic? Do we feel that we can ignore the pressures and judgments of shifting public opinion? Do we acknowledge that some changes with time are inevitable? Are we ready to orient our own thinking and practices to others?

"Regardless of our knowledge of the forest, our success and acceptance as forest users and managers depends on sensing and measuring the changes in public opinion which are taking place. By so doing we maintain a position which permits us to participate constructively in shaping and orienting policy so that it applies intelligently to the combined interest of the forest and the general public. Furthermore, if we are alert to public opinion and its formulation, we can effectively and freely adjust practices and policies under our own control and demonstrate a position of leadership in forest policy formulation rather than a position of reluctant acquiescence to direction and force generated by outside interests." [29]

In fact, the U.S. Forest Service has done an excellent job of keeping up with the times and altering its overall management programs in the light of new needs. For example, the east slope of the Rocky Mountains in Colorado has been undergoing extensive change from the city of Pueblo in the south to Fort Collins in the north. In the 1930's, this was largely cattle country; but since World War II, it has become more and more an industrial and intellectual center, and many informed persons predict that eventually a continuous metropolitan area will run between the two points.

Already the effects are being felt on the national forests. In Roosevelt National Forest, more and more acreage is being given over to recreation rather than being held to its former uses. In the Boulder area, for example, 1,295 head of cattle were grazing in 1960; in 1967, the number had dropped to 859. In the Estes Park area, over the same period the number fell from 813 to 641; while at Laramie River, which is farther north and out of the area of recreational pressure, the number has increased. There is still an overall demand for grazing lands, but those lands near the metropolitan centers are becoming less and less suitable for the purpose. Not only is there need for recreation space, but the cattlemen themselves find the ranges too crowded with people to be satisfactory. In one instance, an excellent piece of grazing land had been leased to two different ranchers in a period of five years; each one found the area so overrun with recreationists that they failed to renew their leases. As a result of this shift in the demand for land, the U.S. Forest Service has been removing grazing allotments, thus leaving more acreage free for outdoor sports. This can be done efficiently and quickly within the original management program, which provides the flexibility to meet situations like this.[30]

The change in times and attitudes can be well illustrated by the hippy invasion that swept Boulder, Colorado, in 1968. When the city proved unfriendly, the hippies moved out to the suburbs, from which they were also dislodged. They then announced they would move into national forest lands. This was a far cry from the oldtime ranger's problems of preventing overgrazing or catching timber thieves. With the adaptability that is characteristic of the U.S. Forest Service, the district ranger decided that since camping was one of the public uses of the national forests, the hippies should be allowed to come just like anyone else. But also like anyone else, they had to obey the usual rules—no camping except in a designated campground, no occupancy for more than fourteen days, and no more than a certain number of people near each other. Furthermore, they would all have to pay the regular fees, which he actually collected from them.[31] Some of the local residents accused him of being a "hippy lover," but they missed the point. Within the flexible framework of the U.S. Forest Service's policy, he was able to avoid creating a crisis, and his adaptability made room for all kinds of Americans as well as all kinds of land use. Yet he still preserved the forests from damage.

Among conservationists, it is not difficult to arouse controversy over the multiple use of the national forests. The camper may be angry who suddenly discovers that one of his favorite spots has been chosen as the site for cutting without his understanding that the national forests are an important source of the lumber we need. The house to which he will return at the end of his trip may well have been constructed from national forest timber. One ranger at the Teton National Forest was inspecting a cut-over area to make sure the lumberman had complied with his contract. Actually the lumberman had done an exceptional job of cleaning up, and the ranger was admiring it when a visitor came up, literally shook him by the shoulders, and accused him of desecrating the forest.

Certainly the principle of multiple use sometimes places the U.S. Forest Service at the center of the battle between conflicting interests, with the extreme preservationists on one side and the more wanton of the commercial interests on the other: and certainly some aspects of it might be modified. Many people who love the national forests would be relieved to see the right of mineral entry restricted. As it stands now, this right is a relic of an older time when the discovery of new minerals within our boundaries took precedence over almost everything else. The principle of multiple use also leads on occasion to what many, including myself, would consider overdevelopment, such as the proposal of the Disney interests to build a large-scale sports center deep in the mountains of California.

But controversy over the merits of multiple use itself obscures the important point that the U.S. Forest Service has been able to achieve a significant degree of selectivity in serving the conflicting demands made on its lands. It has attempted to assign to each tract its best and highest use, and it has been able to work out a master land plan for all the acres it administers. Such broadscale planning has proved possible when the land falls under the supervision of a single agency. The problem is how to extend this sort of thinking to include more federal agencies that affect the use of our land, coordinating their activities toward basic, overall goals, and then to carry the principle even further to encompass state and local agencies. Congress has made one outstanding step to do just that.

In 1962, the U.S. Government Printing Office published a book of more than two hundred pages that may have been one of the most important conservation publications in this half of the century. It was entitled *Outdoor Recreation for America*, and it was the report to the President and Congress of the Outdoor Recreation Resources Review Commission. This commission, whose chairman was Laurence S. Rockefeller, opened the first chapter of its report with these words: "The outdoors lies deep in American traditions. It has had immeasurable impact on the Nation's character and on those who made its history. This is a civilization painfully and only recently carved in conflict with the forces of nature—farms from unbroken prairie and cities from wilderness. The epic of American life is the tale of the pioneer, edging his way westward in the face of unending danger and hardship. When an American looks for the meaning of his past, he seeks it not in ancient ruins, but more likely in mountains and forests, by a river, or at the edge of the sea. The tale is one of discovery, of encounter, of hard-won settlement.

"But there is more to the legacy than the land. From the beginning, one of the strongest currents in American thought has been the idea that the outdoors is a *right* of Americans—not only something to be enjoyed but vital to our spirit. The idea was born in an agrarian society, for though the outdoors was then all about, some feared that it would not always be so. Indeed, Jefferson saw the land as the country's ballast against the rootlessness of city living. . . ."

These words accurately reflected the sentiments of many Americans, but the commission was not content merely with words. After three years of research and many days of discussion among the commissioners, they had concrete and far-reaching proposals to make. "For various reasons," the report said, "the recommendations tend to be more detailed and extensive regarding the Federal Government. The Commission wishes to emphasize, however, that the key elements in the total effort to make outdoor recreation opportunities available are private enterprise, the States, and local government. In relation to them, the role of the Federal agencies should not be one of domination but of cooperation in meeting their respective needs." [32] In other words, the commission recognized that the preservation and effective administration of open space in America could not be the sole responsibility of one or two agencies of government or even of the federal government alone. The problem was much broader than that, and its solution required an overall approach and the coordinated effort of every aspect of government as well as private enterprise. Recognition of this fact represented an extraordinary step forward in American conservation and one that held great promise for the future.

Among the commission's recommendations was the establishment of the Bureau of Outdoor Recreation in the Department of the Interior, a recommendation on which Secretary Udall acted in April, 1962. The choice of the word "recreation" was probably an unfortunate one. It conjures images of highly developed recreational areas, but the bureau's assignment was broader than that. It was really the planning and coordinating agency for the use of all remaining open spaces in the United States.

A few days later, President Kennedy submitted legislation to Congress to augment another of the commission's recommendations, the establishment of the Land and Water Conservation Fund. This fund was intended to provide a central source of money for federal acquisitions of open space and also grants-in-aid to states and municipalities for the same purpose. Before any state or municipality could be eligible to receive funds, however, the state had to complete a statewide survey of its open-space resources and determine what it hoped to accomplish. Its plan then had to be approved by the Bureau of Outdoor Recreation. This wise provision was intended to prevent piecemeal acquisition of land and to encourage the states to take an overall look at their open-space resources. It worked. This was the first time that all those involved in land acquisition began coordinating their efforts.

A few criticisms could be leveled against the Land and Water Conservation Fund. One of the most apparent was the making of grants for the physical development of recreational areas. This was an activity that could well have been postponed for a few years instead of absorbing funds that might better have been used for the immediate purchase of available lands. But such difficulties were minor.

The major problem of the Land and Water Conservation Fund, ever since its inception, has been lack of money. Originally Congress had depended on three principal sources to supply the needed revenue: proceeds from the sale of surplus federal property except that belonging to the military, a tax on motorboat fuels, and user fees at designated recreation areas operated by the federal government.[33] The latter, Congress hoped, would supply a major amount of the funds. Fees were set for various areas, and the Bureau of Outdoor Recreation created the Golden Eagle, a pass that for seven dollars a year would admit the purchaser and people accompanying him in his car into any of the areas without further payment. But by 1966, the amount collected in user fees amounted to only one-fifth the total that had been estimated, $7 million instead of $35 million.[34]

There were many reasons for this. The Army Engineers, for example, who operate recreational facilities at some of their reservoirs, were resistant to being included in the fee system. They did not need the money; they could always get the funds they wanted from Congress. In some places, the fees were difficult to collect. I have been in U.S. Forest Service campgrounds, for example, where it was hardly worthwhile to send a ranger seven miles out of his way to pick up a few dollars; fees, therefore, were collected only on those days when a ranger was making a regularly scheduled visit. People also learned how to cheat. When Congress substituted a hand card for the original automobile sticker, hotels near some of the major national parks bought quantities of them and lent them to their guests. To save less than ten dollars, they would deprive future Americans of some of the magnificent areas that might still be saved.

The greatest weakness of the program, however, was the manner in which it was sold to the public. I do not mean this as a criticism of the Bureau of Outdoor Recreation. None of its personnel, as far as I know, have had any experience in this field, and there is no reason they should have. But the sale of the Golden Eagle violated practically every rule of marketing. I have talked to many personnel engaged in collecting user fees or selling the Golden Eagle. They usually did not understand what it was designed to accomplish. A fundamental principle in a sales campaign is to have well-informed and enthusiastic salesmen. I have walked around designated recreation areas and at random asked visitors if they knew what the receipts from the Golden Eagle were used for. Rarely, if ever, have I discovered someone who did. Another principle of selling is to arouse enthusiasm for the product. But in this case, most of the buyers just thought the Golden Eagle something of a nuisance, even though they were people with a native interest in the out-of-doors. There were, as far as I know, no competitions for its sale—no contest, for example, between the U.S. Forest Service and the Corps of Engineers to see which could sell the most. Yet competition is a fundamental ingredient of a mass selling effort. A selling agency like the National Park Service or the units within an agency such as the individual parks receive no benefit from a good sales record. Yet incentive lies at the roots of most successful sales efforts.

There is no emotional impact to the sales literature that accompanies the Golden Eagle when it is issued. The buyer gets nothing but his pass, no feeling that he is participating in a vital movement that might change the face of America for years to come. I have seen no evidence of any effort to sell the Golden Eagle to people who might not use it but would like to take part in a great conservation effort, particularly if they had some means of showing that they have done so. Yet I believe there are probably hundreds of thousands of Americans who would do so gladly. This would be especially true, I think, if Congress would guarantee an adequate annual sum for the Land and Water Conservation Fund from other sources and let revenue from the sale of Golden Eagles be added to that. Altogether this is an instance in which the federal government needs a skill that it does not possess. It probably could have enlisted it on a volunteer basis from private enterprise if it had gone about it the right way. This was another instance of government not being as self-sufficient as it thinks it is. To make the situation worse, by the spring of 1970 Congress had not even got around to approving the year's program. Thus when the tourist season started, the Golden Eagle cards had not even been printed. As a merchandiser, the federal government was acting like a food store owner who offers turkeys the day after Thanksgiving but does not stock them the week before. If the basic program had not been such a good one, its inept handling would have been ludicrous. But as it was, Congress and the federal government had presided over a major tragedy—the destruction of an imaginative and constructive idea whose beneficial effects would have been felt for many years to come.

Meanwhile, as receipts in the Land and Water Conservation

Fund fell below the estimates, the price of land was rising. In 1967, Edward C. Crafts, Director of the Bureau of Outdoor Recreation, made this gloomy report to the House Committee on Interior and Insular Affairs. "The rapid rise in land prices combined with a number of other factors has placed a strain on the Land and Water Conservation Fund. The States and their political subdivisions are faced with escalation problems in their acquisition programs similar to those of the Federal Government. Their development needs are also pressing and costs continue to rise.

"Combined Federal and State outdoor recreation needs to be financed by the Land and Water Conservation Fund during the next 10 years (fiscal years 1968–1977) are estimated to be about $3.6 billion in 1966 dollars. If price escalation were included in this estimate, the needs would be 40 to 50 percent higher for the period.

"Revenues to the Fund are currently running about $115 million annually. They are expected to total nearly $1 billion during the fiscal year 1968–1977 decade. It seems fairly clear that the Land and Water Conservation Fund will fail to meet the minimum program needs over the next ten years by possibly $2.7 billion, considering both Federal and State needs." [35]

In response to his warning, Congress eventually raised the authorization for the Land and Water Conservation Fund to $200 million a year over a five-year period and provided that funds from the sale of offshore oil leases could be used to supplement its other proceeds. (There is some justice in the thought that people who oiled up the coast of Santa Barbara, California, should give us some parks in return.) But in Washington, an authorization is not the same as an appropriation. Out of the $200 million authorized, the Johnson Administration for the fiscal year 1969 requested only $111,500,000. This meant that for the fiscal year 1970, it could have budgeted $288,500,000 and remained within the original program. It did not; it budgeted only $154 million. But much could be expected from President Nixon. When he was desperately seeking to become the Presidential candidate, he made this unequivocal statement: "In cutting the budget, the President must set his own priorities. While some sectors are certain to be pared, others must be preserved. Among those that should escape the budget knife are appropriations for conservation . . . and for the preservation of natural resources." He linked these expenditures with expenditures for education and said, "Investments here are investments for our children, in the kind of country they will live in and in the quality of life they will lead. This is the last place for Americans to be miserly." That was on May 16, 1968.[36] But Mr. Nixon, the candidate, and Mr. Nixon, the President, were apparently not even relatives. Having made the approval of a hefty pay increase for himself and the members of Congress one of the first acts of his administration, he then began to slash at the already picayune budgets allocated to conservation and natural resources. Not content with the cuts already made by the Johnson Administration, President Nixon's budget reduced the Land and Water Conservation Fund by another $30 million. As his Director of the Bureau of the Budget explained to Congress, there was little likelihood of any further increase in the next few years. Certainly, as regards the Department of the Interior, it was pointless to consider any additional land acquisition programs. By 1973, the department, he explained, would not have completed—even if land prices remained stable—the projects it has already started.

Remember President Nixon, in August, 1969, traveling from his mansion in San Clemente, California, to dedicate the redwood grove? "It is fitting," he said in part, "that a magnificent redwood grove in [the nonexistent] Redwood National Park be dedicated in honor of Lady Bird Johnson, who has done so much to stir in the American conscience a deepened sense of unity with our natural environment." Whose "deepened sense of unity"? Certainly not Mr. Nixon's. His administration had already stated, loudly and clearly, that it could afford to build a supersonic jet or an antiballistic missile, but it could not afford the relatively few dollars necessary to finish the Redwoods National Park, Point Reyes, and a few others, much less start new projects of this sort. What about his remarks concerning "investments in our children" and "this is the last place for Americans to be miserly"? With his torpedoing the Land and Water Conservation Fund, he had not only betrayed every child growing up in America today; he had attempted to destroy the greatest effort the American people have ever made to look at their land as a whole and plan for its future. He had also revealed that his conservation thinking was not of this century; it belonged more to the 1870's than the 1970's.

In 1970, after a year in office, he finally began to realize that the American people had taken his campaign promises seriously and that the environment and conservation were important political issues, important enough to affect an election return. He therefore reversed himself and recommended a slight increase in the Land and Water Conservation Fund and also that Congress spend the money already appropriated. This gave him the basis to proclaim—with accuracy—that he was prepared to spend more on open space in one year than his predecessors had been. But it was a little like trying to put out a four-alarm fire with a garden hose. The need is great, and the time is now—not tomorrow. By 1972, the last opportunity for a truly effective land-use program for the United States will probably have disappeared forever. To make the great dream envisioned earlier become a reality will require the *billions* President Nixon was prepared to spend on highways and other such projects, not the few *millions* he was ready to invest in the future of America. Americans can only hope that he will learn better or that Congress will overrule him.

Our past experience has clearly indicated the benefits that can be achieved by better land-use planning, and one glance around us shows the many opportunities that exist to employ it. But they will not be there long. With each passing year, the chances for a successful program become less and less.

9

The Need for Cooperative Effort

THE major conservation problems—whether they concern water and air pollution, the impact of our transportation system on the countryside, the acquisition of open space, or any of the other important issues—are too complex to be solved by a single individual or agency working alone. Most of them require an intensive cooperative effort by all the governmental agencies, private organizations, and individuals who are concerned. We might still be debating what to do about the North Cascades if the Secretaries of Agriculture and the Interior had not finally ordered their two departments to cooperate on a report and recommendations. If someone had taken the same initiative with the Bureau of Land Management and the National Park Service, much more acreage on Point Reyes would now be in the hands of the federal government. If years ago the Corps of Engineers had tried to work with the National Park Service in the Everglades, that problem might now be solved satisfactorily and at much less expense to the taxpayer.

The case of the redwoods is an example of what can happen when groups work together. There would be no chance today even to consider the establishment of a redwoods national park if it had not been for the pioneering effort of the Save-the-Red-woods League. Yet the league could not have accomplished much, if it had failed to enlist the cooperation of the State of California, both in adding state funds to those raised privately and in providing the necessary administration of the lands acquired. And from the very start, the possibility of establishing a redwoods national park rested entirely on the ability of the federal government to secure the cooperation of both the league and the state.

Earlier I described how a private foundation quietly purchased and held for Allegheny County, Pennsylvania, land that would eventually be needed for parks. This is an important service for a private organization to perform. By acting more quickly than government, it can not only purchase the land while it is still available, it can also prevent the price escalation that has occurred, for example, on Point Reyes. Indeed that peninsula might now be in federal ownership if, at the beginning, some private group had performed the same function.

I have also talked about the work of the Western Pennsylvania Conservancy in helping the Pennsylvania park system acquire badly needed lands. The cooperative effort between the state and the private agency has paid off handsomely. The Izaak Walton League, under the able leadership of Joseph Penfold, played a vital role in establishing what is now the Quetico-Superior Canoe Area. Without the league's close cooperation with the federal government, that magnificent project probably never would have been completed. Among private philanthropists, both the Mellon and Rockefeller families have made outstanding contributions, especially in helping the National Park Service acquire new parks. The American land would have been in a much poorer state today if it had not been for their cooperative efforts.

As a simple example of what can happen when everyone works together toward a mutual objective, I would like to tell the story of Upper Priest Lake in northern Idaho. This part of the state, with its rugged mountains, lakes, and forests represents a sample of what is taking place all over America. Even in the 1950's, it was remote, and land was cheap, selling for fifty cents an acre, if anyone cared to buy it. But new highways placed it closer to centers of population. Spokane, with modern roads, was now only a short distance. Seattle, which used to be a ten-hour drive, soon became a seven-hour one. Many persons from California, finding their own state more and more crowded, preferred to spend their vacations in northern Idaho. Land prices started to rise. Those acres that used to sell for fifty cents began to go for fifty dollars, sometimes even when there was no provision for sewage or access. Although some people were earning money from this, and a few of the selective buyers were making satisfactory purchases, the development was mostly unplanned. Nobody seemed to be worrying about garbage or water, even though the streams are cold and without much bacterial action and therefore cannot stand pollution.

One of the prized features of the region are the two lakes, Lower Priest and Upper Priest, which are connected by a narrow thoroughfare, so it is easy to take a boat from one to the other. Because Lower Priest Lake is nearer to population centers like Coeur d'Alene and Sandpoint, Idaho, and because Upper Priest Lake is accessible only by boat or trail, Lower Priest bore the brunt of the early development. Here the U.S. Forest Service had rented land for the construction of private homes. (This practice on the part of the U.S. Forest Service is a heritage from an earlier day, when there was more vacant land and fewer people. In many instances, it is not renewing such leases, but it then has to recompense the homeowners for the improvements they have made.) On Lower Priest Lake was also concentrated most of the privately owned waterfront property, and at least one mining claim had been filed on the lakeshore. (Just as in the Cascades, national forests, except under special circumstances, are open to mining claims.) The state also owned much of the waterfront and it, too, had rented land as sites for summer homes. The coli count in the once-pure lake was beginning to rise, and it was evident that the seeds of overdevelopment had been planted.[1]

Upper Priest Lake had been spared this because of its inaccessibility. The land on the western shore was included in the Kaniksu National Forest. The land on the eastern shore was an Idaho state forest. There is a significant difference between state forests in the East and in the West. In the East, where lumbering is not a significant part of the local economy, the state forests are primarily recreational areas kept in a less-developed form than the state parks. In the West, they are generally assigned the responsibility of producing money for the school systems. They are not reservations but fund-producers. This meant that owner-ship of the eastern shore of Upper Priest Lake by the state forest system did not ensure preservation of its beauty.

Breaking up government ownership of the shoreline were two pieces of property, one to the northeast and one to the southeast and both held by the same owner. Being flat, these were highly desirable for commercial purposes. The owner did nothing with them for years, but when he finally needed money, he thought the time had come to capitalize on the growing popularity of the Priest Lake area. On one of the two parcels, he erected a metal building that could serve as a store catering to the boatowners who came for the day, and on both of them he placed signs announcing that he had lots for sale. For all practical purposes, it looked as though Upper Priest Lake would be developed as Lower Priest had been, for there would certainly be no incentive to resist the pressures on the rest of the lake solely for the benefit of the people who bought those particular acres.

The Kaniksu Forest supervisor, however, was not content to sit passively by and see this happen. Instead he opened negotia-tions with the owner of the two tracts and discovered he was willing to sell to anyone, including the U.S. Forest Service. Fur-thermore, he did not need the total asking price paid to him at once but was willing to sell his holdings on an installment basis. The sum he wanted immediately, as I recall it, was about $30,-000, not a great amount but more than the U.S. Forest Service had available for that purpose at the time. So the supervisor turned to the West Coast Regional Office of the Nature Conser-vancy, which was willing to make the down payment and enter into a purchase contract with the owner. This stopped any fur-ther development; and as soon as the U.S. Forest Service ob-tained the funds, it reimbursed the Nature Conservancy and took over its contract. Private capital, by acting swiftly, accomplished what public funds could not. Yet public funds, which are far greater, ultimately picked up the cost. The two supplemented each other.

The acquisition of this land by the U.S. Forest Service made it possible for the service to go to the State of Idaho and discuss the management of the state-owned lands on the eastern shore. If the state would cooperate, together they would be able to foreclose any further unplanned development on Upper Priest Lake and manage the area jointly for the benefit of the most people. Impressed by what had been accomplished and interested in maintaining Idaho's beauty and appeal, the state was willing; and a joint agreement was signed by the governor and the regional forester. This clearly stated the agencies' goals: "1. Establish the land within the water influence zone of Upper Priest Lake as a 'scenic area'.... 2. Manage this zone principally for recreation and esthetic purposes and to protect those basic values which are associated with attractiveness of lakeside conditions. 3. Maintain and enhance the zone's scenic recreational values. ...." The agreement spelled out in considerable detail what each agency should do and should not do, including a responsibility on the part of the U.S. Forest Service to ask the Bureau of Land Management to withdraw certain lands from mineral entry, so mines could not be opened near the lake.[2]

One other tract, however, was still a concern. This was a section of land belonging to a railroad. In earlier times, when the railroads were first being built, they were often given alternate sections of land near their rights-of-way. Like many land-use ideas, it seemed a good one at the time; but it has left us an unfortunate legacy. Maps of many of the public lands of the United States, including a number of national forests, look like a checkerboard, with alternate holdings of private and government property. The owners often do not want to exchange their lands for others and permit the government to consolidate its properties. For it is far more advantageous to own a section surrounded on every side by public land than one that is bordered by private property. This one inholding just to the north of Upper Priest Lake was a remnant left from this former practice of dividing our lands. Although it was not close enough to the actual lakefront to present a direct threat to the shore, it was still close enough so that its future commercial development could have had an adverse effect on the U.S. Forest Service's plans. When I last talked to the service, they were negotiating with the company, which had indicated a willingness to exchange the land for acreage elsewhere. They did not want to be the only stumbling block in the way of the comprehensive plan.

In furtherance of its effort, the U.S. Forest Service worked out a master plan in cooperation with the state of Idaho and formally declared the area a scenic one. This places certain restrictions on its future use. Now, instead of the uncontrolled development that might otherwise have taken place, the resources of the two Priest lakes are being better utilized for the benefit of more people. Lower Priest Lake is being kept open for active recreation. The U.S. Forest Service is building more campgrounds, so that more people can use it and enjoy the outdoors. But it is holding this development to Lower Priest Lake. The thoroughfare, which is narrow and cannot accommodate numerous people, is being kept as a "forest environment," as the service calls it. Except for a small dock that was already there, Upper Priest Lake will remain undeveloped. Its beaches, fishing, and magnificent scenery will be available to all. The net result of this planning is more accessibility for more people with—and this is the important point—more variety when they get there, variety provided by wise planning of the resource's use rather than permitting uncontrolled proliferation of buildings, campsites, commercial facilities, and private houses, making the two lakes like many others.

There were two keys to the success of this endeavor. One key was the farsightedness of the U.S. Forest Service, which saw the trend and took steps to reverse it before it was too late. The other key was cooperation. For all its planning, the service could not have accomplished the objective by itself. It asked for and received the help of the Nature Conservancy, a private agency, in preventing the commercialization of the two tracts that were up for sale. This action inspired the confidence of the state of Idaho, which agreed to cooperate fully in carrying out the total plan. And this, in turn, persuaded the railroad to enter into negotiations to release the land it held. It was like a chain reaction.

Once the way had been pointed, and once the first step was taken, the next followed. Most importantly, however, no one organization could have achieved the final goal by itself; it required the coordinated efforts of all of them.

Although the history of conservation in this country is replete with examples that demonstrate both the need for, and the success of, cooperation, these examples are sadly more the exception than the rule. The reasons for this can best be explained by examining in detail the evolution of a significant cooperative program and looking at the forces working for and against it. This will also show some of the problems that handicap the conservation movement and make its efforts less successful than they should be.

The primary objective of the Nature Conservancy is to preserve—by their actual acquisition—areas of land having esthetic or scientific importance. These may be small tracts of a few acres or large ones comprised of thousands of acres; and the Nature Conservancy may, or may not, retain title itself. When it does not, it transfers the title to some suitable agency, perhaps a university, perhaps a governmental agency like the National Park Service or the California state park system. When it does this, it almost always places restrictions on the future use of the land.

This is a laudable objective, but it soon became apparent that both the quantity and the quality of the land that could be purchased or received as gifts by a private agency were inadequate to the nation's needs. Because of the large sums of money needed, the single largest purchaser has to be government, whether federal, state, or local. So the Nature Conservancy began exploring means of helping government overcome the problems it was facing in its land acquisition efforts, thus supplementing public action with private assistance.

Soon after the decision was made to do this, a situation arose in New York State, in which the state needed help. The state park system had long been bothered by an amusement center that operated at the border of one of the state parks in the Catskill Mountains. The center was not only out of harmony with the adjoining park, it also occupied land that logically should have been included within the park boundaries. All attempts to secure this area had been futile until one year the owner ran into financial difficulties, and the amusement center was put up for auction.

Here was the chance that the state had been waiting for; and if it could move quickly, it could prevent the center from being purchased by someone who would continue its operation. But the state could not move quickly. In the first place, it was not permitted by law to bid at auction; in the second, it had no funds immediately available for the purchase. As an experiment, it turned to the Nature Conservancy and asked whether it would bid in the property and hold it for eventual resale to the park system. Such a transaction carries with it a high degree of risk, for under those circumstances, the state cannot legally commit itself to carry out its part of the agreement. Everything has to be done on good faith.

A representative of the Nature Conservancy attended the auction and bid in the property for a price that was within limits of what the state had said it could afford. I now found myself in a strange position. As head of one of the foremost conservation agencies in the country, I had authorized the use of funds, given to preserve esthetically and scientifically valuable lands, for the purchase of an unattractive amusement center, a blight on the Catskill Mountains. I hoped that this ownership would be temporary, but we had no legal assurance on this count. If the deal did not go through, we would all be in a difficult situation, and myself in the worst of all. I mention this to emphasize the high degree of risk that is involved in most constructive conservation ventures. Today, with the need so urgent, this is not a field for cautious people. If we are concerned for the land, we must take chances and live with the worries that accompany them. The problem is to calculate the risks carefully and not become involved in unreasonable ones. That is why a volunteer like myself heading a large conservation agency soon finds he has a full-time job.

The State of New York, however, not only kept its good faith agreement, it did so promptly. Within a short time, it had allocated the funds for the purchase of the amusement center, reimbursed the Nature Conservancy for its auction bid, taken title to the land, and razed the buildings on it. Today it is an integral part of the park, offering a handsome view of the distant mountains. But neither the state nor the Nature Conservancy could have accomplished this by itself. The state was not equipped to buy the property when it came up for sale; the Nature Conservancy did not have the funds to make a permanent investment in the land.

Encouraged by this success, the Nature Conservancy entered into a much larger undertaking with the State of California. This involved almost 10,000 acres a few miles northeast of Santa Cruz. The three co-owners of this tract wanted to give it to the state as a state park to be named in memory of their mother. There was, however, one condition attached to the gift, and that condition was creating a formidable obstacle. One piece of the property had a $400,000 mortgage on it, and the owners could not afford both to give the land and pay off the mortgage themselves. The state would have to do that. Although $400,000 is a large amount of money, it was only a small portion of the value of the entire tract, which was worth millions. Unfortunately the state did not have that amount available at the time the gift offer was made; and although the acquisition of the area was high on its priority list because of the expected population growth of Santa Cruz, it looked as though the offer might have to be declined. If it were, the owners had no alternative but to sell it all to a developer, pay off their mortgage, and rid themselves of the burden of rising taxes. One developer had made them a standing offer of $4 million.

This project concerned me even more than the one in the Catskills because the transaction was far more complicated. The amount of money needed was much larger—far more than the Nature Conservancy could produce—and the state would be unable to repurchase the land as quickly. But some friends of the Nature Conservancy in California came up with an answer. They were willing to endorse a note at a San Francisco bank that enabled the Nature Conservancy to borrow enough money to pay off the mortgage and also meet the interest payments and other expenses. In time, the state was able to buy the property and reimburse the Nature Conservancy for its costs. Today the Forest of Nessine Marks is an outstanding state park.

There was also a corollary benefit as a result of this action. Because the Nature Conservancy had performed a service for the state, it asked for the passage of legislation that placed a restriction on the land: If it were ever used for anything except park purposes, title would revert to the Nature Conservancy, which meant that any agency taking the land would have to condemn it and pay full value for it. The significance of this action transcended the protection it gave the Forest of Nessine Marks. Remembering how the highway department built roads through the redwoods park lands, many of which had been preserved by private donations, this legislation was an attempt to set a precedent that might be followed in the future.

Both of these instances, the park in the Catskills and the Forest of Nessine Marks, demonstrated that there was a significant role for a private agency to play in support of government and the combination could accomplish objectives that neither could attain alone. On the one hand, a private agency could never hope to have the funds that were needed for a sizable, nationwide effort to set aside prime lands, but it did have flexibility. Unlike government, it did not have to adhere to a schedule set up by a legislative body that could not foresee the special opportunities that might arise. It could also take actions that, for government, were unorthodox or forbidden, like bidding at an auction. On the other hand, government could obtain the money. Even though the sums allotted by government, whether federal, state, or local, to conservation purposes are usually small in terms of their total budgets, they are large in comparison with the private funds that can be mustered.

These experiences led the Nature Conservancy to expand this aspect of its work, and it cooperated with several other states and also with the federal government, most especially with the U.S. Forest Service. Many of our national forests are unfortunately pockmarked with inholdings. These have usually resulted from one of two general causes. Either the federal government gave away or sold land from the public domain before the formation of the national forest; or in the case of national forests that have been purchased, it did not buy up all the acreage originally designated in the forest's boundaries. Over the years, the U.S. Forest Service has gradually been consolidating its holdings, particularly in significant areas. This is a highly imaginative agency, and Edward Cliff, the Chief Forester, along with his staff quickly saw the opportunities that the Nature Conservancy's program offered.

Because the U.S. Forest Service is a revenue-producing agency, it has some funds of its own that can be used for the purchase of inholdings. But it has to make the purchases according to a schedule that has been approved by Congress. In the usual course of events, this provides for orderly programming and keeps the operation under congressional control, where it belongs. It poses difficulties, however, when special circumstances arise. A landowner, for example, may suddenly put his inholding on the market. If it is purchased and developed, its value will increase and perhaps place the property outside the reach of the U.S. Forest Service. But the process of changing the schedule of purchases that Congress has approved is burdensome and time-consuming. Therefore the service of the Nature Conservancy in purchasing some of these tracts and then reselling them to the U.S. Forest Service should prove useful. Operating closely with Mr. Cliff, we found that this cooperative effort worked well on a relatively small scale.

The next question was this: Could it be made more helpful and could it be expanded to cover more land and more agencies?

One of the continuing difficulties in the federal government's acquisition of open space has been the rising cost of land. The situation at Point Reyes, where prices began to soar after the announcement of the national seashore, was typical, not an exception. Again and again, the federal government, as well as local and state governments, have found that their original estimates of the cost of preserving open space were well under the actual cost when the time came to make the purchases.

There were several reasons for this. Generally speaking, in the 1960's land was rising at an overall rate of 5 or 10 percent a year.[3] Before the reader rushes out to purchase land as an investment, he should remember that was an overall rate and that the increases in specific areas varied widely. For example, in the period from November, 1965, to March, 1966, the lucky investor who put his money into Indiana farmland would have experienced a profit of 12 percent. The less-fortunate investor who purchased farmland in Oregon, Oklahoma, Kansas, or New Mexico would have had a profit of 1 percent—not enough to cover his carrying charges. The even less-fortunate investor who chose to put his money into farmland in Washington, Arizona, Maine, or New York would have found that his investment had not increased at all. He would have suffered a significant loss if he had included interest charges on the money he used.[4] I mention these figures because many people today believe that all land prices must invariably go up. This is not necessarily true, but the belief is one of the factors that is sending them higher.

Another reason for the increase in the value of land is the increase in our population. We have more people than ever before, and we need to find places to put them. Many think this is the primary cause and that it places a floor below which prices cannot fall in the future. But our past history does not indicate this. At the end of the eighteenth century, the population of the State of New York was a little more than half a million. At that time, Alexander Wilson, the pioneer ornithologist, was looking for farmland that he and his cousin could afford to buy. He finally located some at $5 an acre. In the 1950's, when the population of the state had increased thirty times, there was much land available in New York at $10 an acre. And those were 1950 dollars, which means that the lands, in spite of the tremendous rise in population, cost even less than in Wilson's era. Perhaps the lands were not completely comparable, but the figures, I think, illustrate that even dramatic increases in population, although an important element, will not alone cause dramatic increases in prices.

Another factor that has escalated land prices has been continued prosperity and the desire for what have come to be known as second homes. Because of our federal highway program, vast areas in America have become accessible for weekend visits, and many metropolitan dwellers now have their "place in the country." This demand is not necessarily either stable or logical, and it has resulted in some peculiar price patterns. In the late 1950's, for example, many New Yorkers were buying land in northwestern Connecticut and Vermont, and in both areas the prices were high. But a traveler moving north would have discovered this paradox. As he left Connecticut and entered the Berkshires of western Massachusetts, prices suddenly dropped by substantial amounts. As he continued even farther north and crossed the state line into Vermont, he would have discovered that prices were higher again.[5] In part, this could be ascribed to the Massachusetts income tax, which might well have prevented purchases by people who wanted to establish legal residences in the country to avoid the heavy taxes they pay in New York City. But this was a small portion of the potential purchasers. For most of them, this was not a consideration. Also in part, the difference in price might have resulted from the greater availability of skiing in Vermont than in Massachusetts. But again, this could hardly account for the price spread between areas that are only a few miles apart. The biggest factor, I think, was being in style. It was much more fashionable to speak of "my house in Vermont" than "my house in Massachusetts." The first was chic; the second was not. I mention this to show that the demand for a second home may be based as much on passing vogue as on lasting desire. It is not at all unlikely that in a severe depression, the second homes will be the first to go on the market.

Two other factors have also helped prices rise. The sorry condition of our cities has certainly contributed. If the cities were more attractive, people would not want to escape from them. As it is, if they have the money to do so, they move to the suburbs, creating pressures on the land there, or they want a country place of their own, where they can also escape, at least for the weekend, the noise, dirt, and bustle of the city. The conservationists, too, have made their contribution. Some of them, in their panic to preserve certain areas, have been willing to pay unrealistic prices. One woman, for example, wished to establish a conservation grove of some rare trees. She had a fund to do so, knew just how many acres she wanted and, by telephone to a real estate dealer, offered the entire fund for the specific number of acres. This amounted to several times the going price for that particular type of land, but after her offer, the price of surrounding land leaped upward.

In another specific case, a family owned some upland and some marshland abutting it. A number of years ago, when a state highway went through the property, the marshlands were considered almost valueless, but high compensation was paid for the uplands. Today the reverse is true. A recent appraisal placed a lower value on the uplands than on the marsh. The reason was the demand of conservationists in that area to preserve marshlands. Unfortunately conservationists have not always been as astute as they should have been; and in a number of instances, they have gone into a panic, bid too high, and pushed the prices up, thus defeating their own case.

The principle reason for the rising prices, however, is outright speculation. Nothing else could account for the sudden spurt in prices during the 1950's and 1960's. The American people have turned to real estate with the same enthusiasm with which they turned to the stock market in the 1920's. This is nothing new. Americans had gone through spells of land speculation for many years. Earlier, in describing the Everglades, I mentioned the up's and down's of Florida real estate. Some promoters even brought their prospective purchasers by the busload and sold them lots that were under water. Of course, some of the people who invested in Florida real estate made money, if they invested in the right place and at the right time. But many of them lost and lost heavily. This same phenomenon has occurred and reoccurred across the country. I have also described how land around Lower Priest Lake was being sold, even when there was no access to it or any provision for water or garbage disposal. In 1910, one of the rages was orchards in the Bitterroot area of Idaho. Speculators promised purchasers that they would make their fortunes. At other times, it was developments on the West Coast, developments that eventually came to nothing, although many years later, the land did become valuable again.

Today this speculative fever is being fed by numerous promoters, some of them completely honest and some of them less so. At least once a month, the mail brings me, as well as many other Americans, an invitation to attend a dinner at which some land scheme will be described and acreage offered for sale. The dinner, of course, is free, and it includes cocktails as well. Or if it is not a free dinner, it is an invitation to visit some area in Maine, Vermont, Florida, or some other state where the promoter has been able to purchase a large tract for subdivision. All expenses will be paid by the company, including transportation. This is a costly way to sell real estate, and it reveals how inflated the prices have to be.

Some of these companies operate on a shoestring. One sold its lands and gave the purchaser seven years to complete his payments. These seemed like generous terms to the buyer. Actually they were essential to the operation; and when a buyer wanted to hasten his payments and secure a clear title to his land sooner, he caused consternation. For here was what was happening. The company was buying its tracts on a five-year schedule of payments, counting on the receipts it took in from its customers to finance itself. When one of them wanted to speed up his payments and take title, the company could not give him a deed because often the company itself did not yet have title to the tract from which it had made the sale. When such an embarrassing emergency arose, it gave the buyer title to equal acreage in another area on which it had completed payments. As this transfer was made without the consent or knowledge of the purchaser, it constituted a violation of state law. Finally the practice was uncovered and ended; and the company was absorbed by a concern having greater resources. But nothing of this flimsiness was revealed to the average purchaser. He was merely given glowing pictures of how eventually, if he bought enough land, he could subdivide it himself and make a handsome profit.[6]

Another developer with lands in several states is much better funded and gives every appearance of wanting people to live on its land. (It always helps the developer to get construction started. That makes it easier to sell further lots.) To show the extent of speculation that goes on, this company has what amounts to an ingenious gimmick. After buying a piece of land, the owner can wait for a while and then call the company to find the current worth of his property. If it has risen, he can trade it for a larger tract somewhere else—even in another state—or he can sell the land back to the company and apply the proceeds as the down payment on more land. The company functions almost like a closed-circuit stock exchange.

These cases—and it would be possible to mention many more —indicate the depth of the speculative spirit that now surrounds real estate in the United States. But nowhere is it more apparent than in areas where government has announced the creation of a major recreational project. This is especially true of the federal government because its projects generally are larger and receive more publicity. Here are a few figures collected by the Bureau of Outdoor Recreation that tell what happens. In 1958 the Bureau of Reclamation appraised 309 acres around the future Flaming Gorge reservoir in Utah at an average price of $39 an acre. In 1959, it purchased 195 of these acres for $43 an acre and valued the remainder at only $31 an acre. But that is not what they eventually sold for. In 1965, the state purchased a little more than fourteen of these acres and had to pay an average of $929 an acre.[7] That is an increase of about 3000 percent in seven years. Many other case histories can be cited, all illustrating the same spiral in prices when a recreation project is announced. It has plagued every one of them and has even caused some members of Congress to think that the land acquisition programs of government are accomplishing little except to make speculators rich. And worse, because the Land and Water Conservation Fund has been so underfunded, escalating prices are depriving future Americans of what should be theirs. Much open space that might otherwise have been preserved for future generations will now be dotted with buildings.

Part of the problem results from the workings of government, and I will take the federal government as an example because it affects us all. To varying degrees, however, state and local governments find themselves caught in the same vise. Let us assume that the staff of the National Park Service believes that a certain area might make an excellent national seashore. First, it must obtain the funds to make an on-the-spot survey. It is difficult to keep this quiet, and any speculator can start watching the area. On the basis of the study, the National Park Service then makes its recommendation to Congress, which holds open hearings on the proposal. Now everyone knows what is going on. The next step is for Congress to pass the authorization. This is the initial bill that provides the basis for all future action. It tells just what pieces of land will be included, and this, along with the data contained in the public hearings, gives any speculator all the information he needs. The National Park Service, with its excellent research facilities, has pinpointed an outstanding recreation area, and Congress has told all the world where it is and what Congress would like to buy. The next step in this lengthy procedure is for Congress to pass the appropriation. This is the amount of money that it intends to spend for the first acquisitions. Until that measure is passed, the National Park Service cannot start making purchases. Once the appropriation has been approved and the Bureau of the Budget has released the funds—the Bureau of the Budget has control over the spending of money even after Congress has made an appropriation—the National Park Service can put its land acquisition staff in the field and start buying. The elapsed period usually averages eighteen months. That is all the opportunity the speculators need. By the time the government is ready to buy, the speculators have already been there. Although it has not been proven, there is suspicion that they also sometimes go through wash sales—fake sales that are designed to establish a higher market price.

Government is almost helpless to handle this problem. Congress—and rightly so—is unwilling to write blank checks for the agencies under its supervision. It is reluctant to give agencies like the National Park Service or the U.S. Forest Service a large, unallocated appropriation each year to spend as they wish. Such action would inevitably lead to scandal and claims of favoritism and probably would subvert the whole program. Government is further handicapped by the difficulties of going through condemnation. These hearings are held locally and are therefore weighted in favor of the local landowner as against the rich and wealthy federal government. The awards are thus likely to be high. If only a single parcel of property were involved, that

THE NEED FOR COOPERATIVE EFFORT · 271

would not matter much. But the awards in condemnation proceedings set a value on all similar property in the area. There is no escaping this, and so the government is generally reluctant to take the risk of going to court unless there is no other way.

To handle this problem, Congress has introduced several innovations, including a method by which some monies can be made available more quickly from the Land and Water Conservation Fund. The best solution, of course, would be for Congress to find a third party that would bank the land for it, just as the foundation I mentioned did for the county commissioners in Allegheny County. The process would be risky for the third party because there could be no legal commitment on the part of the government to complete the final purchase, but risks are part of being in conservation. The logical agency was the Nature Conservancy, which had by then accumulated considerable experience in advance acquisition for government.

To conduct a significant program, however, the Conservancy needed more funds than it had. The question was how much more. Its staff, with the help of some of the government agencies concerned, made a study and came up with a remarkable figure. About 6 percent of the amount of a total program could help ensure the program's successful completion. This 6 percent had to be used wisely, but it was enough to tie up the key tracts in most projects, especially because many sellers are willing to receive their payments on an installment basis. (Some are even anxious to, because of tax benefits.) Therefore a revolving fund of $6 million could affect land acquisitions amounting to $60 million or about half the annual allocation to the entire Land and Water Conservation Fund. This could be a sizable program.

But perhaps even more important than the actual land put under option or sales contract would be the establishment of values. If the Nature Conservancy bought a piece of land and then eighteen months or two years later resold it to government at cost, plus the interest charges, that had accrued, this would establish a market value. For actual sales are an influential determinant. One of the men who most clearly saw this was former Assistant Secretary of the Interior Stanley A. Cain. He thought that the program might be used to establish a whole land-price pattern within a given area that could be used to combat the exorbitant demands of speculators.

Six million dollars, however, is a large sum for private conservation to raise. Even the largest foundations do not have that kind of money for conservation. The Ford Foundation, which is highly imaginative in philanthropy, was then adopting a new policy that it called "project-oriented investment." This meant that instead of making all its investments for the profit that might be in them, it would invest some of its capital in projects that had social significance. Under this new policy, it was willing to enter an unusual agreement with the Nature Conservancy. It would underwrite loans at commercial banks for the $6 million. Even though loans were increasingly difficult for anyone to get, two large commercial banks agreed to go along with the idea and lend the money at the prime rate, the lowest rate at which they make loans even to their best and most secure customers.

My purpose in briefly describing this single activity is severalfold. It illustrates how complex conservation action has become. No longer is it primarily limited to lobbying for legislation or to what conservationists like to call "confrontations" on particular issues. It has, instead, come to have all the ramifications of any enterprise in these modern times. Another purpose in describing this operation is to show the difficulty of establishing a large-scale cooperative effort in conservation, not because the people are unconcerned and not because their objectives differ, but because their backgrounds and experience make it difficult for them to get together.

Take, for example, some of the agency officials involved in this undertaking. One of the intellectual stumbling blocks was the amount of money at the disposal of the Nature Conservancy —$6 million. One of them was quite frank about it. The fund was far too small, he said, to make any significant contribution. And others agreed with him. Unlike Samuel Boardman of Oregon, who fashioned a 2,400-acre park out of an initial gift of less than 120 acres, those were people who had to have everything at hand or they could do nothing. The secret of many successful ventures in conservation has been the ability to build something great from a small beginning.

Even the Bureau of Outdoor Recreation took the same line. At the time that this program was being discussed, it produced a report that said in part, "Another possible way of resolving the land escalation problem is through the use of private philanthropic funds and organizations for the purchase of key recreation lands which could then be held for future Federal, State, or local acquisition and development. It would amount to the establishment of a private revolving fund for this purpose. This would be an excellent means of supplementing and complementing the Land and Water Conservation Fund and of maximizing the effective use of the Fund."

But, the report concluded, "It is considered doubtful by some officials that private and corporate philanthropy would be willing to commit substantial sums for the acquisition of lands to be held for possible use of public agencies for outdoor recreation purposes. Lands to be held for any length of time require management and would require expenditures for this purpose. In addition, it is considered highly improbable that funds in any substantial amounts—$50 million to $100 million or more—would ever be made available by private philanthropy." [8]

The report was correct in one respect. It is hardly likely that private philanthropy could produce $50 million to $100 million for this purpose. Private philanthropy is not that wealthy. But the report missed the mark on two other points. One was that private philanthropy would or should hold the land "for any length of time." This is outside the realm of practicality. If a revolving fund of the sort the bureau was contemplating is to be successful, it must revolve, and revolve quickly. The speed with which it turns over and therefore the work that it can accomplish would be a major appeal to its contributors. No one particularly wants to give money for the purchase of a piece of land and then see that money tied up for years, while the government decides whether it will complete the transaction. The foundation in Allegheny County that bought the park land expected the commissioners to act as soon as the land transactions had been com-

ELEVENTH HOUR · 274

pleted. And they did. For a program like this to work, this is
the same attitude that the federal government must also take.

Although the bureau recognized the need for land management and the costs that would have to be incurred if the property
was held for any period of time, it failed to recognize that this
was probably one of the lesser expenses. Someone would have
to run the fund, and with all its assets tied up in nonproductive
investments, there would be no income to pay the staff. Each
year, the total amount in the fund would grow smaller and
smaller until it went out of existence.

Furthermore, the amount of $50 million to $100 million is
not only unrealistic from the point of view of fund raising; it
is not necessary to solve the problem. If the money turns over
every two years, and if an expenditure of 6 percent can hold the
program together, $100 million would support a Land and
Water Conservation Fund of a billion dollars annually, an
amount not likely to be appropriated.

The difficulty here is one of attitude. I grow weary of private
entrepreneurs who utter the familiar cliché about government
personnel and politicians never having to meet a payroll, and
I sometimes reply that the trouble with some businessmen is that
they have never had to meet an electorate or a legislative body.
But there does tend to be a difference in their way of thinking.
The government staffer has to operate within a set of rules. He
does not have the opportunities that exist outside government
to try new ideas. Therefore when he approaches a problem of
this sort, he thinks of it in the conventional terms to which he is
accustomed—outright purchase of the area with full payment
made currently. Therefore, he thinks he needs a larger sum of
money than he does for a holding operation. Real estate developers do not work this way, and government might learn something from them in the imaginative use of money.

The reactions of Congress were also interesting. I visited with
the chairmen of the committees in the House and the Senate to
explain what the Nature Conservancy was trying to do. They all
agreed that land-price escalation was a serious problem, but they
all had difficulty believing that a private, nonprofit agency could
really help them. In addition, they were all suspicious. The initial

remark of one distinguished senator was simply this: "Who's going to get something out of this?" My reply was that I knew what I would get: a headache. He then amended his remark to say that he meant who would build up a bureaucracy and make jobs for themselves. It was difficult for him to understand that a group of private citizens were attempting to develop a means of helping Congress solve a problem that it had proved it could not solve itself. Another committee chairman said, "Why this could become a Bobby Baker affair!" Even after convincing these Congressmen that the Nature Conservancy was an honest organization, they still had reservations. Suppose the Nature Conservancy became the means by which the agencies or private conservationists pressured Congress into buying tracts that it would not otherwise purchase? Their rationale ran something like this. Someone outside Congress would persuade the Nature Conservancy to buy an area and then accuse Congress of endangering the Nature Conservancy if it did not complete the transaction. In some respects, this is a logical argument, but it completely overlooks two points. One, there is no legal agreement that the government must purchase the land; two, the Nature Conservancy, in handling federal projects, does not enter one that has not been authorized by Congress. That would seem to be surety enough.

But the suspicion lingered on. It came up again when the House Subcommittee on Appropriations was discussing Mason Neck, Virginia. This is an area on the Potomac River just below Mount Vernon. It is a key tract in the federal government's comprehensive plan for the river and can provide thousands of acres of open space within a short drive of Washington. It is also one of the rare nesting places for eagles and an area that also has much history, for it is close to historic Gunston Hall, which a private association has saved and is maintaining.

The Nature Conservancy was asked to help preserve Mason Neck from development. The project was enormously complicated. The value of the property ran into the millions of dollars; several owners held title to it; and no one agency wanted all of it or had the funds to purchase it all. Three agencies, however, were deeply interested in parts of it. The Commonwealth of Virginia

wanted some of the acreage for a state park, and the Northern
Regional Park Authority, a local agency, also wanted a section,
and the U.S. Fish and Wildlife Service was interested in obtaining the marshland that was the nesting site of the eagles. The
only solution was to find an organization capable of buying up
the entire tract and then dividing it among the participating
agencies. This was not a case of purchasing it all at once. Because
the three government agencies would have partial funds available
only from year to year and thus had to make their own purchases
on an installment basis, the purchase from the original owners
had to follow the same pattern and be weighed against the probable appropriations to three entirely separate government agencies. If the schedule was not reasonably well coordinated, the
difficulty of meeting the interest payments on the sums borrowed
to finance the project could have resulted in the forced resale of
the property for development purposes. It is much to the credit
of everyone concerned that this complicated project has pro-
gressed as smoothly as it has and that the people of Washington
and northern Virginia will, in the future, have two outstanding
parks and a wildlife refuge nearby and that a significant step
will have been taken in carrying out the comprehensive plan
for the Potomac.

But here is the testimony before the House appropriations
subcommittee:

"MRS. HANSEN [chairman]. You said the lands around Mason
Neck are in immediate danger of residential development. Didn't
Nature Conservancy buy about $3 million worth of this land?

"MR. GOTTSCHALK [Director, Bureau of Sports Fisheries and
Wildlife]. Nature Conservancy has taken options to buy or has
bought approximately $3 million worth of property in this gen-
eral area. Again, as a means of aiding in the preservation of this
area, and stopping the escalation problem.

"MRS. HANSEN. The land which they have taken options on is
not the land you seek to acquire, is it?

"MR. GOTTSCHALK. Some of it is.

"MRS. HANSEN. This brings up the subject I discussed last year.
Do they [the Nature Conservancy] pressure you to buy these
lands immediately?" [9]

So there it was again, the same discouraging question, and no other comment by the subcommittee. Nothing about whether the overall program was working, nothing about whether it could be developed more fully to prevent land-price escalation from continuing to erode the Land and Water Conservation Fund. Nothing even about the willingness of private citizens to come to the assistance of their government. This was not, I am sure, in any way the result of negligence or lack of interest. Mrs. Hansen is a capable, courteous woman. But it was perhaps the result of lack of understanding and experience. It is highly doubtful that most members of Congress have any conception of the type of thinking and the sort of work that has to go into a program of this kind or even what is involved to make it operate successfully. The skills needed to become a legislator are not those needed to negotiate a delicate real estate transaction and obtain the appropriate financing from commercial banks. There is a breach here that needs to be crossed.

Interest rates are also something that government agencies and Congressmen have difficulty in understanding. Many of them do not realize that interest is not figured by the year or even by the month. It is figured by the day, so a delay of four or five days in forwarding a check can be expensive if the project is of any size at all. Compensating balances are beyond the ken of most of them. These are the checking account balances that banks insist a borrower must maintain as part of the terms of the loan. For example, the compensating balance may be set at 15 percent. That simply means that for every million dollars borrowed, the borrower must keep a balance of $150,000 in the bank. This is expensive and is a part of the cost. Businessmen are familiar with this practice; government agencies and legislators are not, and it provides another stumbling block in the way of their understanding what private enterprise can, and cannot, do to help. I should add that this lack of comprehension of the cost of money is not confined to the federal government. One state for which the Nature Conservancy had purchased an important tract of land had not applied for matching federal funds at the time it was scheduled to repurchase it. Therefore it could not complete the transaction. It failed to see that there was any urgency about this for the Nature Conservancy and that additional interest costs were going to push the price above what they had thought they would have to pay.

With one limitation, a program such as the one I have outlined works well. In fact, it already has in notable instances such as Upper Priest Lake and Mason Neck. The one current limitation is the interest rate. When interest costs are higher than the annual increase in land value, then, of course, it is pointless to borrow money to purchase land in advance. The only result will be additional expense. But whenever the land is likely to increase in value faster than the expense of paying the prevailing interest rate, then it is well worth the government's while to have a private agency borrow the money to make the purchase before the government funds actually become available.

Although, as I have pointed out, this program has been successful, it has not been as successful as it should have been. The Nature Conservancy was slow in getting it started, and the government was slow in seeing its potentialities and in realizing what was required to make it work. The slowness was not caused by lack of interest or absence of the desire to solve a critical problem. It was caused primarily by narrowness of understanding and experience.

This is one of the single greatest obstacles to cooperative efforts in conservation. Too many people and too many agencies are operating without comprehending what other agencies and people are doing or could do. The basic cause for this is ignorance more than anything else. But ignorance can always be overcome by effort.

The conservation problems facing this nation are tremendous. They are also, in my opinion, capable of solution. But their solution is going to require the coordinated and cooperative action of every person and every organization concerned. No one person, no one group can do it alone. Earlier in this book, we have seen what can be accomplished when men and organizations work together on these problems. The Izaac Walton League did wonders with the U.S. Forest Service in the Quetico-Superior; Oregon has attained a miracle along its coastline by utilizing and coordinating every resource available to it; the forest supervisor at the Kaniksu National Forest saved Upper Priest Lake from overdevelopment by the same method. The possibilities are enormous. If conservationists would agree on broader policies, whether land-use plans for larger areas, a set of objectives for the entire Everglades region in Florida, or how to preserve large sections of our coastline, or prevent air and noise pollution, and if they all—government, private agencies, and individuals— would coordinate their activities, using the best facilities of each, the results, I believe, might change the face of America within a few years. But they cannot do much if they handle every project on a piecemeal basis, with each agency or person working alone.

10

The Part of Government

IN solving our conservation and environmental problems, the nation has three principal sources of leadership—individual citizens, the private conservation agencies, and government —federal, state and local. Among the latter, the federal government has the dominant role. Because of the tax structure, it can provide the funds; and because many conservation problems have interstate ramifications, we need its authority. It also reflects, to one degree or another, the capabilities and deficiencies of state and local governments. The pattern of action is often similar; only the scale is larger.

During the 1960's, federal action on conservation issues became more intense than ever; and in January, 1969, when the administrations of Presidents Kennedy and Johnson came to an end, many conservationists were quite satisfied with what appeared to be eight years of solid accomplishment. Much remained to be done, as every conservationist knew, but never before had there been such general and enthusiastic talk about conservation issues, both inside government and out. Never before had the private conservation agencies shown such growth in their memberships. Never before had involvement in conserva-

THE PART OF GOVERNMENT · 281

tion been so fashionable. And in response to the mood of the country, Congress had never before passed so much conservation legislation. Water pollution, air pollution, wildernesses, national parks, financial aid to the states for open space acquisition, scenic highways, scenic rivers—all these questions and many more had been the objects of Congressional measures. Yet, as the reader knows, when the hard realities were added up they did not seem equal to either the needs or the opportunities. What went wrong?

Certainly not the timing. That was exactly right. The Eisenhower Administration had been relatively sterile in terms of conservation. President Eisenhower was not an anticonservationist; he was an aconservationist with little understanding of, or sensitivity to, the concept. As long as he owned his own acres at Gettysburg, he seemed satisfied and unable to sense that millions of Americans who were less fortunate than he needed the help of government in creating an environment in which they might want to live. Although the President thought of himself as representative of all Americans, his attitudes were sometimes those of the limited, smalltown businessman with whom Norman Rockwell used to adorn the covers of the *Saturday Evening Post*. This was true in the case of conservation.

Yet this may have been fortunate. The United States was recovering from the shock of two major wars and the discovery that it was in bitter competition with the Soviet Union. It needed time to adjust to the new, but unstable, society that was rising from the ashes of World War II. If a massive environmental program had been launched at that period, it might well have proved premature and therefore have been doomed to fail. After battling with the Germans and the North Koreans, the nation simply was not ready to struggle with questions of conservation.

Those years, however, were not entirely lost. During them, Americans in increasing numbers became aware of their environment to a degree they had never been before. They saw their streets and highways clogged with traffic and their cities capped with smog. They found their water and air growing steadily dirtier and discovered that areas where they had once engaged in recreation were becoming either overcrowded or were closed. At the same time, as the result of better pay and greater leisure, they turned more than ever to the outdoors. This direct experience with the natural world, coupled with the admonitions of the conservationists and the scientists, produced a questioning attitude that had not existed before. More and more people began asking why the world's richest nation could not produce a more satisfactory environment. Impatience started to well up over our inability to cope with such problems; and by 1961, the stage was set for action.

President Kennedy was just the person to capitalize on the opportunity that offered itself. Politically astute, he recognized that here was a human issue that had been neglected by the Republicans and one that would give to his administration the air of freshness he so much wanted it to have. He also understood that the issue was one to which the people were ready to respond and that it could provide a program that stressed the higher values he wished to introduce into American life. In addition to the timing of his inauguration, he had a further advantage as a conservation-minded President. He looked the part. Young and athletic, he personified the type of American generally associated with the outdoors and healthy activities. So the movement, under his direction and with the assistance of his Secretaries of the Interior and of Agriculture, Udall and Freeman, quickly gained momentum.

The later shortcomings came from a number of causes, which are worth examining as guideposts for the future. The greatest villain of all was, of course, the Vietnam War. When President Johnson, following the unwarrantedly optimistic advice of his generals and admirals, involved himself in the escalation of that struggle, he dealt the conservation movement a blow from which it may never recover. For in spite of his repeated insistence that the United States could afford both guns and butter, the opposite was true. With each call from General Westmoreland for more men and materiel, the cost of the war soared upward, absorbing more and more of the federal budget. Other programs had to be cut, and those dealing with conservation were among the ones that suffered most. Two figures illustrate what happened. Just for defoliating plant life in Vietnam, the Johnson Administration spent $168 million; in its last year, the administration spent little more than that, $184 million in trying to control water pollution throughout the entire United States.[1]

But even with the war, there might have been a hope of conservation expenditures that were realistic if the military had not acted as if the public purse were bottomless. Nothing could have been more damaging to the country than the manner in which expensive programs were initiated by the Pentagon, rushed through the Armed Services Committees of both the House and the Senate, approved by the Appropriations Committees, and then passed with hardly a question being raised. Although some Congressmen and Senators waged a valiant and lonely fight against these careless procedures, the majority were all too acquiescent.

The military has many means of preventing effective scrutiny of its proposals and actions. By pleading the nation's security, it can classify the factual material needed for realistic debate and then hint darkly that the danger is greater than the public knows. It can talk about "letting down our fighting men," or it can parley in terms of defense contracts for home districts, a device that grows in importance as military expenditures rise. If all else fails, it can produce the final argument that even if it is wrong, it is better to err on the side of safety than to risk the danger of being conquered.

Yet all too few questioned why we did not obtain better protection for less expense. In 1966, during the Johnson Administration, the United States was spending $63 billion a year on armaments, and the NATO countries as a whole, $86 billion. The Soviet Union was spending only $47 billion; and the Warsaw Pact countries, a total of $52 billion, or less than the United States alone.[2] This disparity is likely to continue. Even before President Nixon took office, there were reports in Washington that the Chiefs of Staff hoped to get an annual budget of $100 to $110 billion.[3] The attitude toward military budget requests was summed up by Secretary Laird in an almost unbelievable statement that he made on Armed Forces Day, May 16, 1969. "Even if we eliminate cost overruns, improve our cost estimates, cut out the unnecessary items and keep our systems simple, we are not going to come up with a low defense budget," the Secretary said. "No, even if we are successful in eliminating the war in Vietnam, our highest priority—we are still not going to come up with a drastically reduced defense budget—at least this Secretary of Defense will not recommend drastic reductions in defense spending, under presently foreseeable circumstances." [4]

Perhaps this approach to military expenditures could be justified by the successful accomplishment of a mission, but this has not been the case. In the same speech, Secretary Laird stated the purpose of the military. "The job of the Department of Defense," he said flatly, "is to maintain peace." As the Secretary spoke, there were growing tensions along the Korean and Chino-Soviet borders, Czechoslovakia had been invaded only a short time before, the Near East was in flames, a savage civil war was raging in Nigeria, and the United States was engaged in one of the bloodiest wars in its history. Certainly if the mission of the military was the imposition of peace on the world—a sort of *Pax Americana* administered by the Pentagon—the result had been an almost complete failure, in spite of expenditures that in 1966 amounted to approximately 40 percent of the world's total for armaments.[5]

The reason these expenditures have such heavy impact on all conservation programs is their relative magnitude. In his speech on Armed Forces Day, Secretary Laird said: "There have been cost overruns in other areas as well. The initial review I asked to be made uncovered total overruns in excess of $1.7 billion and the review is still in progress."

Those overruns, although only amounting to approximately 2 percent of the defense budget, were equal to almost the entire federal budget for natural resources in 1970, if the costs of the Corps of Army Engineers were excluded.[6] It was far greater than the entire amount authorized, but not even appropriated, for the Land and Water Conservation Fund for a five-year period. It was about eight times as large as the President's budget for water pollution. Put another way, the cost of the single atomic attack submarine that sank in San Francisco Bay in 1969 was about the same as the initial, and major, appropriation for the purchase of the Redwood National Park.

In his Armed Forces Day speech, Secretary Laird continued,

"The real issue boils down to whether the American people—
the real source of decision in this democratic system of ours—
want to keep paying the high price real security in this uncertain
world demands." But that is not the real issue. The real issue is
whether the military can provide true protection at a realistic
cost. Until they can, the cause of conservation will suffer dread-
fully.

A solution could perhaps be brought about by certain changes
in our government. One of the most important could be the ter-
mination of the seniority system for appointments to Congressional committees. This system which pervades all of Congress is,
at best, questionable. In a few instances, it places men of great
ability in power, but too often it merely rewards those who have
safe seats and long lives. If they can keep on being reelected and
outlive their contemporaries, they will sooner or later find themselves committee chairmen. The general public, of course, has
no say in selecting them. This may be all right for insignificant
committees, but it is certainly not appropriate for committees
that control more than 40 percent of the federal budget, the lives
of the men in the armed forces, and the nation's security. Those
positions demand the best brains and ability in the United States.
They also demand fresh approaches to current and future problems, not minds that have the intellectual sterility that results
from entrenchment in power. Whatever Congress does about
seniority in general, there is no doubt that four committee chairmen should be rotated at regular, stated intervals—the chairmen
of the House and Senate Committees on the Armed Forces, and
the chairmen of the two Appropriations Subcommittees. Given
the traditions of Congress, the change is radical. Given the needs
of conservation—to say nothing of the needs of the country
generally—it is the least that is due the people of this nation.

The same principle applies to the Joint Chiefs of Staff. Few
generals have ever so outmatched the enemy in terms of men and
materiel than General Westmoreland, and yet few generals with
such advantages have ever had so little success. In any organization but the military, he would have been quickly retired, but
instead he was appointed to the Joint Chiefs of Staff. That again
is a position in which the safety of the country requires the finest

abilities and the freshest brains, not men who have made mistakes and are devoted to defending them. We must learn to apply to the performance of generals and admirals the same standards that we apply to everyone else. Only in that way can we cut military costs.

When the Johnson Administration permitted the escalation of the Vietnam War, it opened a Pandora's box of problems that may well haunt us for generations. It certainly destroyed any hope of a truly realistic conservation program until a date that may be too late. And conservationists must understand that their best plans will not be realized until military expenditures are brought under reasonable control.

Military expenditures alone, however, do not account for the failure of the Johnson Administration's conservation program to reach its full potential. Other costs, too, always seemed to come ahead of it, and conservation held a low priority at budget-making time. In 1959, natural resources spending on the part of the federal government accounted for only 1.5 percent of the total. It rose to 1.9 percent in 1960 and then climbed gradually to a high of 2.3 percent in 1965. After that it started to decline and the budgeted amount for the fiscal year 1970 accounted for an estimated 1.8 percent. These figures become even more startling when it is recognized that they include the appropriations for the Corps of Engineers of the Army. These represent a substantial part of the total, generally speaking about a third. Eliminating them from the 1970 figure, for example, reduces the amount spent on natural resources to 1.24 percent of total federal spending.[7]

Some reassessment of natural priorities is long overdue. As a nation, we must establish our sets of values more clearly. No one can quarrel with the magnificent achievement of reaching the moon, but somebody must decide whether it is more important to explore space now than it is to create a favorable environment for the people who have to remain behind. Or whether six-lane highways are more needed than some place to go on them. Questions like these were left largely unanswered by the Johnson

Administration, and as long as they were, the final achievements in conservation were necessarily limited.

A further financial problem developed through the willingness of Congress to vote the authorization of large-scale programs and then its failure to vote the appropriations necessary to carry them through. This affected every sort of program, whether it was the national seashore at Point Reyes or an adequate program for the abatement of water pollution. The effects of this approach were far-reaching. In the first place, the public was misled into thinking that more had been accomplished than actually was. The public does not seem to know that the dedication of a national park or the announcement that Congress has passed a water pollution control bill is just the beginning. Unless the money is forthcoming, the program will stagnate. So it hears a great deal about these issues, assumes they are being handled properly, and starts thinking about something else. We need to be kept informed as to what actual progress is being made. This failing was not peculiar to the Johnson Administration. Republicans are equally subject to it.

In addition to misleading the public, the failure to provide adequate financing at the time a program is started is also discouraging to subsequent administrations. A considerable amount of money has to be provided to complete the old program without the political advantage of being able to announce anything new. This was certainly true of water pollution, as an example. Even the authorizations were inadequate to the need as evidenced by the avalanche of applications for grants-in-aid the legislation provoked, and the actual appropriations were even smaller. Thus the best a new administration could do would be to devote far more of its budget to this problem merely to handle the program created by existing legislation. It could not in the process take credit for a new idea. The Nixon Administration has complicated this problem even more by further postponing the cost of water pollution abatement, thus continuing the pattern set by earlier administrations.

This is a dispiriting situation. No one—least of all, a politician —wants to spend his time finding the money to complete other people's projects. He is more likely to leave them unfinished and start ones that he can call his own. In the field of conservation, we must learn to scrutinize new efforts far more carefully to determine whether they will actually be carried out. We should not permit ourselves to become overly enthusiastic about undertakings that have little chance of becoming realities. As it is, it is too easy for a Congress or an administration to initiate a program, enjoy acclaim for farsightedness, and then fail to vote the necessary appropriation so that the program becomes a practical impossibility.

Lack of coordination has also marred the achievements of government in conservation. One of the many examples, as we have seen, was provided by the Everglades, where the National Park Service was trying to maintain the park, while the Corps of Engineers and the Department of Transportation were taking steps that would tend to destroy it. This example was not at all unique. Although the Department of the Interior likes to refer to itself as the custodian of our natural resources, no one was in overall charge. There is no department in the federal government that has final responsibility for conservation and our environment in the same sense that the Department of Defense has responsibility for our military security. Until such a department is established, the Department of the Interior, which is the closest to one we have, should be given more authority, if not by congressional action, at least by presidential support. At the same time, some thought might be given to removing from it some of its responsibilities for the commercial utilization of our resources.

By the fall of 1969, it had become apparent that the Nixon Administration was up against the same problem of lack of coordination. There was considerable evidence it lacked the capability to handle conservation issues as a whole. Not only had it slashed the conservation budgets beyond what many thought was an irreducible minimum, it was showing signs of confusion and cross-purposes. At about the time the Director of the Bureau of the Budget was telling Congress that the National Park Service would not receive enough funds over the next few years to complete the projects it had already started, the Secretary of the Interior was announcing a whole new program for the service.

This program was to bring parks to the people. It would cost $6.8 billion for the next five years! This was just about equal to the entire budget of the Department of the Interior for the same period.[8] The idea was to take the emphasis off the great western parks and concentrate on the urban areas, where there is so little open space of any kind. Most of the money was to go in grants-in-aid for the urban centers to develop better park systems. One billion dollars, however, was to be used by the National Park Service to acquire and develop such parks itself. Not long after, on December 10, the secretary announced a proposal for an entirely new national park. In view of his previous statement, one might have guessed it would be near New York, Chicago, Pittsburgh, or one of our other large metropolitan centers. It was not. It was to be located on the island of Guam.[9]

This sort of confusion will continue until some administration can provide a better method of programming our activities to meet our greatest needs. Up to the present time, each administration has relied heavily on accomplishing this through the budget-making process, and none of them have succeeded. The budget, when it is first presented to Congress, presumably represents the administration's view of the total needs of the country, and in some ways it does. On the instructions of the President, the Bureau of the Budget has prepared a single document that outlines the President's program and assigns his financial priorities. But the resemblance to a coordinated whole is more in the form than the substance because the budget is made up of bits and pieces that have been more or less jammed together. Each department and independent agency submits its request for the coming fiscal year, and the Bureau of the Budget then tries to make the total conform to the President's wishes, both as to the amount of money needed and the programs that he favors. The procedure is orderly, and it is much to the credit of those who carry it out that it works at all. Budgeting an operation as large as the federal government is not easy, particularly with all the pressures exerted by political influences. So it is little wonder that few people look at the effects of each individual program on the total environment. The problem is just too complicated.

After the budget arrives in Congress, it is broken down into

ELEVENTH HOUR · 290

its component parts, each of which is assigned to a subcommittee for study, and it never becomes a whole again. Each measure is taken up and voted on separately, and a Congressman who today votes approval of an air pollution bill may tomorrow cancel out his action by favoring a measure that will result in the increased use of cars. And he may do so without even seeing the connection.

Congress is aware of this problem. By May, 1969, no less than thirteen bills had been introduced to establish a superagency to coordinate our handling of the environment. One would have set up a Presidential Council on Environmental Quality. Another would have established a Committee on the Environment. And yet another would have abolished the Department of the Interior and placed all its conservation functions in a new department. Some of these proposals were far-reaching, but as *BioScience,* the journal of the American Institute of Biological Sciences, commented, we were in danger of discussing so many ideas that nothing would be actually done. And it placed the word "done" in capitals.[10]

That danger is real. The problem is so complicated that it is admirably suited to endless debate by committees and commissions, all of them publishing reports that no one reads. None of these committees or commissions is likely to have any real authority because it is improbable that the various departments and agencies—as well as the special interests many of them represent—will surrender their present prerogatives to a superagency able to dictate on everything affecting the environment. That is just not in the nature of human beings or of government.

The difficulty is in finding some middle path between the insignificant and the impossible. No one can be impressed by the ability of the Corps of Engineers and the National Park Service finally to agree on the location of a salt water plug in Canal 111. Such a plug was essential to keep a large section of the Everglades National Park from further flooding by salt water. Agreements such as this are the least the taxpayers should expect from their government. What is startling is that arriving at the agreement took so much effort and time, both of which are costly. Such accords between agencies and departments should be almost routine and probably could be quickly brought about by the intervention of the White House. But even if successful, they do not set a real precedent. The objective is too small and limited to attract attention or to represent a real accomplishment. On the other hand, nothing is to be gained by trying to set up an agency or a commission that is doomed to failure before it starts.

On May 29, 1969, President Nixon took a course that has been too often followed by government. With a sweeping pronouncement, he established by executive order the Environmental Quality Council. This council had extraordinary breadth of responsibility. "I am asking the new Council," the President said, "with the assistance of the Citizen's Advisory Committee, to examine the full range of variables which affect environmental quality. I expect the group to review existing policies and programs and to suggest ways of improving them. Its members must project the impact of new technologies and encourage scientific developments which will help us protect our resources.

"I am hopeful that the Environmental Quality Council will foster greater cooperation in this problem area between our government and the governments of other nations, between the various levels of American government, and between governmental and relevant non-governmental organizations."

As if that were not a sufficient assignment, he added, "Finally, I would suggest that this new body must anticipate new problems even as it focuses on present ones. It is not enough that it provide answers to the questions we are asking today. It must also pose the new questions which will face us tomorrow." [11]

The assignment, of course, was completely impossible to fulfill. Under the best of circumstances, no council could undertake all the President asked of it and do it well. And these were not the best of circumstances. While the council was charged with every aspect of our environment, both present and future, the administration that created it was not even deciding whether it wanted parks in the metropolitan centers or a park in Guam; it was cutting the Land and Water Conservation Fund and at the same time announcing a whole new park program of $6 billion;

and it had not even made appreciable progress on Point Reyes, the Everglades, or many of the other smaller issues facing us. Furthermore, the citizen members of the council were to receive no reimbursement except their expenses, and nothing in the executive order was to be construed as giving the council any authority over any department.

Such councils—and this is no reflection on the citizens who have agreed to serve and do their best—are a politician's device for getting rid of a problem. They give grounds for making a grand pronouncement and then provide a means for obscuring the issue.

On January 1, 1970, President Nixon also signed the Environmental Policy Act of 1969, which established the White House Council on Environmental Quality, whose duties include advising the President on environmental problems and helping him prepare an annual report on the environment. The council is also supposed to make recommendations on legislation that significantly affects the environment. Yet within less than two months after the bill was signed, the administration was supporting an act to permit greatly increased commercial logging in our national forests without submitting any report from the council. The council had been quickly bypassed.

Commendable as the Environmental Policy Act was—and it represented an important step forward—if we are going to face up to the questions of our environment, we need a much more practical approach.

To bring about any important change in the government's attitude toward the environment will take experimentation, but it is far from impossible. Congress has numerous members who are concerned about what we are doing to our land, but they need leadership. This has to be provided by the administration.

As the first step, the President should appoint an adviser on conservation and the environment and give him the same rank as the advisers on foreign and domestic affairs. This man should not be a theorist, but a practical person who is accustomed to getting things done. His first assignment would be to break the problem down into manageable components. In spite of its complexity, this can be done. His next assignment should be to divide

the problems up into those that must be solved now, because
the opportunity to do so will not last forever, and those that
could be postponed for future action. Next he should subdivide
these problems even further into those that can be handled by
executive action and those that require congressional legislation.
Much could be achieved by the President working through the
executive agencies that are directly under his control, if he
knew, step by step, what he wanted to do. Those measures that
require Congressional action should be presented in the context
of a long-term plan. If they were, and if they were balanced
against the other needs of the country and strongly supported by
the President himself, I believe most of them would pass. And if
the adviser could draw around him four or five intelligent, realistic people, who would work with him quietly, I believe we could
restore order out of the existing chaos. I feel equally certain that
we will make no appreciable progress on the present piecemeal
basis.

In the enthusiasm for conservation generated during the Kennedy and Johnson administrations lay one of the greatest resources that government could have used—the large number of
intelligent and capable men and women in this country, willing
to work on conservation problems. These include lawyers, doctors, scientists, accountants, artists, writers, photographers, business executives, and others, all with the skills and the judgment
that are so badly needed. But this resource has never been properly tapped.

There are several reasons for this. First of all, conservationists as a whole tend to be highly emotional, and they unfortunately are sometimes not selective in their targets. Often they will
shoot down their fellow conservationists with the same vehe-
mence they would use on a building developer. I have never
asked directly, but I assume that the National Park Service and
the U.S. Forest Service, for example, receive as much or more
criticism from conservationists than they do from any other
single group. I have heard national park superintendents freely
referred to as "heavy-handed" by conservationists, and I have
talked with an important public information officer of the U.S.

Forest Service who was obviously jittery just because I was a conservationist. (He later admitted to me this was the case; he had been attacked so many times.) Again and again, the most violent charges against our conservation agencies come from the conservationists themselves. There is some justifiable cause for this. The conservationists are playing a self-assigned, and sometimes necessary, watchdog role, because our conservation agencies are not always wise in their judgments, as they themselves would admit. But many conservationists carry this role too far.

Others, however, are highly constructive in their thinking and ready to help, but they have difficulty in defining their role or even in setting up communications with the appropriate officials. I think this difficulty arises not only from the government's sensitivity to criticism but also from the inability of many government officials to understand the part that private individuals could play or the sacrifices they are willing to make. It is extremely discouraging to go to Washington to explain a program meant to be helpful to government, only to be received with skepticism or indifference.

One experience during the Nixon Administration will illustrate what I mean. A private individual offered to underwrite the expense of compiling in a single, basic report all the information that had already been collected about the Everglades. He thought this might help to clarify the situation, and he laid down only one condition, that the federal government appoint a high-level committee of representatives of the departments concerned, along with some citizen members, to supervise the report. I went to Washington—on my own time, as usual—and presented this offer to one of the highest officials. His aide took careful notes, and the following week I received a telephone call from the man who was next in order to the one I had seen. He insisted I had called him, which I had not, and then the conversation turned to the Everglades. I repeated the offer. After several weeks had passed, I wrote the first man and said that I was wondering whether any decision had been made to accept it. Weeks after that, I received a call from an official in the National Park Service. He said he was supposed to reply to my letter but did not know what the offer was. I repeated it to him again, thus making it the third time I had outlined the gift offer to someone in responsibility. Needless to say, I heard nothing further. The idea died in limbo, and I was embarrassed to go back to the prospective donor and tell him what had happened.

Granted that the idea was not revolutionary—possibly it was not worth carrying out—and granted that the amount of money, $40,000 to $60,000, was not large, nevertheless government cannot afford to be so indifferent to the offers of assistance made by private citizens.

Private individuals and organizations have demonstrated that they can be effective in assisting government. I have cited numerous examples and could add many others. The Old Dominion Foundation underwrote the National Park Service's study for the Cape Cod National Seashore, when federal funds were not forthcoming. The amount of money needed was not large by government standards, but it focused attention on the possibilities of the seashore. In another case, a state wanted to publish an especially handsome booklet to arouse interest in a conservation cause. Under the law, however, it would have had to put the booklet out for bids and accept the lowest one. This would have affected the quality of the printing, so a private agency stepped in and did the printing for the state. The results were handsome. In spite of their relatively limited funds, private agencies can be of great assistance to government.

The question is whether government can learn to tap these resources more effectively. I believe it can. On a limited but useful scale, the National Park Service has demonstrated this by its imaginative use of outside talent on its master plan teams. But this is only a small step in the right direction. The philosophy should be greatly broadened and extended to other agencies and to larger undertakings. If done well and carefully, this would greatly increase the effectiveness of any conservation program.

To succeed, however, such an effort must be launched by an administration whose sincerity about conservation is unquestionable. That is where the Johnson Administration labored under a handicap. The President himself, although quick to realize the political implications of conservation, did not have much previous background in the subject. Some of his messages and proposals were excellent, but a lurking suspicion remained that he would have dropped conservation if he had not thought there were votes in it.

The shrinking percentage of the national budget that he was willing to devote to conservation underlined this suspicion, as did the failure of his administration on certain critical issues. It was Mrs. Johnson who delivered the address at the dedication of the dam that created Lake Powell, one of the most controversial of conservation issues; and it was his Secretary of the Interior who was in the middle of the fight to dam the Colorado River in the Grand Canyon. Experiences like these, in spite of the generally good record, destroyed confidence in what would happen when economic interests were pitted against conservation. The administration seemed to have a tendency to slide over to the economic side.

Although the total accomplishment during the period was certainly significant, it did not meet the needs of the country or, given the mood of the people, the potential for achievement that existed. Mired in Vietnam, trapped in escalating military budgets, too willing to settle for programs that looked well on paper but were not properly funded, and unable to mobilize fully the strength of the growing volunteer movement, it never quite succeeded in doing all that it might have.

The Nixon Administration also had the opportunity to come to grips with these problems, but all the signs indicated that it would not. By the fall of 1969, it had, especially through its budget cuts, created the impression that it was not truly interested in conservation in spite of the campaign promises made by the President and the establishment of the grand-sounding Environmental Quality Council. It appeared that the President was not sufficiently concerned to pay the price required, provide adequate funding, resist the pressures of special interests, and set up the machinery that would make a well-planned conservation program possible.

This sentiment was only intensified by his Budget Message in 1970. He attempted to take conservation and the environment away from the Democratic Party as a campaign issue, but his budget recommendations showed no appreciable change in emphasis. His water pollution abatement program largely postponed the cost of that effort even further, while placing the greater burden on the states. His program for controlling air pollution was open to the suspicion that it might result in a lowering of air quality standards. His recommended expenditures for the acquisition of open space were hardly sufficient to meet the needs of America's future generations. Yet there was still plenty of money for additional highways—far more than for all the conservation programs put together—money for more travel in outer space, for further work on the supersonic jet transport, additional nuclear explosions; and the military budget, while shaved slightly from its all-time highs, was still enormous. There was no truly significant shift in priorities.

Yet the hour was late. From the point of view of conservation and the environment, the President had wasted much of the first twelve months of his administration in trying to pare down programs that were already pared to the bone and without initiating any of the bold, new moves that the deteriorating situation required. True, the President came to office with no appreciable understanding of, or experience with, environmental problems, but the job of the President is to exert leadership in fulfilling the nation's needs. This is one of the most urgent. If the President loses the opportunity, it will not be merely his own that he has lost. It will be an opportunity that the American people will never have again.

11

The Private Agencies

I F government agencies often do not coordinate their conservation activities, private organizations are sometimes worse. They indulge in an enormous amount of duplication and wasteful competition, which not only is harmful in itself but also discourages potential donors and other supporters, who are confused by the large number of organizations, their conflicting claims, and their obvious overlapping.

Frequently I am asked whether we need so many conservation agencies. In my opinion, we most certainly do not. Hardly a month passes that I do not receive an invitation to join some newly formed organization or to subscribe to a new conservation publication. Many of these new agencies are underfinanced, understaffed, and inexperienced. Most of them are founded for one of two reasons. Either a specific conservation problem has arisen and the persons concerned do not know which existing agency can help them, and so they form their own. Or they are, regrettably, expressions of the egos of their founders who like to be on boards and hold officerships. Most of them have to start from the beginning all over again, going through incorporation, writing bylaws, ordering letterheads, and learning about conservation. They absorb an enormous amount of energy and funds that might be better directed. Unfortunately there is no one agency in conservation to which a donor or someone interested in a conservation issue can turn for unprejudiced advice concerning the effectiveness of the organizations. He must find his own way through the wilderness.

It is not that I favor merging all the organizations into two or three superagencies. Such a course would probably result in bureaucratic monstrosities, incapable of sufficient flexibility to meet the challenge. Furthermore, small, local agencies are needed to meet small, local conditions. Many towns in Connecticut, for example, now have land trusts. Their purpose in many instances is identical with that of the Nature Conservancy—to save important areas of open space. But their interests do not conflict, and the Nature Conservancy encourages their formation and often provides them with technical help and advice. (It also offers another useful service by agreeing to take over the properties should the land trust go out of business. This relieves the minds of donors who are concerned that a small organization may be entirely dependent on the enthusiasm of a few people.)

Such land trusts play an extremely useful role. Being on the spot and sensitive to local conditions, they can discover opportunities that might be unobserved by a national organization like the Nature Conservancy. On the other hand, many projects will arise that they are too small to handle or that require more experience than they have available. In those instances, a larger organization is a necessity. A good example occurred when a group of citizens in Westport, Connecticut, thought the town should acquire one of the relatively few offshore islands in Long Island Sound, Cockenoe. The town was within the district covered by the Aspetuck Land Trust, a new but highly effective local group. Consultation between the two agencies resulted in the decision that the Cockenoe Island was too sizable for the land trust, and so the Nature Conservancy handled it, while the land trust continued to concentrate on its important, but somewhat smaller, activities. Such a division of responsibilities is efficient, and the smaller, local organizations will always play a significant role, but there is a limit to how many we need.

Also it is not just the proliferation of smaller agencies that causes the confusion. The larger organizations often find themselves in direct competition with each other. Agency X, for example, was offered $20,000 with which to purchase and preserve an area of coastal marshland in the Northeast. The donor knew of no specific area, so Agency X had to find a tract for sale at that price. The necessary investigation took many weeks, during which the donor grew increasingly restless over the time required. Finally Agency X located a satisfactory area but on review discovered it was not sufficiently diversified to be representative. In the hope that it could enlarge the tract, Agency X began negotiations with other groups to assist in the purchase of additional acreage. The final result might have been the establishment of one of the most important tidal marshland research stations in the Northeast, as well as the preservation of a large area for its esthetic and wildlife values.

Not understanding why this process took so much time, the donor approached Agency Y and asked them to buy the land originally selected by Agency X. Without any hesitation, Agency Y agreed and rushed a field man out to start negotiating with the landowners. The results were unfortunate. All chance of a research station vanished, although such a station might have made an important contribution to our understanding of marsh life. Less land was saved than might have been. And the first agency had squandered the time it had spent trying to develop a more comprehensive and worthwhile plan. The procedure was wasteful. Conservation does not have the resources to behave like that.

As another example of this instinct for competition, I recall that when I first became associated with the Nature Conservancy, its board was anxious to set up a chapter in western Pennsylvania, only because it had noted the outstanding success of the Western Pennsylvania Conservancy, an organization that bears a similar name but is completely unrelated. It took considerable persuasion to make the board understand that this was the last place to start a chapter, because the job was already being well done, and it was pointless to engage in unproductive competition.

Conversely when the Nature Conservancy received newsworthy financial assistance from a foundation, the head of another large conservation organization issued a memorandum to all his directors. The foundation, he argued, should have supported his own group instead; and because the Nature Conservancy had been able to attract financial help for this type of project, his organization should enter the same field. Apparently he never stopped to think that the task was being accomplished and that he should continue to concentrate on the activities in which he was already successful and useful.

There are notable exceptions to such conduct. Alston Jenkins, the head of Philadelphia Conservationists, once called me about an island off the coast of Florida that might be preserved. His organization did not have sufficient resources to do it itself, but he was willing to assist the Nature Conservancy if it would undertake the project. The Nature Conservancy assumed the leadership, and Mr. Jenkins faithfully carried out his agreement, raising a substantial part of the money needed. A further example of such cooperation is the program initiated by the National Audubon Society whereby its representatives meet regularly with the Nature Conservancy to discuss land acquisition opportunities. These meetings are designed to prevent competition and duplication of effort.

Such examples, however, are all too rare; and much of the effort that might be devoted constructively to conservation is dissipated. One reason is overprofessionalism.

Few countries engage in as many volunteer activities as America, and few place a higher value on participation in volunteer work. Nonpaying positions on the boards of nonprofit organizations offer considerable prestige and are often the gateway to social recognition. Yet in spite of the importance attached to the volunteers' role, many successful volunteer agencies are almost completely dominated by their professional staffs. This is especially true of those engaged in conservation, a condition that is the source of much of the interagency competition with its waste and duplication. When men think their livelihood or their prestige is at stake, they quickly lose their objectivity and become aggressive. Conservation is no longer a cause in itself; it is a means of earning an income, and they will fight to protect or expand their jobs.

A more objective attitude could be attained by the better organization of private conservation agencies and the use of effective management controls. Generally speaking, the problem divides into two parts: one that applies to all groups, no matter what their field, and another that applies more specifically to conservation.

The first can be solved with common sense and the application of modern management techniques, but in conservation they are not. At the Nature Conservancy, we have gradually taken a number of steps that I would think normal for an organization of its size and activity, but other agencies are surprised when they learn what we do. The duties of all officers, both volunteer and professional, are carefully written up, and their responsibilities and authority described in some detail. These are not merely job descriptions in the usual sense but are intended to establish the orderly relationship of each officer to the others. They do much to prevent overlapping authorities and confusion. Just as a corporation might, we have monthly reports from each division head. These are not lengthy, but they quickly show where each division stands. And every year, in addition to the budget, the management draws up an overall plan of expected accomplishments and actions, which is composed of the plans for each division and what is expected of the officers, including the chairman. This provides guidelines for judging performance; but more than that, it makes clear what everyone is supposed to do and the priorities they should follow. Although these and other practices are normally used in many corporations, it took quite a few years to install them, which reflects, I think, the general ignorance of management techniques that prevails in most conservation agencies. But this is only a small part of the question, and one that is relatively easily handled.

The important issue is the relationship between the volunteers and the professionals, both of which have significant roles. To be effective, any major conservation effort must have the support of a full-time staff. These are the people who are on the job every day and do not have to drop a project suddenly because of the pressures of their own work. This type of continuous attention is often absolutely necessary, and I have seen important undertakings lost because key volunteer figures were unable to devote the time and lacked the skills and necessary information, and there were no professionals to back them up. Furthermore, the professionals know more about current conservation programs and activities. This is not easy. Every day that I go to my mailbox I return to the house with somewhere from one to ten conservation publications, announcements, press releases, or other information. It seems almost impossible to keep up with this material. Yet it is important to know just how to apply for government funds for the purchase of open space, what states also make grants-in-aid, what the laws are on condemnation, and where to go for assistance with water pollution problems. Technical questions like these arise frequently, and the volunteer worker rarely knows the answer.

There are other assignments that also require full-time professionals. Fund raising, except on a small scale, cannot be carried out without someone to direct it. Legal advice is needed on a regular basis. The vice-presidency of the Nature Conservancy provides another example of the necessity for skilled professionals. This job is entrusted with the financial management of millions of dollars and requires the services of someone who really knows finance. Fortunately the man who fills the position is a former deputy comptroller of the navy, who later pursued a successful career in banking and investments. No industry could afford to have a volunteer financial officer; neither can a large conservation agency. Just like every other field, conservation needs its experts.

On the other hand, in many agencies difficulties can also develop with full-time staffs, and it seeems to me that there are two patterns that occur all too frequently. In one, the professional staff becomes so efficient in pursuing limited objectives that there is no room for the volunteers. At the best, they are errand boys in their local districts. At the worst, they do not participate at all, merely paying their dues each year and receiving the organization's publications. These may be excellent, and reading them may make the member informed on conservation issues, but his relationship to his organization is about that of a subscriber of *Newsweek* to *Newsweek*'s management. What conservation loses when this sort of situation arises is the active participation of many people who might make a significant contribution to the cause. Even more, it loses the imagination and breadth of view that could be brought to bear on conservation problems. Too many issues are handled just as they have been for years, and too often the same faces appear again and again. The movement is extremely short of manpower, and it is unfortunate if potential assistance is lost.

At its worst, overprofessionalism of the staff can do great damage. Those who go into conservation professionally are often dedicated—and sometimes zealous. As the years pass and they learn more and more about the subject and their ideas of what is right become more certain, their zealousness may take over. They lose patience with their membership, then their boards of trustees, and then their volunteer officers and decide that they alone know what is correct to do. Often by this time, they are so well entrenched that it is impossible, or nearly so, to dislodge them. (I could write a manual on how a professional head can take over his organization completely. There are certain simple steps to follow, and he may take them without even knowing he is doing so.) When the organization comes under the complete dominance of its professional leader, the tragic consequences affect both the man himself and the whole cause of conservation. The man becomes more and more egocentric and more and more certain that he alone knows the answers to problems of conservation. Deprived of the balanced judgment that might be exercised by his volunteer board and officers, he becomes increasingly extreme. When he does so, he alienates people who might otherwise be supporters of his cause and whom his cause needs. Or he fights over issues that, appearing unreasonable to many people, again separate him from the public whose help he could use.

Our resources are already too small for the task. We cannot afford to squander them in this fashion. Whether such emotional upsets occur more frequently in conservation agencies than in other organizations, I am not prepared to say, but I rather suspect they do. I think this is because of the nature of conservation and its propensity for attracting highly emotional people.

Here, then, is one of the principal responsibilities of the volunteers, especially those serving as officers or on boards or committees. They should establish and maintain appropriate checks and balances, so that the best, not the worst, abilities of their professional staffs are utilized. Unfortunately many volunteers in conservation fail to understand this role and either abdicate it or overplay it. When they overplay it, the results are almost as disastrous as when they abdicate it. They, too, become overzealous and often assume functions that should be left to the professional staff. By their interference, they disrupt the orderly workings of their organization and limit its effectiveness as well as its growth.

Often the conflict between the extremists among the volunteers and the professionals leads to infighting that dissipates energies and time that might better be devoted to conservation itself. I regret to say that internal struggles in some conservation organizations, both large and small, have been a major preoccupation. Such struggles are a waste and an important reason why the conservation movement has not been more successful than it has.

What is needed is recognition of the difference between the two roles—professional and volunteer—how one can provide continuity and technical knowledge, while the other can provide breadth of experience and judgment that would be unhireable. Maintaining the balance between the two is basically a question of management. It can be solved if conservation can attract more management-minded people who accept such attitudes as the normal method of operation.

Most organizational success results from advance planning; but planning in conservation, whether by private or government agencies, is often either too limited or too visionary. In government, most of the planning that is done falls into one of these two categories. Either some agency is working on plans for the entire environment that are too sweeping to be carried out, or the planning is too narrow in scope. The National Park Service, for example, in its master plans for individual parks includes such items as the routes of future roads and the location of camping facilities. These plans are extremely useful, but before that, bigger planning needs to be done, for the park is rarely an isolated unit. It has a distinct relationship to other nearby parks and even to the national park system as a whole. The Easterner who goes West for a vacation trip does not consider each park individually. In his mind, one supplements another, and together they create his vacation. Furthermore a national park may be surrounded by national forests that play a supporting role in handling the visitors. In many instances, the National Park Service and the U.S. Forest Service consult together on their respective roles, but even such planning, helpful as it may be, is not sufficient. The least that should be done—and still be entirely practical—is for the two agencies, along with the Bureau of Land Management, to discuss their needs and responsibilities on a regional basis and over a long term.

That this does not occur with greater frequency is not so much the fault of the agencies concerned with conservation as it is a direct result of the effects of politics. Although certain Congressmen seem to be eternal, elected again and again and creeping by means of seniority to the top ranks, the general atmosphere in Washington is transitory. Everyone in the departments knows that the Cabinet secretaries will not endure more than eight years and that the bureau heads may change with a new administration; everyone knows that the majority sentiment in the House can be severely altered in not more than two years and that the Senate, although more stable, can also change quickly. This knowledge tends to give everything an air of immediacy. There is little point in spending time and money on a plan that may take years to materialize, because by then the political mood may be entirely different. Under these circumstances, it is surprising that there is as much planning as there is, not that there is so little.

Yet the private agencies, working with private funds, have no such limitations imposed on them; they are free to do whatever they want within their budgets. Nevertheless few of them do much long-range planning either.

By plans, I do not mean studies. Conservationists love studies. The number of trees cut down each year just to provide the paper conservationists use to publish their studies must be quite considerable. As an example, between 1900 and 1968, 5,470 technical papers were written on the estuaries and coastal waters of the eastern United States.[1] This is at a rate of approximately a paper and a half every week for sixty-eight years. Yet this figure represents merely a small proportion of the total papers written, and only those covering the technical aspects. Add to these the land-use studies that have been issued, the reports of conservation agencies on the subject, the magazine articles that have been written, the volumes of congressional hearings that have been printed, and the proceedings of various symposia, and the total would fill a small library. But as evidenced by the present state of our coastal lands and estuaries, no one has come up with an effective workable plan for preserving them. As the pile of printed material continued to mount higher and higher, the coastal lands continued to disappear.

Although studies are useful, and often basic, in planning, planning itself is something quite different. Planning defines a problem, sets up an achievable objective, weighs the available means of attaining it efficiently, the order of the steps to be taken, and the priority of each one. This is the sort of planning that is so absent in the private conservation movement.

Of course, there are notable exceptions. The long struggle of the Wilderness Society for the passage of the Wilderness Act is an example of a private organization setting a long-term goal and working steadfastly toward it. The result has been a basic change in American conservation concepts. But unfortunately few private agencies have set such clear and definite objectives and then formulated plans to reach them. In one case, I have, out of real concern, asked the executive head of a private agency the purposes and objectives of his organization only to be told that there is no printed literature available describing them, he himself cannot quite say what they are, and that the best source of information is to read their annual report. As he expressed it, that would give me a general idea of what they do. But an annual report is an historical record, only telling what has happened in the past. It does not look to the future or establish what the organization hopes to accomplish. Earlier I mentioned the executive director who proposed to his board that it immediately duplicate the activity of the Nature Conservancy. His motivation was obvious; he thought the activity was financially successful, and so he wanted to take part in it. Clearly he had no real objective of his own, or he would not have been willing to switch so quickly. This general vagueness is reflected in much of the promotional material published by conservation agencies in their own behalf. The wording is emotional but nonspecific, and few state what the organization hopes to do during the coming year, much less over a longer period.

Part of this vagueness arises from the necessity of taking advantage of special opportunities that is an essential part of conservation. The field is so large and complex that it is not always possible to forecast tomorrow's needs or to foresee the opportunities that may occur for favorable action. But much of the vagueness arises from other causes.

One of these is lack of management control. Few conservation agencies are directed with sufficient precision. If they were, there would be more evidence of planning because planning is one of the most important instruments of management. Not only does it provide for the effective attainment of carefully predetermined goals, but it also offers a means of measuring an organization's effectiveness. When the Nature Conservancy, without having set for itself standards of performance, had saved some 20,000 acres of land, the members of the board congratulated themselves on having done a good job. Because they had never decided among themselves how much land it was possible to save, it became difficult to persuade them that they could have preserved considerably more. When they had passed the 100,000-acre mark, they again congratulated themselves. But remaining within reasonable limits of speculation, the amount could have almost been double that in the same period of time. Measured against its own past record (or the record of other conservation agencies), its achievement had been remarkable. Measured against its potential, its performance was considerably less.

In industry, the concept of "share of market" is well known.

In its simplest terms, it means that a company estimates the total market for a particular service or goods and then determines whether its share of the total is going up or down. The advantage of this technique is clear. It strips away the confusion that arises from changing opportunities. The manufacturer of widget X may be pleased that his sales have risen 20 percent over a year ago; he may not be so pleased when he learns that the demand for widget X has soared and that his own share of the total market has shrunk from 15 percent to 10 percent. He has obviously not taken advantage of his opportunity.

A similar technique could be applied to conservation. A variety of conditions affect the probability of reaching any conservation objective at a given period of time—the availability of federal, state, and private funds, the temper of the public, the attitude of legislative bodies, and other considerations. These can be identified and even to some extent measured. Once this has been done, the probability of reaching the objective can be determined, and the eventual success or failure of a particular program can be estimated. That, in turn, provides a means of judging the effectiveness of the program and of the people in charge of it.

For a number of years, I have tried to persuade some of my fellow conservationists to apply this sort of concept to their activities. As it is, too many of them are pleased when their membership rolls increase or when they have had success in a particular endeavor. Like the manufacturer of widget X, they measure their performance against their own record for the last year or the last few years, not against the total opportunity or need. In the 1960's, this country demonstrated a demand for conservation action that was historically unparalleled. Weighing their attainments against this demand, few conservation agencies have much to be proud about.

Until they adopt the fundamental concept of "share of market," effective planning is not possible, for the first step in planning is to decide what the organization should, and could, accomplish in the future and how effective it has been in the past. Failure to use this technique in conservation comes largely from the management inexperience of the volunteer boards and

from resistance on the part of the professional staffs. It is much
pleasanter to report success on a rising market than it is to report
a failure to seize opportunities. If this resistance could be overcome, the way would be opened to far more effective conservation activity, with the agencies concentrating their efforts on
clearly defined goals instead of dissipating their energy as they
now all too often do.

The way would also be opened to better cooperation between
the agencies, something that is sorely needed. From time to time,
the agencies get together to trade mailing lists or to discuss a
specific, and usually limited, conservation problem. In early
1969, for example, a group of them met to take action on the
airport affecting the Everglades, as a result of which a protest
was sent to Secretary Volpe of the Department of Transportation.
These exchanges, however, are relatively superficial. No one
I know about has sat down, outlined a total conservation problem, and then persuaded each agency to play a clearly defined
role in its solution, according to an advance plan. At this stage
in the development of the movement, this may be impossible.
To an extent, professional jealousies would interfere. The head
of Agency X is not likely to surrender to the head of Agency Y
a role that he thinks he is already playing, even if he is not playing it well. This obstacle could be easily overcome, however, by
having the volunteers, whose professional jobs are not at stake,
assume an active part in such an arrangement. Indeed, I hope
that some day someone will take the initiative in establishing a
permanent organization that will draw together the most experienced and best-informed conservationists for just such objective
discussions of the major conservation issues and how they can
best be handled on a coordinated basis by the agencies. An organization like this would not have to be large, and it would not
require much money; but it could, I believe, have a significant
effect on conservation.

Even if it were formed, it would have to overcome a number
of obstacles. The principal one would be the inadequacy of the
conservation movement's planning machinery to support concentrated, cooperative action on predetermined issues. This is a
tragic situation for the country, but it will continue to exist until

conservationists learn that the problems they are attempting to handle are not susceptible to solution by old-fashioned, outdated methods. They demand the best of modern management techniques. Perhaps an organization such as the one I have suggested could help point the way. I hope somebody starts one and at least tries.

Like most human activities, conservation has its own technologies—its techniques for achieving the practical results it desires. And because nothing remains static in our society, these technologies must be constantly varied and enlarged to meet changing conditions. Not that the old technologies have to be completely discarded and replaced by new ones. Often the old technologies can be used and reused to handle particular situations, but they tend to become less and less universally applicable. We have not entirely dispensed with candles just because we live in a country where electric power is taken for granted in most communities. Candles still serve an esthetic—and sometimes useful—purpose, but we do not depend on them for the majority of our lighting needs. Conservationists, unfortunately, sometimes rely on candlelight in an era of electricity.

The impact of changing conservation technologies can be illustrated by briefly reviewing the work of the Nature Conservancy. Although I have been connected with a number of conservation organizations in one capacity or another and although I have carefully studied and observed the operations of most of the major ones, I am using the Nature Conservancy as an example because I am most familiar with it. It traces its roots back to a committee formed in 1917 by the Ecological Union for the purpose of encouraging the preservation of natural areas for scientific research. Even at that relatively early date, the need for such areas was clearly foreseen, and this group of scientists tried to meet it. In 1952, they looked back at what they had accomplished over the intervening years and came to the sad conclusion that it had amounted to extremely little. As far as I know, not a single acre had been preserved directly as the result of their activity.

Many factors contributed to this inability to accomplish practical results, but probably the most significant was the application of an outmoded technology to a current problem. The technology might be called educative-scientific, and it is still used by conservationists today, sometimes in special circumstances with good results. Basically it assumes that if a respected scientist or scientists in a field related to natural history will speak out loudly and clearly for the preservation of a certain area, concern for the environment, or for the cause of conservation generally, positive action will follow. This action will be taken by private individuals and institutions out of a number of motives—respect for the scientists, a desire of the individuals to align themselves with scientific intellectuals, and the wish to convert what might have been a rather amateurish interest in natural history into a constructive and more formal occupation. As a technology of conservation, it traces its origins to nineteenth-century Great Britain, where it proved to be highly effective.

More than most nations, Great Britain has had a long, serious, and gentlemanly interest in the countryside. The phrases "country squire," "country gentleman," and "country vicar" do not, as they would among other nationalities, connote rural nonentities. Quite the contrary. They bring to mind rugged, pipe-smoking individuals, walking across the moors and fields in all sorts of weather and clearly superior to their more sophisticated, but less masculine, cousins in the heavily populated cities. This concentration on, and admiration for, ruralism is an essential part of British character, at least among certain classes. There is something symbolic in Shakespeare's magnificent descriptions of nature, some of the best ever written, and his eventual retirement to a small country town, when he could have lingered on in London. London is not, to the upper classes of Great Britain, what New York is to the same groups in the United States. It is more of a place to visit than a place to live, and hotels like Brown's have owed their existences to this fact of British life. The list of writers who followed Shakespeare in extolling the countryside would include men like Herrick and White, each looking at it from a somewhat different point of view but each hailing its virtues. It was no accident, therefore, that when William Wordsworth wrote his revolutionary poetry (too often, we forget that it was shockingly revolutionary in its day), he chose country scenes and country people for much of what he had to say. His simple people were not city beggars, but farmers. And he could unabashedly enjoy the daffodils. In short, he was an Englishman.

This British interest in the outdoors persisted throughout the nineteenth century and continues today among much the same classes. And it provided a fertile ground for the educative-scientific technology of conservation. What Britisher of wealth, leisure, and country interests could resist the call of biological scientists concerned with field investigations? So the country houses became filled with collections of birds' eggs and nests, rocks, butterflies, and the other impedimenta of the amateur naturalist. And the professional scientist could always find a welcome for his person and his ideas. (It helped, of course, if he also had the marks of a gentleman.)

This particular conservation technology has also worked well in the United States in the past, and sometimes it still does. Its success demands, however, a special human environment. There must be wealth, not new wealth, but wealth that is at least second, and preferably third, generation; there must be leisure; if not outright retirement, then long vacations; there must be a strong Anglo-Saxon social orientation; in short, there must be an approximation of a nineteenth-century upper-class British atmosphere. Given these circumstances, the skillful scientist will find himself accepted as a social equal by those far wealthier than he. He will be invited to dinner and as a weekend guest with no thought that he cannot repay his hosts on similar terms. But he will be expected to advise his host on the planting of trees and the proper management, appreciation, and study of his holdings—how to inventory the snakes, if herpetology is his host's interest, or how to increase the well-being of the deer herd. He will be expected also to advise his hostess on the hanging of bird boxes and the cultivation of wild flowers and to identify the rarer specimens collected by her offspring. (In such a society, "nice" young boys always had a butterfly net. It was practically a mark of class, and certain types of people could immediately recognize in a young butterfly-net-holder the child of a peer.) In these surroundings, the duties imposed on the scientist are not onerous and, if carried out with a degree of social grace, can produce impressive rewards for the scientist's institution or for the conservation projects in which he is interested.

It would be possible to point out specific areas in which this conservation technology can work—and is working—today, but to do so might make both sides self-conscious and thereby disrupt some highly constructive undertakings. But generally speaking, in the second quarter of the twentieth century this technology became outmoded in the United States. During those years, the country recovered from World War I, then plunged into the hectic economic growth and speculation of the twenties and finally dove into the despairs of the thirties that ended in World War II. There were only a limited number of British-type country gentlemen of wealth, sitting before their fires and reading scientists' reports on natural areas. And these few were not being reached by this group of scientists who formed the committee of the Ecological Union. The technology used by the committee was not suited to the time or the task.

Early in the 1950's its members, on reviewing their small success, decided to form a separate unit, which they named the Nature Conservancy and later incorporated under the laws of the District of Columbia. It continued to play a rather ineffectual role until its then head, Dr. George Fell, suggested what amounted to a new technology—the use of a revolving loan fund to assist local groups who were interested in saving natural areas. This single idea brought the Nature Conservancy to life. Generous contributors provided the necessary seed money, and the Nature Conservancy embarked on a conservation role in which revolving funds continue to play the dominant part and will probably do so until land becomes too expensive to purchase. This technology, it proved, was ideally suited to the third quarter of the twentieth century, when the United States was filled with activist people, who wanted to do something about land preservation and do it themselves. They included, of course, some people with leisure and wealth, but for the most part they were in the middle-income brackets and incapable of making large, single donations. The revolving funds provided them with the tool they needed for local action. They could negotiate a pur-

chase contract for a suitable piece of land in their locality, make
the down payment, and then conduct one of the greatest of
American rituals—a fund-raising campaign.

How typically American the arrangement was! How beauti-
fully adapted to the needs and temper of the era! I had no connection with the Nature Conservancy at the time—I had not even
heard of it—so I am free to say that I think that Dr. Fell's inno-
vation in conservation technology was one of the great contributions to conservation during that period. It has resulted in saving
thousands of acres of land.

But a basic technology demands supporting skills and services
just as the advent of electricity demanded equipment, manufacturers, line men, and electronic experts before it became widely
used. To be useful, a revolving fund of the type I have described
needs people who can keep it revolving, and this is what the
Nature Conservancy lacked—the public relations personnel who
could make the local fund-raising campaigns successful, the
financial men who knew how to handle the funds, the planners
and managers who could complete the individual projects. Skills
such as these were largely missing. The Nature Conservancy was
equipped to judge the scientific value of a project and, out of
the funds it had already raised, it was able to advance the needed
down payment. But as inevitably as the sun rises in the East, it
took on a project that was far too large for its capital, was practically impossible to finance by the proposed methods, and was
not well planned either as to completion or as to purpose. This
one project almost wrecked it. It looked for a while as though
the Nature Conservancy would either have to abandon it, which
would have meant a substantial loss of capital and prestige, or be
swallowed up by it. The worst thing the project did was to
threaten the destruction of the new conservation technology, because a revolving fund implies that the funds are revolving. In
this case, they were static.

The Nature Conservancy, however, took steps to extricate itself from the position in which it found itself. By various devices
—including straight fund raising—it reduced the size of the
project in relation to its total assets and its other activities. This
was a gamble, and it worked. But it took another step, which

was even more important. It began a concerted campaign to attract the people, both among its staff and its volunteers, who could make a revolving fund revolve. In other words, it hastily built up the supporting skills and services that the new technology demanded. The result has been much more land preserved and increased support from many sources.

A further development in its conservation technology came with the realization that there were insufficient private funds available to do the job. This led to the program of assisting government that I have already described and the preservation of thousands of additional acres. Another change in its technology came with the development of more imaginative use of its money. Historically, most nonprofit organizations have been extremely conservative in the handling of their funds, conservative to a degree that no profit-oriented group could afford. The Nature Conservancy was no exception to this rule. Whenever it contracted to supply a loan from its revolving fund, the exact amount was set aside for that specific purpose, although often months would pass before the money was actually used. Sometimes it never was. This practice, of course, was not in accord with modern finance; so following the procedures of a commercial bank, the Nature Conservancy began to make estimates of the amounts that were usually drawn down at any one time and thus arrived at a formula whereby the revolving fund could be safely committed to a dollar value greater than its total. This resulted in more land being saved with the same basic number of dollars. Numerous other more modern practices were introduced into the Nature Conservancy's handling of its money—in effect a new conservation technology had been developed—and the practical result was to increase by at least seven times the amount of land that could otherwise be preserved.

There is, however, a continuous countersurge against the adoption of new technologies in conservation. Not only is there usually strong opposition to each one as it is being developed, constant pressure also exists to revert to technologies that are completely out of date. Several members recently proposed to me that we would perform a useful land-saving function if we carried out in every state work similar to that done by the Indiana

THE PRIVATE AGENCIES · 317

Natural Areas Survey. This survey, ably headed by Dr. Alton A. Lindsey, has resulted in the identification of the principal natural areas of Indiana, descriptions of each one, a designation for their best future use, and a determination of their ownership. I know of no other survey that is more comprehensive or useful, and Dr. Lindsey and his associates deserve congratulations for what they have accomplished. Their survey will have much use.

But as a nationwide land-saving technology, this device is outmoded. The Indiana survey cost $35,000 and took two years. Extrapolating this expense over forty-nine additional states results in the sum of $1.7 million. It can be argued that Indiana has a relatively greater number of natural areas than most states and therefore their inventory was unusually expensive. On the other hand, it can also be argued that some states, like Alaska, would cost considerably more. In any case, the total expense involved is certainly in the neighborhood of $1.5 million. The first premise of this technology, therefore, is that such a sum of money is available for that purpose. If so, I do not know where, because most donors giving that amount would prefer to see it spent directly on land acquisition. The second premise is that the lapse of two years while the surveys are being made would prove insignificant. With rising prices and heavy pressures on land, this is debatable. The third premise is that such surveys would arouse unusual interest in preserving natural areas and produce the money to purchase them on a systematic basis. This premise, too, is questionable. Natural area surveys are extremely useful to the research scientist, and many of them should be made, but it is doubtful that they could be an effective land-saving technology. On the other hand, they would have been ideal in the 1930's. Making an inventory would have been a perfect undertaking for the WPA (and I speak here of the WPA in its best sense), land prices were still low, and the areas could have been subsequently purchased in a slowly rising economy. It is unfortunate that no one developed this idea more fully as a technology at that time. It might have been spectacularly successful. But today it is outdated. Nevertheless the pressure to use it continues, largely because a small group of conservationists, once having thought of the idea, out of sentiment cannot drop it.

Other members have advanced, in almost impassioned terms, the proposal that the Nature Conservancy should establish endowed research facilities at more and more of its areas. This is possible in certain exceptional instances, where a donor is specially interested in doing so. But as a general policy, it is not possible. Even if it were a commendable technology for increasing the preservation of natural areas, it could not be successful in this economy. At the time the members made this suggestion, land prices were escalating at an average rate of 10 percent annually while the Nature Conservancy had little hope of earning more than 6 percent on its own funds. Thus every $60,000 spent on endowed research would have been at the expense of $1.1 million in land that might have otherwise been saved; and with each year, the spread would have become greater by another $40,000. Most large contributors would see this inherent weakness immediately. As a land preservation technology, this might have worked in an era when land prices were lower and the pressure on natural areas less intense by creating a wider awareness of natural area values. But such a program today would be a little like trying to pump up the tires of the fire engine after the fire has started.

This preoccupation with older technologies is painfully evident in much that is written today about conservation. Because the subject is topical, many articles are now appearing that are written by individuals who are unfamiliar with the field. This in itself is good; the issues need far greater publicity than they have ever received. But many of these articles fail to advance new ideas; they merely present conservation problems in the same old terms, generally, as a fight waged by protesters.

Some while ago I had lunch with an editor who had been assigned by his publisher to develop a conservation section for his publication. I knew what his publisher wanted, because he had told me—a fresh approach to conservation that would make a significant contribution. The editor had wisely been consulting many persons, but the approach he was going to take was clear. He saw conservation in the traditional terms of protest and fight. As he put it, he wanted to know in advance where the hot-spots like the redwoods would develop, and he was anxious to lend the prestige of his magazine to the ensuing battles. His support will always be most welcome. Such battles will continue to be important in conservation, and every lucid voice speaking out in defense of conservation ideals will help. But the opportunities for his publication were far greater, for he could have taken the lead in developing a more modern approach to the subject. But he was restricted by the expectations of his readers. They thought of conservation in the old terms of constant confrontations and struggles over limited objectives and that is what he would have to give them.

Yet what conservation most desperately needs is new ideas, new technologies, new methods of achieving practical results, new thinking that takes into account the changing times. In addition, it needs the prompt acceptance and utilization of these new ideas, because the latest approach can itself become quickly outdated in our fast-moving world. The Nature Conservancy's program of cooperation with government provides an excellent example of the necessity for speed. Although imaginative, the program unfortunately got off to a slow start, largely because the Nature Conservancy's own board had difficulty adapting to new ideas and because government also had the same problem. This conservative attitude on the part of the agency and those whom the program was designed to help certainly impaired its usefulness and cost the nation many acres of land that might well have been saved. If the program could have been fully committed by 1966 or 1967, it would have preceded some of the subsequent escalation of the Vietnam War, the rise in land prices, soaring interest rates, and the gradual deterioration of the government's land acquisition efforts. It is completely within the realm of possibility that the total additional lands preserved could have amounted to 100,000 acres. Once developed, a new technology must be implemented quickly.

An idea that has been frequently discussed is to purchase lands and to resell portions of them to recover funds for additional purchases. This is dependent, of course, on a continually rising market for land but, given those circumstances, might open new opportunities, particularly as it would be possible to restrict the use of the lands sold. But a proposal to set up such a program within one state drew a sharp rebuke from a former member of the Nature Conservancy's board of governors. Even talking about such a program was to him abhorrent and distasteful. Obviously what he wanted was a reversion to the older technologies, forgetting that high land costs made it impossible for private capital to be as effective as before and that government money was in short supply. He had no idea of how to compensate for this situation; he just did not want this new technology even considered.

In the case of land preservation, the new technologies must take into account the shortages of funds that exist in comparison to the high cost of land, and they must also increase in effectiveness. I, for one, am becoming disenchanted with the practice of purchasing one piece of land here and another there. Every such piece saved is, of course, better than nothing; and an organization dependent on private contributions from all over the country has to be, to a certain extent, opportunistic. If the people of a particular area want to save a specific acreage, it may not be possible to broaden their interest. In such instances, there is certainly no point in turning down their offers because of their parochialism. That particular piece of land will be saved, and at least that much will be done. But an agency with a purpose like the Nature Conservancy's must somehow develop a technology that expands the results from its acquisitions, just as with its revolving funds and its imaginative use of money at has expanded the results achieved with a relatively small amount of capital. One way might be for it to say that it would undertake a certain action, if another agency, either government or private, would undertake a supplementary action. In this way, a single acquisition might be used as leverage to procure additional preservation of nearby areas. But even after such a technology is developed—and it should be developed fast or it, too, will be out of date—the Nature Conservancy will have to acquire the necessary supporting skills and services. For a program like this would require more knowledge of general conservation problems, more familiarity with land planning, and a better understanding of other agencies and other conservation techniques than the organization now has. Lying ahead of it, therefore, is hard intellectual work and considerable planning if it wants to keep up with the changing times.

The Nature Conservancy is not alone in having to face such problems. Not long ago, I picked up a copy of a magazine published by a conservation organization that is dedicated to education. Two full pages were devoted to an article that dealt at great length with the different words used to describe various groups of animals, fish, and birds, such as a skein of geese, a clatch of ducklings, and a skulk of foxes. As every reader must have known, school children are enchanted when they first come across this vagary of the English language and may spend part of an afternoon playing with it, trying to think of new examples. But it is a game that they soon tire of, and they rarely play it after they leave second grade. But here it was, two full pages' worth of it, in a magazine ostensibly designed for adult readership and concerned with the critical issues of today's conservation.

What had happened, of course, was the application of an outmoded technology to a current problem. For behind the words about skulks and skeins was the vision of a nineteenth-century gentlewoman sitting beside her fire and enjoying this delightful quaintness and with plenty of time to indulge in it. But this is the third quarter of the twentieth century, and such people exist only in rapidly diminishing numbers and are not the doers.

The education of the public on conservation issues is largely a matter of communications, and the method of communication should be modern in order to reach a contemporary audience. This is an age of rioting in the streets, campus disruptions, war in Vietnam, television with all its immediacy—an age in which Marshall McLuhan is the guru of communications. However much we may regret it, it is not an age of skulks and skeins. Except in antique shops, the nineteenth century is out of style.

Yet what an opportunity for education exists in the present mood of the people. Never have they wanted so much to learn about conservation. Never have they been so readily stirred to action, and this action could be more effective, if only they knew better what to do. In the younger generation alone lies an enormous potential resource for conservation, if their energies can be channeled by a conservationist able to communicate with them. The opportunity is there. Conservation contains much of the humanistic element that attracts youth today. The riots at Columbia started over the destruction of a park; and the undergraduate newspaper, *The Spectator,* was as interested in the university's selling Clausland Mountain to Rockland County for preservation as was the New York *Times.* On the West Coast, one skillful conservationist won an important issue by enlisting the support of the hippies. Their work and their enthusiasm turned the tide.

People such as these, and many others whom conservation needs, can be reached, but the methods will have to be more vigorous and modern. As far as the ability to arouse the public is concerned, the Sierra Club has done an excellent job, sometimes too excellent a job, for it has gotten emotions so high that the basic issues have occasionally been obscured. But their communications, particularly their newspaper advertisements, are of the times. They are sophisticated and look as though the agency that prepared them thought the club was a lively account. The club has been developing a contemporary communications technology to meet contemporary problems.

The whole range of conservation thinking and activity is permeated by this contrast between the old and the new and the continual struggle to keep up to date. Not long ago, I saw the report made by a field representative to his headquarters office on a burning conservation issue. It concerned the construction of an airport on which work was already well advanced. He had two immediate recommendations. One was to conduct a study of the general effects of the project, and the other was to study the hydrology of a particular tree that might be adversely affected. Both of these recommendations were highly commendable, but they would hardly solve the problem of the airport's construction. By the time the studies were completed, so too would be the airport.

Studies have been, and will continue to be, vital to conservation. But studies tend to take time, and this is a fast-moving era. We need a faster technology for gathering the information required to support a conservation cause than to send out a leisurely study team. It is not impossible that the leading conservation organizations between them could build up a pool of information on potential conservation problems and thus have it readily available the moment a problem arose. They could go even further than that. They could devise a means of rapidly analyzing a problem and determining the essential elements in achieving the practical results: Is the question one for political action? If so, which forces should be brought to bear? Is the question one in which economics form the basic issue? In almost every case, one or more of such aspects dominate, and the pooled information could be stored in a computer so that the pertinent knowledge could be retrieved easily and put together in a manner that should get action. Anything like this is impossible today. Aside from the unfortunate jealousies that sometimes exist between agencies serving a worthy cause, there is no machinery, no technology, capable of this approach. Perhaps the time has come for someone to sit down and figure one out.

This is one of the great tragedies of conservation. While industry and other activities are making heavy investments in research and development to ensure their successful functioning in these fast-moving times, conservation is not. Too much of its energy goes into the reapplication of old technologies; and when these fail, the conservationists have only themselves to blame. The movement needs far more people who are willing to take an intellectual as against an emotional attitude toward its problems, who are willing to analyze them and seek not merely solutions, but methods of obtaining solutions. Until this occurs, the conservation movement will continue to lag behind the times and not perform effectively. Fortunately, as it increases in popularity as a cause, it is attracting more and more new people. Among them may be the very ones with the fresh approaches and ideas that will help to move it forward in the development of radically new technologies.

12

The Conservationists

T HE first sight of the Grand Canyon is an unequaled experience, and I have often thought of the amazement that must have overwhelmed Don López de Cárdenas and his twelve followers when, in 1540, they became the first Europeans to stand at its edge. To me, part of its fascination is its vastness, its magnificent colors, and its strange formations with the light playing over them; but part of its fascination is also that you can be so close to it and not see it. I know of no natural sight in the world that is so large and yet so invisible from a short distance.

Because this was to be my wife's first visit to the canyon and my first to the North Rim, I consulted with George Collins of Conservation Associates as to where to go. Mr. Collins had once been a National Park Service ranger on the North Rim, so I knew his advice would be good. He immediately suggested Point Sublime. (Many of the features of our national parks were named at the turn of the century and sound as though they had been.) Aside from affording an excellent view of the center of the canyon, Point Sublime can only be reached by a long road that is classified as primitive. This designation means that in wet weather it becomes impassable and, even in dry, is difficult. It also means that those who take it are, for the most part, the ones that care. Thus, for that first grand view, we would be away from the crowds.

During the time we were at the point, few people came; and as I had expected, those who did were mostly appreciative of the sight that lay before them. (One was the ranger who was on duty at the park entrance when we came in. I am always impressed by the rangers' personal interest in the wonders they are assigned to protect.) Among the visitors, we fell into conversation with a couple who came up in a camper, and of course, we talked about the beauty we were seeing. I mentioned that this was considered one of the finest views of the canyon. If that was the case, the woman asked, why didn't the National Park Service put in a better road? I explained as best I could that there was not enough space at Point Sublime to park many cars and that anyway it was nice to have a spot that was somewhat difficult to reach and therefore more isolated. In the course of talking, I happened to refer to myself as a conservationist.

The reaction was completely unexpected. These people were obviously interested in the same things I was, but at the sound of the word "conservationist," the man's temper immediately flared up, and he demanded to know whether I was a member of what he called the "Sahara Club." Few times in my life have I been quite so taken aback by the ferocity of an attack, and I realized that the small area that makes up Point Sublime could not hold us both unless we reached some sort of understanding quickly.

On questioning, it turned out that he was an employee of the Bureau of Reclamation, an agency that has often suffered from the attacks of conservationists, although, I should add, in my opinion not often enough. But this was not the only reason for his rancor. He had developed a deep antipathy, to use too mild a word, to all conservationists for what he considered their extremism. He was in favor of open space, he explained, but he did not see why the conservationists insisted on saving everything. As he gradually calmed down, we discussed his interests and some of the things he does. Most of his spare time he spends outdoors; and with his camper, he and his wife have visited and enjoyed many of our great natural sights. In talking with him, I found that we had a large community of interest, and he perhaps learned that not all conservationists were quite what he had thought. In fact, we parted on the best of terms with good wishes for each other's future travels.

But that chance conversation on the edge of the Grand Canyon set me to thinking again about the nature of conservationists, and how some of them alienate people from whom they might otherwise draw needed support. No one knows better than I that conservationists as a group are wonderful persons—concerned, sensitive, energetic, and generous. But anyone who has worked with them for a length of time must also admit that they contain within their ranks some of their own worst enemies, people who have unknowingly hurt the cause and created problems that impeded the movement as a whole. For the very characteristics that make conservationists alert to the condition of their environment and willing to fight for its betterment sometimes become exaggerated and self-defeating.

Practically all conservationists are sensitive. If they did not eagerly respond to the world around them, take joy in the sight of a glacier creeping down a mountainside or in the sound of waves breaking against a rocky shore, they would not have entered the field. It is this sensitivity, this appreciation of the natural world, this capacity for enjoying sheer beauty that makes them willing to struggle to preserve the things they love. But sensitivity arises from emotionalism, and this creates a danger to conservation.

In itself, emotionalism can be a highly desirable human quality. Out of it have come great pictures, music, and books; all the arts depend on it. It provides the foundation for many of our forward political movements; certainly the United States would never have come into being without the emotional drive of the early patriots like Thomas Paine and Samuel Adams. And in conservation, emotionalism provides the means of arousing others, of communicating with them, and stirring them into action. Cold, clear logic alone would not have enabled John Muir to save the Yosemite Valley, the Audubon Society to institute its early programs for the protection of our vanishing wildlife, or the members of the Washburn Expedition to work for the dedication of the Yellowstone to the people. Yet this emotionalism, if uncontrolled, can lead to extremism, and extremism is what had so aroused the ire of my acquaintance at Point Sublime and, unfortunately, the opposition, or at least lack of support, of many others.

This extremism takes different forms, some less overtly emotional than others. The overintent bird watcher provides an example of the first. Clad in extravagant clothing, completely self-absorbed, and often humorless, he presents a ridiculous figure. A fine newspaper photographer once accompanied a bird walk, and the pictures he obtained are a delightful commentary on human beings, almost like an album of photographic Daumiers of the conservation world. But when someone like myself looks at them, the smile they occasion soon dies, for I realize that this is what many people think all conservationists are—self-important middle-aged and elderly men and women chasing a bird across a field or through the woods. The bird-watching image has done grievous harm to conservation. Looking for birds is good sport and leads to knowledge and appreciation. But I sometimes wish that the lunatic fringe of those who pursue it would either temper their ways or stay out of sight—at least when we have a major conservation project under way.

Extremism manifests itself in other ways, too, not just in a small group making conservation seem silly. It often leads to injudicious statements and planning. In one town, a group of citizens protested a landfill operation that was swiftly destroying a tidal creek and marsh, one of the few left in that area, or, as a matter of fact, in that entire state. The cause was good, and the group might have won except for a major mistake. The landfill (which is a polite word for garbage disposal) was attracting rats, they claimed, and they had a dead one to prove it, carefully preserved in a housewife's freezer. In an attempt to gain publicity for their cause, they demanded that the mayor come to a meeting and see the dead rat for himself. He arrived, accompanied by members of the local press. At the appropriate moment, one of the citizens fetched the dead rat and waved it in front of the mayor's eyes. Having grown up in the country, the mayor immediately recognized it for what it was—a muskrat. By the time the laughter had died down, hope of saving the marsh had almost vanished. A little more thinking and a little less emotionalism might have done a better job.

When conservationists seriously say, as some of them have actually done, that they will block any attempt to erect another power plant in their rapidly growing state, they are doing more harm than good. Power plants are ugly, but no conservation effort will prevent their construction if the people of an area need more electricity. What conservation can accomplish is to make the plants less obtrusive and cause their sites to be chosen with greater consideration for their effect on their surroundings. But extremists drive away those people who might rally to the support of these more limited, but also more realistic, objectives. They repel the moderates who make up the majority of the population. Yet it is on these moderates that the success of conservation ultimately must come to depend, for the hard core of the conservation movement today consists of extremely few persons. It desperately needs additional help.

I am not in the least advocating a surrender to anticonservation interests, but the charge of the Light Brigade did not win the war. Throwing oneself in front of a bulldozer, calling a developer names, or being highly emotional at a legislative hearing may be useful—sometimes. There are occasions when only the loudest voice will be listened to. But as Newton B. Drury, whom I consider one of the wisest of all conservationists, once said to me, although it can be fun to lose one's temper and carry on in an extreme manner, the principal question is, will doing so help the cause?

This intensity on the part of conservationists also tends to make them parochial in their attitudes. Instead of looking at the total problem, they are likely to concentrate on a single aspect of it to the detriment of all others. As an example, a group of conservationists were discussing the preservation of a large island off the coast of one of our southern states. Among those present were several whose primary concern was setting aside natural areas for scientific research. They pressed hard to determine whether the plans for the island provided for public access and were delighted to learn that no landing piers would be built and that no camping would be allowed.

Considering that island alone, their concern was legitimate. We must save areas for research if we want to know more about ourselves and our environment. But none of those who argued so strongly in favor of holding this island inviolate had informed himself about that state's coastline, and the situation was far more complex than any of them either knew or cared to know.

For various reasons, some economic and some geologic, the state had a relatively undeveloped shore front. Here and there, various forms of development had penetrated to the ocean, but the majority of the coast was still unbuilt upon. This meant the state had an unusually large amount of coastline whose use could be determined in advance—provided, of course, that the money was forthcoming.

Many people were aware of this, including the state government, which had its own objective—to build up the tourist trade on which the state was already partially dependent. Not being wealthy, it needed the additional revenue. Because scientific research produces almost no direct income, this activity had a low priority in the plans of the state. Recreational development was what it wanted; and with this in mind, it was planning the construction of a large marina on one of the islands and talking about building causeways between several others. This, it might be argued, made the preservation of the one island under consideration more important than ever, and to an extent that argument was correct. But closing the island to all camping and boating whatsoever would certainly increase the pressure on all the others. They might be completely ruined for anything but recreational uses. Yet some of them might have unique values that ought to be preserved.

Was there a better way than suddenly withdrawing from all public use a large section of coastal area? Was there some means of fitting this island into a total pattern of coastline use and still making certain that appropriate areas were reserved for research and to support wildlife? Might not some mild concessions on the use of this island have formed a good bargaining point with the state to prevent the overdevelopment of some of the others? These were questions that this group of conservationists did not discuss. In their obsession with their single interest, they did not take into account the far-reaching implications of removing such a large area from public use or that by doing so they might have an adverse effect on the bigger goal they wanted to attain.

Too many areas locked up for research—and we sorely need research—or too many made inaccessible except to the fortunate few will result in their eventual destruction. Public pressure will either open them up, perhaps in an uncontrolled fashion, or the public will fail to respond to their defense when highway departments or airport planners or other developers try to take them over. Their protection requires the involvement of as many people as possible—consistent with their best use. Most people are not much interested in what does not affect them directly. If they derive no apparent personal benefit from an area and find themselves excluded from it, they will not be concerned about what eventually happens to it.

So we must maintain a balance. We need the areas for research, but we also need to satisfy the demands of those who wish to engage in active recreation. At the same time, we should provide for those people who wish to enjoy the natural environment, perhaps not in its pristine state, but without its having been distorted by overdevelopment and overuse. What is rare among conservationists is the person who is interested in all three types of areas and who understands that each is part of the whole. Somewhere there can be a middle ground, with each group having a place for what it wants and with each piece of land being used for its highest purpose. But this middle ground will not be reached by those who press only for their own special interest without regard for the desires of others.

This limited point of view has a debilitating effect on the conservation movement. It breaks it up into bits and pieces, whereas in the handling of many problems we need a national attitude and we need to draw on national resources. The head of one private organization with an unusually large membership told me how parochialism affected his membership rolls. A local group, concerned about one aspect of the total conservation problem, would join up together. The following year, if their special problem had been solved or if his organization had been unable to do anything about it, they would all, because of the narrowness of their interest in conservation, resign together. The expense of these local mass enlistments and subsequent resignations amounted to a considerable sum of money. It also impaired the effectiveness of what he could accomplish.

At the Nature Conservancy, experience has shown the relative ease in most instances of raising money locally for a particular project and the difficulty of raising it for national operations. More than one donor has written a check for $50,000 or $100,-000 for a specific project but has been unwilling to make any contribution at all to the nationwide effort. One active member contemptuously refused a request for help on a national fund-raising campaign with the remark that raising national funds was entirely the responsibility of the staff and the money should be obtained from foundations, not from the public. His comment underlined a large part of the problem. First, it revealed a complete lack of understanding of how funds are raised; foundations do not generally give grants for continuing operations. Second, although he had been laboring long and hard in the cause, he did not appreciate the benefits he was deriving from membership in a national organization. The revolving funds from which he and his associates were obtaining loans had not been provided by the area in which he was working; on a number of occasions he had called on the national staff for technical help, without which one of the projects in which he was most interested would have been impossible; in another instance, he and his associates had had to call on outside help from other volunteers in a neighboring state; and one of his largest and most significant projects would have ended in a complete tangle without the national influence of the Nature Conservancy.

Conservation is too large a problem to be solved piecemeal. Although small local groups can, and do, play an important role, there are strict limits to what they can accomplish. They need the help and the resources of larger organizations and a larger and broader point of view. This is what this man did not understand. Somehow, in his opinion, all these other questions took care of themselves. He was preoccupied with his own tiny area, his backyard, as it were. As long as its environment was preserved, he did not care what happened to the rest of the country, although he was glad to accept help from other sections when he needed it.

An extreme example of parochialism occurred when I received a letter from a man living near the mouth of the Connecticut River, deploring the thought that federal funds might be used to preserve it. This river, one of the most beautiful in New England, has not as yet become highly developed along considerable stretches of its banks. Over the years, many plans have been advanced for saving its beauty. None of these plans ever materialized, while the price of the land continued to rise. In a final effort to preserve what was left, Senator Abraham Ribicoff of Connecticut sponsored a study by the Department of the Interior. If the plan were ever effected, it could represent the best hope for the preservation of the river, but probably it will die because of insufficient funds. But my correspondent—an oldtime economic royalist, I suspect—was indignant over the thought that federal funds might be used, although he himself lived near the river and enjoyed it. He resented federal interference in what he considered a local question. Whether he was afraid his income tax would go up or whether he thought the federal government would exercise undue control, I am not sure, but in any case, in his limited view, he saw this project as something that should be undertaken entirely by the state, a state that was already beset with fiscal problems and helpless to act.

Conservation is too broad a subject for limited points of view like that. If we are going to be successful, we need people with the emotional and intellectual capacity to look at problems as a whole and to recognize their interrelationship, and who do not concentrate all their energies and the energies of others simply on the solution of isolated questions that happen to interest them personally. We need people who regard conservation as a national problem and know that we must rally all our resources—government, private organizations, and individuals—if we are to meet successfully the challenges we face.

In addition to the extremists and the parochialists, there is a third group of people whom conservation seems to attract in undue numbers, and they are perhaps the most damaging of all. These are the self-important people who find in conservation the excitement and significance that appears to be denied them in their daily routines. Anyone who has been in conservation long will recognize them. On a small scale, they are the ones who offer to lead the nature walk, not because they are interested in stimulating knowledge about nature, but because the assignment gives them an opportunity to display what they know. When they receive a question from someone less informed than themselves, they reply, of course—but condescendingly. They make clear their superiority to the questioner.

In other aspects of conservation, they reveal themselves in different ways. At meetings, they are the ones who have learned some of the language, kept an eye on some of the legislation, and met some of the movement's more important leaders. When they speak, they are not so much trying to influence the issue under consideration but to demonstrate how much they know. After a short while, they become self-styled leaders themselves and perhaps hold positions in one or two organizations. Often they work hard, putting in long hours and running from one meeting to another; but the work they do is not so much for the cause as for themselves.

People like this, of course, exist in almost any activity. They appear in business and in charitable organizations; they can be found in politics and health and welfare projects. But having had direct experience with many of these activities, I can say that the people I am writing about are especially prominent in conservation. This is not merely an accident. Conservation provides them with special opportunities. In the first place, conservation is a righteous cause, and righteous causes unfortunately attract self-righteous people. Any criticism that is leveled at an ardent conservationist comes from sources that the conservationist disdains to start with, so it does not affect him personally. In fact, he may enjoy it, obtaining from it the satisfaction that comes from being attacked by an obvious evil. That is one of the best ways to assure himself that he is really good.

The emotionalism that I spoke of earlier also plays a part. Emotional groups provide good backgrounds for the self-important. When many people are at a high pitch anyway, it is easier for the self-important person to assume a dominant role. If the group in general is working at a somewhat lower key and have therefore kept their sense of humor and their sense of proportion, the egotist is likely to run into opposition. Someone will make fun of him or put him in his place. But when everyone is operating with a high degree of emotionalism, the self-important person can stand out as a hero.

There is another reason why conservation draws these people. There are few causes left today in which a person can become a martyr quite so quickly. With the increasing technical knowledge required in so many fields, entering them may take years of training and experience. One cannot become the head of a hospital in the slums without first earning a medical degree. One cannot become a missionary among some savage tribe without first going to divinity school. It is even difficult to work among the poor without training in social work or to play a role in rebuilding a city without knowing about finance, engineering, or many other subjects. Conservation, however, seems deceptively simple. As I hope the reader now realizes, it, too, is a complicated field, but on the surface, particularly when it is broken down into limited, local activities, it takes no experience or training to enter it. If a highway department, for example, is about to take over a highly desirable natural area, that area may be defended by the person who screams the most. Even if the defense succeeds, that does not strike at the real heart of the issue; and although the particular tract may be saved, many others like it are probably being lost at the same time. This is something that the self-important person does not see. Completely absorbed in what he is doing, he can persuade himself that the angels are on his side.

But the problem with these self-important people is that they do damage. Like the extremists, they alienate many of the more intelligent personnel we need so badly. A skilled lawyer or accountant, who may have exactly the knowledge required to solve a particular problem, will find himself repelled by the person who continually wants to hold the center of the stage. As a consequence, the lawyer or accountant drops out, and the self-important man or woman remains. Furthermore these people will not step aside to make room for new people, who might have more to offer. Their positions have become important to their egos, and so they continue to cling to their petty prerogatives year after year. I have seen this happen too often, and it has produced a rigidity and conservatism in the movement that has been extremely harmful.

Recruiting new conservationists of the type so needed today is not easy, because the requirements of conservation have changed drastically. Most people, when they think of conservationists, have several stereotypes in mind, a bird watcher perhaps, or a vocal outdoorsman who represents a curious blend of Thoreau and John Burroughs. Their vision of these stereotypes affects their interest in becoming involved. Actually, these stereotypes are not the people who are bearing the burden of responsibility. The needs of modern conservation, as the reader has seen, are many and varied, and so are the people that fill them. This is sometimes difficult to explain.

Not long ago, we were invited to a friend's for dinner. Ordinarily I would have accepted quickly, but this time I hesitated because the purpose of the dinner was to introduce me to a young man who wanted to devote his life to conservation. I like such people; but after talking to many of them of all ages, I know they generally fall into a pattern and that there is little I can do to help them. It was true in this case, too.

Our friends live at the edge of a pond once famed for the excellence of its ice. Today it serves no commercial purpose but provides a haven for ducks when the storms are blowing on Long Island Sound and the birds are seeking safety from the high waves and strong winds. Because our friends' house was once the ice house, it is on the very edge of the water and thus is an ideal place from which to observe the pond's wildlife. Always when we go there, our host has some particular bird that he would like to have us see, in this instance a wood duck which had overstayed the season (it was late winter) and whom our friend had taken to feeding each evening at dusk. When the surface of the pond appeared black, the trees turned into silhouettes, and the first stars sprinkled light across the darkening sky, there was a slight ripple in the water off in the distance; and as it came closer to us, we could see it was caused by the wood duck, beautiful as those birds always are. Then, when our host had fed it, we returned inside and sat before the fire to talk.

There was no question that the young man had enjoyed with his entire being every moment of that interlude outside. He had grown up as a boy in one of our northern states and had spent most of his vacations in the woods. One river in particular had become his special favorite. He had canoed on it and fished in it, and had become a great lover of the outdoors, seeing in that river a symbol of what America might be if only enough people cared to preserve it. (He did his part by joining in the annual clean-up that collected thirteen gunnysacks of beer cans from its shores each year!) He had now graduated from college, taken up two careers one after the other, and decided they were not to his taste. His mind kept returning to the river, and this had led him to consider conservation.

It was then my sad task to disillusion him. First, I had to tell him that outside of government, there are not many jobs available. There are only a handful of national organizations engaged exclusively in conservation, and they have few full-time employees. At the Nature Conservancy, we had about twenty-five until a generous donor made it possible to acquire four or five more. (That twenty-five also included clerical help.) The Sierra Club, when I last checked with them, had, as I recall, about sixty-five, and it has since reduced its staff. As with the Nature Conservancy, this number included their stenographers and clerks and also the staff that handles their extensive book publishing program. These figures are indicative. I have never seen a survey, but I would be surprised if the number of full-time conservationists employed by national private organizations amounts to more than a thousand, and the number is probably lower. (For those who are interested, the pay, however, is good and getting better.)

There are, of course, smaller organizations across the country that are local in character. Many of these are nature museums and centers, which serve a useful and important function by educating the public. They are staffed by capable, dedicated men and women, but the character of the professional jobs is often limited in scope. This is because the organizations usually deal with a small geographic area. They were not, I think, what this young man had in mind.

In short, if he and others like him want to avoid working for government—and many people do—the opportunities for a career in national conservation are not numerous.

But this was not the truly discouraging news I had to give him. That concerned the essence of the important work being done today in conservation. To him and many others—both those seeking a professional career and those wanting to make a volunteer contribution—it is disillusioning to find that more land is now saved and more conservation problems solved by a man behind a desk than by a man in the field. Their impression of conservation work has been gathered from reading John Muir and John Burroughs and seeing photographs of leading conservationists climbing mountains or camping in deserts. But the resulting impression is not accurate in terms of modern needs. Conservationists, even effective ones, still find occasion to visit and enjoy the areas they are attempting to preserve, but these are not the times when they are doing their most significant work. That unfortunately usually has to be done in a city or an office.

The day I talked to the young man, I had spent every hour on conservation; and here, I told him, was an abbreviated list of the problems in which I had been engaged. One concerned a decision on the manner in which the Nature Conservancy would apply for tax exemption on its lands within a particular state, a problem that was complicated by some special considerations of that state's law. The money involved amounted to thousands of dollars and could represent substantial savings for a hard-pressed conservation agency. (We are all hard pressed; there just is not enough money to do what needs to be done.) Furthermore, tax exemption would permit us to continue with several other projects which would otherwise be prohibitively expensive. I had also discussed with our staff some policy questions regarding the employment of lawyers. We deal with many of them, and this was an effort to establish certain guidelines over aspects of their activities. Part of the day, I had spent on the establishment of a scientific committee: what its duties would be and to whom it would report. Without such considerations of organization, it would not be as effective as it should be. At lunch, I had met with four other men to consider the strategy for raising $350,000 to save an important piece of land. The entire day had been occupied with similar questions; and aside from going to lunch, I had not been outdoors once. I could have, of course. Only a few miles from our house are two magnificent Nature Conservancy tracts, which I like to visit and walk over. But when I am doing that, I am not saving an acre of land.

So I tried to explain to the young man that the wood duck we had watched in the deepening dusk was the end result of conservation, but not conservation itself. Looking at the wood duck had solved no questions, preserved no land, purified no stream, cleansed no air, or added not a single tract to the system of wildlife refuges where wood ducks can feed and breed. Except for my own personal enjoyment, these had been wasted moments; and I have sadly learned that the deeper my involvement in conservation became, the less time I had to spend in the outdoors watching the life and the scenery that I love so much. Those who wish to make a basic contribution to conservation can count on hanging up their bird glasses, putting away their trout rods, and storing their hiking boots in the attic. If they can find time for vacations—and the task is so enormous that they may not—perhaps this equipment will be useful to them. But it will play little or no role in their most important conservation work.

The reasons for this become obvious once the conservationist thinks about it. Like so many other activities, conservation today has become more and more complicated. John Muir could lead the fight for the Yosemite Valley almost single-handed and with the aid of his pen. The same tactics applied today would probably not be nearly as successful. Too many diverse questions are involved in a large conservation operation for one man to be able to do everything. We once made a list of the skills we would like to have represented on the board of the Nature Conservancy, skills that we must use again and again. They included law, science, finance, administration, fund raising, and public relations. The need for some of these is apparent. Fund raising, for example, is essential to provide the money for administrative expenses and for the purchase of land. Science is necessary for the evaluation and management of the lands we hold. The need for financial skills, however, is less apparent and therefore provides an excellent example of what can be accomplished in modern conservation by using apparently unrelated skills.

While making a long-range plan for the Nature Conservancy it occurred to me that we were faced by an unresolvable dilemma. One service we offer is that of being a watchdog over lands a donor may wish to give another organization. In such instances the donor places certain restrictions on the use of the land (for example, he may wish it kept largely in its natural state), and the Nature Conservancy agrees to see to it that those restrictions are kept up. This is a useful service because it inspires confidence in donors who might not otherwise give their land for fear it would be abused in later years. But there was only one way the Nature Conservancy could insure this service. That was to build up an endowment fund that would guarantee its continued existence.

But here came the dilemma. With the difficulty of raising money and the need for buying land quickly before it became developed, what justification could be made for holding monies in endowment funds that, from an immediate conservation point of view, were sterile? A million dollars in an endowment fund would at that time have earned approximately $40,000, certainly a sizable sum but hardly enough to warrant withholding a million dollars from direct land-saving activities. The longer I pondered this problem, the more certain I became that there was no solution. Then I had an idea. Why not set up a special type of endowment fund, the principal of which would be invested in the normal manner, while the income, as it usually is, would be used for operating expenses? We could add, however, this proviso—that the securities in the fund could be pledged against bank loans for the purchase of lands. This could be done in instances in which we were sure of reimbursement of both the purchase price and the interest costs. Thus a million dollars in such a fund would not only produce $40,000 a year of income, it also would supply us with $750,000 of bank loans. (Under banking practice, the full amount of the securities cannot be borrowed.) Several of us discussed this idea at some length, and finally we presented it to our board, which voted to adopt it. Thus we established our Guaranty and Income Fund.

For many months, the monies we were able to raise for this fund lay unused except as investments. To our staff, who had had no financial training, the idea of borrowing money was uncomfortable; but at last an occasion offered itself that was so suitable everyone agreed to try it. My friend and a member of the board, Dr. George Cooley, who heads his own investment firm, agreed to try to arrange the financing. He is a persuasive negotiator and thoroughly versed in banking techniques. To my great surprise—and also, I suspect to his—he found he could obtain the loan without pledging any specific securities. The bank was willing to make the loan against the general assets of the Nature Conservancy, which greatly simplified the whole procedure. Furthermore, it opened up to us larger credits than we had expected, and in a relatively short time, we were eligible for bank loans totaling more than a million dollars.

But that is not the end of the story. The Ford Foundation, which had proved itself a good friend of the Nature Conservancy, wanted to help with the program of making advance land acquisitions for government agencies. As I mentioned earlier, this could have been done with a capital grant, but the resources of the Ford Foundation, vast as they are, are nonetheless limited. Because of the Nature Conservancy's successful use of bank credit for conservation purposes, the foundation, too, thought of using borrowings and decided they would guarantee a line of credit of $6 million. Thus in a short space of time the effective revolving funds of the Nature Conservancy were increased by more than $7 million, an amount it could not have raised outright.

This came about because Dr. Cooley, who loves the outdoors as much as anyone, was willing to trudge through the city streets, often alone and sometimes in company with me, in search of the first receptive banks, applying his considerable financial skills to a conservation problem with outstanding results. What he did could not have been accomplished by any of the conservation stereotypes.

There have been many instances in which I have found that my experience in business and banking was far more useful to conservation than any knowledge I might have acquired about natural history or ecology. Let me cite a few instances. Our vice-president and I spent a day in New York talking to two bankers. The final result was an arrangement that could save the Nature Conservancy up to $20,000 a year. Anyone who has attempted to raise money knows what this amount means. The Nature Conservancy has also introduced many banking techniques into its operations. In addition to making loan forecasts similar to the forecasts of commercial banks, which permit it to overcommit its funds, it handles its cash flow just as a corporation would. This has enabled the organization to save far more land because it has made its dollars go further. As another example, the first grant it received from the Ford Foundation resulted from a management-type study of the organization and what it might be able to do, given certain circumstances. The report was not unusual for a business; it was unusual for a conservation agency.

Activities such as these—and I have selected only a few examples—are a far cry from what most people, including the young man that evening, imagine conservation to be. Yet they are the essence. Without them, the more appealing, and more obvious, aspect of the job will not get done. Those who wander over some of the additional lands saved because of the Nature Conservancy's imaginative use of money and credit—imaginative, that is, in straight business terms—could well ponder the means that bring success in modern conservation.

Sometimes I—and those who think like me—have been accused of being cold and practical, but that is not the issue. The issue is obtaining results. I, too, would much rather spend my time in the field than behind a desk or on the telephone; and

down of some management function, not from any external cause. This, I believe, could be said of almost every other conservation agency in the country.

This was the story I had to tell the young man who was so interested in the outdoors and who saw in conservation work a means of making his career there, and it was a disappointment to him. It is also what I have had to tell many other devoted and dedicated people. If you want to make a truly significant contribution toward saving the environment, you can count on spending most of your time inside. The outdoors will be for others and for you, only in your leisure moments—if you have any.

But if you do have the skills and abilities that are so desperately needed, particularly those of management, you will find in conservation a great challenge, and the work that you do will last for many generations.

Yes, the results of the conservationists' labors will last for generations, but the work immediately ahead of them is staggering. We have hundreds of years of neglect to repair, and hundreds of years of confused thinking to correct before we return to the conservation concepts of our forefathers. We were given this beautiful country of ours, with all its magnificent beauty and variety and its natural resources. Although most Americans are aware of the richness of our land and that much of our power and strength comes from it, fewer are aware of the absolutely incredible beauty we have inherited. A man could spend several lifetimes doing nothing but absorbing the sights he can find in the United States. In the first chapter, I mentioned a few of them, but those were only samples. Men like Ansel Adams and Edward Weston have spent their entire careers trying to capture it on film. They have done well, but they have only covered a small part of the total. To waste this beauty or destroy it would be as stupid as throwing a brick through the stained-glass window of an ancient church or to slash a fine painting with a knife. Those last two actions would not be civilized. Neither is the destruction of the beauty we have been given.

But through carelessness, oversight, and often outright greed, we have not used our heritage well. Here and there, we have made a gain. We have set up the first national park system in the world, and we have passed a Wilderness Act. But the little we have done has not been commensurate with the opportunity we were blessed with. We have fallen far short of our potential.

Now we have to take stock of ourselves and decide first what our priorities will be. Do we want a super-jet transport more than we want an Everglades or a Point Reyes? Giving up the transport does not mean that we will all have to stay home. It will only mean that a relatively small handful of our population will have to travel just a little more slowly than they might otherwise. Do we want additional highways and traffic congestion more than clear air and peace of mind? Are we willing to substitute more efficient public transportation for the privilege of driving our automobiles everywhere? Do we think the protection of the natural resources of this country is worth only a little more than 1 percent of our national budget, or do we think these blessings are worthy of more attention than that? In the first chapter, I mentioned our lack of national purpose, that we do not yet know what we want our country to be. It is time, now, that we made up our minds, and the first order of business is to establish national priorities.

We have also to reexamine the role of government. We cannot afford to have departments and agencies canceling out each other's work, and we have to give more authority to those charged with protecting our surroundings. To do this, they will need more funds. We cannot expect them to carry out their programs with unrealistically small budgets. In turn, we have every right to expect them to coordinate their programs and occasionally to sacrifice their own short-term interests and resist the short-term pressures brought to bear against them for the broader, and longer-term, good of the country.

We must learn to look at our conservation problems with a wider view. We must rid ourselves of parochialism and emotionalism and the interprofessional jealousies that mar so many of our efforts. After all, none of us should be doing this for himself alone. We are doing it for one another, because it is *our* country. We must learn to coordinate our work for an overall purpose that is greater than anything we can accomplish by ourselves.

And we must enlist people, all sorts of people, who have the skills and abilities that are so sorely needed. For, after all, conservation is people. It is people who do the destruction, who create the demands on our resources, that make conservation necessary. It is also people who accomplish the good that conservation does.

If you have not done so already, come and join us.

But many ask what is the worth of conservation? Are not the ill-effects we see around us the necessary price of progress? Progress is a much-abused word, and I have never been able to determine its meaning. A slum is certainly not progress. A man coughing with a deadly cancer that might have been caused by air pollution would hardly call that progress. A child who cannot find a beach on which he can dig and splash certainly would not consider that progress. The man who loves the woods but discovers there are no longer woods would not think of his situation as progress. Progress is an empty word, used by empty minds to cover their lack of thought. There can be room for most things in this country of ours with its great vastness. To provide that room would be real progress.

In the first chapter, I tried to show some of the direct benefits that result from conservation. We know it has economic value, that it is often good business. This has been demonstrated time and again and is the subject of numerous reports. We are not always exactly sure how great the economic value is in a given situation because it is sometimes difficult to measure. But we know that people prefer—and will pay for—pleasant surroundings in which to live and work and take their vacations and raise their families. And they will pay heavily for them if they can afford to.

There are also incalculable benefits in the proper use of our land and space. We learned, during the Dust Bowl days, that we cannot drive a plow through any piece of land and remain a secure and healthy people. Less directly, but perhaps no less realistically, we are learning that we may not be able to cut down every forest, build a highway in every park, dam every river, and place our factories just anywhere, without also suffering damage, if not to our pocketbooks, at least to our spirits.

What distinguishes a human from other forms of life is not his ability to provide for himself or to perform useful functions. Many forms of life are equally adept at filling these two roles, whether they are bacteria breaking down sewage or beavers building dams and thus providing a higher water table. What truly distinguishes man is what arises within himself. He alone creates music and poetry and appreciates beauty. And if he destroys beauty, he destroys a part of himself.

A world denuded of trees and running brooks and spiders' webs woven in the grass and the early spring song of a cardinal, his feathers flashing red in the sun, is not a human world. It would be a dead and sterile place like the surface of the moon, which our more adventurous have finally reached, but where none of us wish to live. For living, we need life. Not only our own lives—but all life. That alone should be a reason for conservation.

Conservation is not, as some would lead us to believe, the complete denial of one activity against another. Instead, it is a search for balance, a means of keeping things in their orderly places. It is a concept of a civilized mind.

Acknowledgments

IF I were to list the many people who have influenced my thinking in the field of conservation, who have patiently made information available to me, or who have worked with me on conservation problems, the acknowledgments for this book would run for many, many pages. I am grateful for what these people have done and believe that I can best thank them by continuing to work for the cause to which they have contributed so much.

There are, however, several persons and organizations who have played specific and important roles in the actual preparation of this book. The first of these is Ernest Brooks, formerly President of the Old Dominion Foundation, a trustee of the Anne S. Richardson Fund, and an active conservationist for many years. Indeed, his faith and that of the Old Dominion Foundation in the promise of the Nature Conservancy during its early and faltering years did much to make its later achievements possible.

When I was readying myself to write this book, I told Mr. Brooks how much I wished I could further enlarge my understanding of today's conservation by examining at first hand a number of issues with which I had not been immediately involved. On learning of this desire, he arranged to have the Anne

349

S. Richardson Fund give me a grant to cover the expense of independent travel across the country, looking at any conservation problems I wanted to. The freedom this provided me to conduct my own studies is a gift for which I will always be grateful; and although the Anne S. Richardson Fund is not responsible for any of the opinions set forth in this book, the results of my travels gave new dimensions to my thinking about conservation in the United States. Altogether I drove more than 15,000 miles to various localities that I might not otherwise have been able to visit, and discussed aspects of conservation with hundreds of people.

I would also like to thank the Conservation Foundation for serving as custodian of the grant.

As usual, I owe a debt of gratitude to Mrs. C. R. Horton, Jr., who read portions of this book and gave me her reactions to them.

ALEXANDER B. ADAMS

Notes

The following abbreviations are used in the notes:

BOR   Bureau of Outdoor Recreation, U.S. Department of the Interior
CF   Conservation Foundation
IWL   Izaak Walton League
NO   *National Observer*
NPS   National Park Service, U.S. Department of the Interior
NYT   New York *Times*
NWF   National Wildlife Federation
USFS U.S. Forest Service, U.S. Department of Agriculture
WMI   Wildlife Management Institute

Where the source of information is either personal interview or personal observation and that fact might not be apparent from the text, I have used the abbreviations PI and PO to so indicate.

Chapter 1

[1] USFS, *Highlights in the History of Forest Conservation*, p. 2.
[2] *Ibid.*
[3] *Ibid.*
[4] Farrell, p. 74.
[5] MacDonald, p. 147.
[6] *Ibid.*, p. 157.
[7] *Ibid.*, p. 245.
[8] William Penn Tercentenary Committee, p. 78.
[9] Thoreau, p. 243.

10 Bakeless, p. 104.
11 Gates, pp. 9–10.
12 Wallace, p. 2.
13 *Ibid.,* p. 114.
14 *Ibid.,* p. 110.
15 California Department of Parks and Recreation, *Economic Impact of California State Parks,* p. 1.
16 Swanson, p. 32.
17 *Ibid.,* p. 36.
18 Krutilla, pp. 780–1.
19 Hall.

Chapter 2

1 Douglas, p. 7.
2 Joel Kuperberg, Naples, Florida, PI.
3 Douglas, pp. 200–45.
4 *Ibid.,* pp. 251–4.
5 Gates, pp. 321–35.
6 Douglas, pp. 268–9.
7 *Ibid.,* pp. 282–6.
8 *Ibid.,* p. 309.
9 *Ibid.*
10 Gates, p. 325.
11 Douglas, p. 309.
12 Dau, p. 297.
13 Douglas, pp. 312–19.
14 *Ibid.,* pp. 324–5.
15 Tebeau, pp. 167–9.
16 *Ibid.,* pp. 169–70.
17 Brookfield, pp. 63–8.
18 *Ibid.,* pp. 69–73.
19 Tebeau, p. 172.
20 Douglas, pp. 332–8.
21 Dau, pp. 310–14.
22 Douglas, pp. 345–8.
23 *Ibid.,* pp. 373–5.
24 Schneider, p. 37.
25 Douglas, p. 376.
26 *Ibid.,* pp. 378–9.
27 Central and Southern Florida Flood Control District, *Conservation in Action.*
28 Tebeau, pp. 173–9.
29 Douglas, p. 380.
30 Tebeau, pp. 179–80.
31 Unless otherwise indicated, the material in this section comes from PI and PO.
32 Raftrey, speech, March 14, 1969.
33 Tebeau, p. 182.
34 Central and Southern Florida Flood Control District, undated press release.
35 Raftrey, *op. cit.*
36 This and the following Nix's report, October 15, 1968.
37 Raftrey, *op. cit.*
38 NYT, April 27, 1969.

[39] NYT, October 19, 1969.
[40] *Ibid.*
[41] Schneider, p. 38.
[42] Raftrey, *op. cit.*
[43] NPS release, May 18, 1969.

Chapter 3

[1] Smith, pp. 5–8.
[2] *Ibid.*, pp. 70–2.
[3] *Ibid.*, pp. 126–34.
[4] *Ibid.*, pp. 172–7.
[5] *U.S. Government Manual*, p. 160.
[6] Smith, p. 277.
[7] Athearn, pp. 187–8.
[8] Hawgood, p. 159.
[9] Athearn, p. 259.
[10] Gates, p. 636.
[11] Athearn, p. 260.
[12] *Ibid.*, pp. 260–1.
[13] Gates, pp. 639–40.
[14] *Ibid.*, p. 652.
[15] *Ibid.*, pp. 653–6.
[16] *Ibid.*, p. 661.
[17] *Ibid.*, pp. 661–4.
[18] *Ibid.*, pp. 664–5.
[19] *Ibid.*, pp. 672–3.
[20] *Ibid.*, pp. 674–6.
[21] *Ibid.*, p. 686.
[22] *See* appropriate sections of the *U.S. Government Manual*.
[23] *Congressional Record*, Friday, March 7, 1969.
[24] U.S. Senate Subcommittee on Executive Reorganization, October 17, 19, and 20, 1967, p. 14.
[25] *Ibid.*, pp. 58–60.
[26] Faubus, December 10, 1965.
[27] NYT, December 17, 1967.
[28] Dragoo, pp. 87–93.
[29] Evans, pp. 7–11.
[30] U.S. Bureau of Reclamation, *Colorado-Big Thompson*, p. 4.
[31] U.S. Bureau of Reclamation, Hoover Dam, pp. 6–8.
[32] *Ibid.*, pp. 12–13.
[33] *Ibid.*, pp. 13–14.
[34] *Ibid.*, p. 15.
[35] Carter, p. 1600.
[36] Moss, pp. 89–94.
[37] Department of the Interior release, February 1, 1967.
[38] U.S. Bureau of Reclamation, *1967 Crop Summary Sheet for the Columbia River Basin.*
[39] NYT, May 4, 1969.

Chapter 4

[1] Eisenhower, *At Ease*, pp. 156–7.
[2] Eisenhower, *Mandate for Change*, p. 501.

3 *Ibid.,* pp. 547–9.
4 U.S. Bureau of Public Roads, *Federal-Aid Financing.*
5 U.S. Department of Commerce, *A Proposed Program,* p. 93.
6 NYT, August 25, 1968.
7 Westport, Connecticut, *News,* July 2, 1969.
8 John A. Paulus, City Manager, Rye, N.Y. letter, March 23, 1966.
9 *Ibid.*
10 Waterbury, p. 4.
11 *Ibid.,* p. 8.
12 *Ibid.,* p. 9.
13 *Ibid.,* p. 3.
14 U.S. Bureau of Roads, *Geometric Design Standards,* p. 4.
15 Robert McKernan, Director of Public Relations, New Haven Railroad. Information supplied, March 29, 1966.
16 Information supplied by the Connecticut State Highway Department, May 16, 1966.
17 McKernan, *op. cit.*
18 Personally conducted marketing studies on the desirability of branch locations for businesses.
19 Westport, Connecticut, Public Site and Building Committee, Appendix III.
20 *Ibid.,* pp. 2–3.
21 *Ibid.,* p. 12.
22 McCarthy, p. 34.
23 Westbury, p. 7.
24 McCarthy, p. 36.
25 Dr. William J. Ronan, Chairman of the Metropolitan Transportation Authority, quoted NYT, August 21, 1967.
26 Bueche, p. 4.
27 S. Smith Griswold, Federal Pollution Abatement Chief, quoted NYT, September 29, 1966.
28 Robert S. Morse, Chairman, Panel on Electrically Powered Vehicles, quoted NYT, October 19, 1967.
29 Hoover, p. 1.
30 NYT, August 25, 1968.
31 Jasperson, unpaginated.
32 Bulletin issued by Save the Scenic Valley, Columbus, Ohio.
33 Discussions with local citizens and reference to the records of the Columbus Board of Elections.
34 Lyn Shepard in the *Christian Science Monitor,* June 18, 1968.
35 President's Council on Recreation and Natural Beauty, *From Sea to Shining Sea,* p. 201.
36 NYT, August 8, 1969.
37 NYT, May 20, 1968.
38 NYT, July 17, 1969.
39 NYT, July 12, 1969.
40 *Wall Street Journal,* October 31, 1969.

Chapter 5

1 NYT, August 11, 1969.
2 NYT, August 24, 1969.
3 NYT, November 30, 1968.

[4] Nixon, Message to Congress, June 16, 1969.
[5] Mohawk Airlines, *Air Traffic Jams.*
[6] Sherrill, p. 77.
[7] NYT, August 6, 1967.
[8] NYT, January 12, 1967.
[9] NYT, April 6, 1969.
[10] NYT, May 18, 1969.
[11] NYT, March 19, 1967.
[12] NYT, November 10, 1968.
[13] NYT, April 30, 1969.
[14] NO, May 27, 1968.
[15] Sherrill, p. 81.
[16] Sayre, June 19, 1958.
[17] Love, p. 24.
[18] U.S. Department of the Interior, *The Third Wave,* pp. 31–3.
[19] Hill, p. 33.
[20] NYT, June 29, 1969.
[21] U.S. Department of Health, Education, and Welfare, *A Strategy for a Livable Environment,* p. 13.
[22] U.S. Senate Committee on Public Works, *Steps Toward Clean Water,* p. 1.
[23] Quigley, September 19, 1966, p. 7.
[24] IWL newsletter, November 17, 1966.
[25] NYT, July 3, 1969.
[26] Quigley, September 19, 1966, p. 13.
[27] NYT, May 19, 1969.
[28] NYT, October 8, 1969.
[29] NYT, October 24, 1969.
[30] NYT, September 4, 1969.
[31] U.S. Senate Committee on Public Works, *op. cit.,* p. 3.
[32] CF newsletter, March 17, 1969, p. 4.
[33] CF newsletter, February 24, 1967, p. 3.
[34] CF newsletter, March 17, 1969, p. 4.
[35] NWF, *Conservation Reports,* October 3, 1969, p. 396, and October 10, 1969, pp. 407–8.
[36] Lowell Weicker, Jr., *News,* October 19, 1969.
[37] Fairfield County, Connecticut, *Courier,* October 16, 1969.
[38] U.S. Senate Committee on Public Works, *op. cit.,* p. 3.
[39] NYT, June 24, 1969.
[40] NYT, August 20, 1967.
[41] NYT, December 27, 1967.
[42] NO, April 29, 1968.
[43] NYT, January 12, 1967.
[44] NO, September 8, 1969.
[45] U.S. Senate Committee on Public Works, *Air Quality Act of 1967,* p. 9.
[46] *Ibid.,* pp. 13–15.
[47] CF newsletter, July 21, 1967.
[48] U.S. Senate Committee on Public Works, *op. cit.,* pp. 6–7.
[49] NYT, September 27, 1969.
[50] NYT, February 5, 1969.
[51] NYT, October 19, 1969.
[52] Higdon, p. 6.
[53] Nelson, p. 4.

[54] *Ibid.,* p. 4, and Wurster, pp. 810–11.
[55] *Consumer Reports,* July, 1969, p. 411.
[56] *Consumer Reports,* August, 1969, pp. 478–80.
[57] Committee on Persistent Pesticides, National Research Council, pp. 24–5.
[58] *Ibid.,* p. 25.
[59] NYT, August 16, 1969.
[60] WMI bulletin, May 9, 1969.
[61] NYT, October 29, 1969.
[62] WMI bulletin, May 9, 1969.
[63] NYT, April 30, 1969.
[64] *Consumer Reports,* July, 1969, p. 411.
[65] Hersh, *Secret Arsenal,* p. 27.
[66] NYT, May 22, 1969.
[67] Hersh, *op. cit.,* p. 27.
[68] NYT, May 22, 1969.
[69] NYT, June 29, 1969.
[70] NYT, October 31, 1969.
[71] Hersh, *Dare We Develop . . . ,* p. 78.
[72] *Ibid.,* p. 86.
[73] *Ibid.,* p. 26.
[74] NYT, March 5, 1969.
[75] NYT, September 24, 1969.
[76] NYT, October 18, 1969.
[77] NYT, April 6, 1969.
[78] NO, September 22, 1969.
[79] NYT, April 15, 1969.
[80] NYT, August 24, 1969.
[81] American Civil Liberties Union Bulletin, October, 1969.
[82] NYT, August 26, 1969.
[83] NYT, October 30, 1969.
[84] Norwalk, Connecticut, *Hour,* November 5, 1969.
[85] Kneese, pp. 174–5.

Chapter 6

[1] Howard, p. 780.
[2] U.S. Department of the Interior, *Population Challenge,* p. 10.
[3] Howard, p. 780.
[4] Lilienthal, p. 91.
[5] NYT, November 15, 1968.
[6] U.S. Senate Committee on Interior and Insular Affairs, hearings, July 17, 1968, p. 58.
[7] U.S. Department of the Interior, *op. cit.,* pp. 16–7.
[8] NPS release, August 22, 1962.
[9] U.S. Senate Committee on Interior and Insular Affairs, *op. cit.,* p. 56.
[10] *Ibid.,* pp. 57–8.
[11] *The Hidden Dimension* by Leonard Hall deals with this question.
[12] NYT, November 4, 1969.
[13] NYT, November 9, 1969.
[14] American Forest Products Industries, Inc., *Government Land Acquisition,* p. 37.
[15] NYT, October 24, 1969 (Nancy Moran).

[16] Most of the following is based on personal observation and personal interviews over a period of years with persons connected with the city's redevelopment.

Chapter 7

[1] U.S. Department of the Interior, *The North Cascades*, pp. 26–32.
[2] NYT, August 12, 1967.
[3] Freeman, April 7, 1967, pp. 6–9.
[4] U.S. Department of the Interior, *op. cit.*, p. 128.
[5] *Ibid.*, p. 144.
[6] *Sierra Club Bulletin*, November, 1968, p. 6.
[7] U.S. Department of the Interior, *op. cit.*, p. 35.
[8] *Ibid.*, p. 35.
[9] U.S. Department of the Interior, *Land Use Survey—Proposed Point Reyes National Seashore*, p. 2.
[10] Collins.
[11] U.S. Department of the Interior, *op. cit.*, p. 4.
[12] *Ibid.*, p. 15.
[13] *Ibid.*, p. 20.
[14] *Ibid.*, p. 20.
[15] NPS, *Point Reyes National Seashore.*
[16] PI.
[17] PI.
[18] PI.
[19] NPS, *The Giant Sequoias of California*, p. 5.
[20] NPS, *The Redwoods*, p. 22.
[21] *Ibid.*, p. 30.
[22] *Ibid.*, p. 27.
[23] *Ibid.*, p. 28.
[24] *Ibid.*, p. 30.
[25] *Ibid.*, pp. 29, 36.
[26] *Ibid.*, pp. 36–8.
[27] *Ibid.*, p. 19.
[28] *Ibid.*, p. 28.
[29] PI.
[30] U.S. Senate Committee on Interior and Insular Affairs, hearings, April 1, 1968 and May 18, 1968, Part II, p. 393.
[31] NWF report, September 13, 1968, p. 281.
[32] *Ibid.*, p. 281.
[33] BOR, release, July 3, 1969.
[34] WMI newsletter, February 28, 1969.
[35] NYT, August 28, 1969.
[36] NYT, August 25, 1969.
[37] *Ibid.*

Chapter 8

[1] Virginia Division of Parks, *Seashore State Park.*
[2] California Department of Parks and Recreation, *Point Lobos Reserve.*
[3] PI.
[4] Morris, p. 15.
[5] NPS, *Our Vanishing Shoreline*, p. 27.
[6] *Ibid.*, pp. 11–12.

7 Johnson, *Remarks,* pp. 2, 4.

8 Freeman, April 7, 1967, pp. 9–11.

9 Oregon Legislature, Highway Interim Committee, p. 1.

10 Oregon State Park Department, *Samuel H. Boardman.*

11 Armstrong, p. 1.

12 *Ibid.,* p. 2.

13 *Ibid.,* pp. 4–5.

14 *Ibid.,* p. 5.

15 *Ibid.,* p. 8.

16 Boardman, October 17, 1951, pp. 2–4.

17 *Ibid.,* p. 4.

18 PI.

19 USFS, Northern Region, *Mandate for Management.*

20 USFS, *National Forest Wilderness and Primitive Areas.*

21 USFS, *Development Program for the National Forests,* p. 6.

22 *Ibid.,* p. 13.

23 *Ibid.,* pp. 6–7.

24 USFS, *The Second Billionth Dollar.*

25 NPS, *Administrative Policies for Natural Areas of the National Park System,* pp. 12–13.

26 *Ibid.,* p. 68.

27 USFS, Intermountain Region, *Multiple Use, Mandate for Management.*

28 USFS, Northern Region, *Mandate for Management.*

29 Connaughton, February 23, 1968, p. 3.

30 PI.

31 PI.

32 Outdoor Recreation Resources Review Commission, pp. 5, 13.

33 Crafts, February 8, 1967, p. 7.

34 NYT, January 30, 1966.

35 Crafts, *op. cit.*

36 CF newsletter, October, 1969.

Chapter 9

1 PO and PI.

2 State of Idaho and USFS, pp. 1–2.

3 BOR, *Recreation Land Price Escalation,* p. 8.

4 *Ibid.,* p. 9.

5 PO.

6 PI.

7 BOR, *op. cit.,* p. 10.

8 *Ibid.,* p. 25.

9 U.S. House Subcommittee on Appropriations, Department of the Interior and Related Agencies, 1968, Part 2, p. 337.

Chapter 10

1 Unsigned editorial, *The New Republic,* May 17, 1969, p. 6.

2 U.S. Arms Control and Disarmament Agency, p. 9.

3 NYT, December 19, 1969.

4 Melvin Laird, May 16, 1969.

5 U.S. Arms Control and Disarmament Agency, *op. cit.,* p. 14.

6 Figures from the CF newsletter, March 17, 1969.

7 *Ibid.*
8 BOR, Northeast Outdoor Memo, September 30, 1969.
9 NPS release, December 10, 1969.
10 Barker, pp. 457–8.
11 Nixon, statement, May 29, 1969, and Executive Order 11472.

Chapter 11

1 Federal Water Pollution Control Administration, *Clean Water for the Nation's Estuaries,* p. 62.
Other sources for information in this chapter are implicit in the text.

Chapter 12

The sources of information for this chapter are implicit in the text.

Bibliography

The following bibliography is limited solely to those publications to which I have made specific reference in the notes. It is not intended to be a comprehensive listing on the subject of conservation, and therefore I have omitted many excellent works and many that have had a profound effect on my own thinking.

American Forest Products Industries, Inc., *Government Land Acquisition*. Washington, D.C., American Forest Products Industries, Inc., 1965.

Armstrong, Chester H., *Oregon State Parks—History 1917–1963*. July 1, 1965. Available through the Oregon State Park Department.

Athearn, Robert G., *High Country Empire: The High Plains and Rockies*. Lincoln, Nebraska, University of Nebraska Press, 1960.

Bakeless, John, *Daniel Boone: Master of the Wilderness*. New York, William Morrow & Company, 1939.

Barker, Ann, "Policies for the Environment: Too Many Cooks?" *BioScience*, Vol. 19, No. 5 (May, 1969), p. 457.

Blake, Daniel R. *See* Wallace, Robert F.

Boardman, Samuel H., *Short Sand Beach State Park*. Typed memorandum, October 31, 1962.

Brookfield, Charles M., and Griswold, Oliver, *They All Called It Tropical: True Tales of the Romantic Everglades National Park, Cape Sable, and the Florida Keys*. Coconut Grove, Fla., The Data Press, 1964.

Bueche, Arthur M., *Technology and the Pollution Problem*. Schenectady, N.Y., General Electric Company, 1966.

361

California Department of Parks and Recreation, *The Economic Impact of California State Parks: 1966–67*. Sacramento, Calif., California Department of Parks and Recreation. Mimeographed report.

——, *Point Lobos State Reserve*. Sacramento, Calif., California Office of State Printing.

Carter, Luther J., "Grand Canyon: Colorado Dams Debated." *Science*, Vol. 152, No. 3729 (June 17, 1966), p. 1600.

Central and Southern Florida Flood Control District, *Conservation in Action*. West Palm Beach, Fla., Central and Southern Florida Flood Control District.

Collins, George, *Preliminary Report on Point Reyes National Seashore*. Interdepartmental report of the National Park Service, June 30, 1957.

Committee on Persistent Pesticides, National Research Council, *Report of Committee on Persistent Pesticides to Administrator, Agricultural Research Service, U.S. Department of Agriculture*. May 27, 1969. Reproduction of typewritten copy.

Connaughton, Charles A., *Forest Land Use Policies*. Mimeographed copy of speech at the Oregon Logging Congress, Eugene, Oregon, February 23, 1968.

Crafts, Edward C., *Statement before the House Committee on Interior and Insular Affairs*. February 8, 1967. Mimeographed copy.

Dau, Frederick W., *Florida, Old and New*. New York, G. P. Putnam's Sons, 1934.

Douglas, Marjory Stoneman, *The Everglades: River of Grass*. Coconut Grove, Fla., Hurricane House Publishers, Inc., 1947.

Dragoo, Don W., "Prehistoric Kinzua." *Carnegie Magazine*, Vol. XL, No. 3 (March, 1966), p. 87.

Eisenhower, Dwight D., *At Ease; Stories I Tell to Friends*. Garden City, New York, Doubleday & Company, Inc., 1967.

——, *Mandate for Change: 1953–1956*. Garden City, New York, Doubleday & Company, Inc., 1963.

Evans, Brock, "Hells Canyon on the Snake." *Sierra Club Bulletin*, Vol. 53, No. 9 (September, 1968), p. 7.

Farrell, John T., ed., *The Superior Court Diary of William Samuel Johnson: 1772–1773*. Washington, D.C., The American Historical Association, 1942.

Faubus, Orval E., Letter to Lt. Gen. William F. Cassidy, USA, Chief of Engineers. Little Rock, Arkansas, December 10, 1965.

Freeman, Orville L., *Address to the Sierra Club*, April 7, 1967. Mimeographed release issued by the U.S. Department of Agriculture.

Gates, Paul W., *History of Public Land Law Development*, with a chapter by Robert W. Swenson. Washington, D.C., U.S. Government Printing Office, November, 1968.

Griswold, Oliver. *See* Brookfield, Charles M.

Hall, Edward T., *The Hidden Dimension*. Garden City, New York, Doubleday & Company, Inc., 1966.

Hawgood, John A., *America's Western Frontiers: The Exploration and Settlement of the Trans-Mississippi West*. New York, Alfred A. Knopf, 1967.

Hersh, Seymour M., *Chemical and Biological Weapons—The Secret Arsenal*. New York Times Magazine, August 25, 1968, p. 26.

———, "Dare We Develop Biological Weapons?" *New York Times Magazine*, September 28, 1969, p. 28.

Higdon, Hal, "Obituary for DDT (in Michigan)." *New York Times Magazine*, July 6, 1969, p. 6.

Hill, Gladwin, "The Great and Dirty Lakes." *Saturday Review*, Vol. XLVIII, No. 43 (October 23, 1965), p. 33.

Hoover, J. Edgar, "Message from the Director." *FBI Law Enforcement Bulletin*, December 1, 1968, p. 1.

Howard, Walter E., "The Population Crisis Is Here Now." *BioScience*, Vol. 19, No. 9 (September, 1969), p. 779.

Idaho, State of, and the U.S. Forest Service, *Agreement*. June 21, 1965. Xeroxed copy.

Jasperson, Robert W., *Freeways, Parks and . . . The Powers of the Highway Commission*. San Francisco, Calif., Sierra Club Reprint Series, 1946.

Johnson, Lyndon B., *The Century of Change*. Remarks of the President at the signing Ceremony for Assateague Island Seashore National Park Bill, Washington, D.C., September 21, 1965.

Kneese, Allen V., *Economics and the Quality of the Environment—Some Empirical Experiences*. Washington, D.C., Resources for the Future, Inc., April, 1968.

Krutilla, John V., *Conservation Reconsidered*. Washington, D.C., Resources for the Future, Inc., 1967.

Laird, Melvin R., Address to the Military Order of the World Wars, Chicago, Ill., May 16, 1969.

Lilienthal, David E., "300,000,000 Americans Would Be Wrong." *New York Times Magazine*, January 9, 1966, p. 25.

Love, S. K., "Quality of Water in the Upper Ohio River Basin," in *Man and the Waters of the Upper Ohio Basin*. Pymatuning, Pa., Pymatuning Laboratory of Field Biology, 1956.

MacDonald, William, ed., *Select Charters and Other Documents Illustrative of American History: 1606–1775*. New York, The Macmillan Company, 1899.

McCarthy, Joe, "Problem: The Long Island Expressway—Solution: Close

Down Long Island." *New York Times Sunday Magazine,* March 19, 1967, p. 34.

Mohawk Airlines, *Air Traffic Jams.* Undated folder published by Mohawk Airlines.

Morris, Jonas V., "Assateague Island." *National Parks Magazine,* Vol. 43, No. 257 (February, 1969), p. 15.

Moss, Laurence I., "The Grand Canyon Subsidy Machine." *Sierra Club Bulletin,* Vol. 52, No. 9 (October, 1967), p. 89.

Nelson, Gaylord, Senate Speech, July 12, 1966. Mimeographed copy.

Nix, Frank, *Everglades National Park Water Supply.* Homestead, Fla., Everglades National Park, October 15, 1968.

Nixon, Richard M., Statement by the President, May 29, 1969, and Executive Order 11472.

————, *Preparing for the Future of Air Transportation.* Mimeographed copy of message to Congress, June 16, 1969.

Outdoor Recreation Resources Review Commission, *Outdoor Recreation for America.* Washington, D.C., U.S. Government Printing Office, January, 1962.

Oregon Legislature—Highway Interim Committee, *Beach Access Program.* Mimeographed report, June 3, 1968.

Oregon State Park Department, *Samuel H. Boardman.* Typed memorandum.

President's Council on Recreation and Natural Beauty, *From Sea to Shining Sea: A Report on the American Environment—Our Natural Heritage.* Washington, D.C., U.S. Government Printing Office, 1968.

Quigley, James A., *State Interests in the Spreading War on Water Pollution.* Speech presented before the Southern Governors Conference, September 19, 1966. Mimeographed by the Federal Water Pollution Control Administration.

Raftrey, John C., *Everglades National Park: The Future.* Speech at the 33rd Annual Meeting of the Florida Academy of Sciences, Gainsville, Fla., March 14, 1969.

Sayre, A. N., Mimeographed and untitled report on the conservation of water resources. Washington, D.C., Geological Survey, 1958.

Schneider, William J., "Water and the Everglades." *Natural History* (November, 1966), p. 32.

Sherrill, Robert, "The Jet Noise." *New York Times Magazine,* January 14, 1968, p. 24.

Smith, Frank E., *The Politics of Conservation.* New York, Pantheon Books, 1966.

Swanson, Ernst W., *Travel and the National Parks.* Washington, D.C., U.S. National Park Service, 1969.

Swenson, Robert W. *See* Gates, Paul W.

Tebeau, Charlton W., *Man in the Everglades: 2000 Years of Human History in the Everglades National Park*. Coral Gables, Fla., University of Miami Press, 1968.

Thoreau, Henry David, *Cape Cod*. New York, Thomas Y. Crowell Company, 1961.

U.S. Arms Control and Disarmament Agency, *World Military Expenditures, 1966–67*. Washington, D.C., U.S. Government Printing Office, 1968.

U.S. Bureau of Outdoor Recreation, *Recreation Land Price Escalation*. Washington, D.C., U.S. Department of the Interior, January 4, 1967.

U.S. Bureau of Public Roads, *Federal-Aid Financing and the Highway Trust Fund: 1965*. Washington, D.C., mimeographed report, 1965.

————, *Geometric Design Standards for the National System of Interstate and Defense Highways*. Washington, D.C., mimeographed report, 1964.

U.S. Bureau of Reclamation, *1967 Crop Report Summary Sheet* (for the Columbia Basin Project). Mimeographed sheet.

————, *The Story of the Colorado—Big Thompson Project*. Washington, D.C., U.S. Government Printing Office, 1962.

————, *The Story of the Hoover Dam*. Washington, D.C., U.S. Government Printing ffice, 1966.

U.S. Department of Commerce, *A Proposed Program for Scenic Roads & Parkways*. Washington, D.C., U.S. Government Printing Office, 1966.

U.S. Department of Health, Education, and Welfare, *A Strategy for a Livable Environment*. Washington, D.C., U.S. Government Printing Office, 1967.

U.S. Department of the Interior, *Land Use Survey—Proposed Point Reyes National Seashore*, Washington, D.C., National Park Service, 1961.

————, *The Population Challenge . . . what it means to America*. Washington, D.C., U.S. Government Printing Office, 1966.

————, *The Third Wave*. Washington, D.C., U.S. Government Printing Office, 1966.

U.S. Department of the Interior and U.S. Department of Agriculture, *The North Cascades*. Washington, D.C., U.S. Government Printing Office, 1965.

U.S. Federal Water Pollution Control Administration, Southeast Region, *Clean Water for the Nation's Estuaries, Proceedings of the Georgia Public Meeting, Jekyll Island, Georgia, Feb. 29, 1968*. Published by the author.

U.S. Forest Service, *Development Program for the National Forests*. Washington, D.C., U.S. Government Printing Office, 1961.

————, *Highlights in the History of Forest Conservation*. Washington, D.C., U.S. Government Printing Office, August, 1968.

U.S. Forest Service, *National Forest Service Wilderness and Primitive Areas*. Washington, D.C., U.S. Government Printing Office, 1965.

———, *The 2nd Billionth Dollar in National Forest Receipts*. Washington, D.C., U.S. Forest Service, April, 1966.

———, Intermountain Region, *Mandate for Management*. U.S. Forest Service.

———, Northern Region, *Mandate for Management*. Missoula, Montana, U.S. Forest Service, 1967.

U.S. House Committee on Interior and Insular Affairs, *Hearings on a Redwood National Park, April 16 and 18, 1968*. Washington, D.C., U.S. Government Printing Office, 1968.

U.S. House Subcommittee on Appropriations—Interior and Related Agencies, *Hearings. 1969*. Washington, D.C., U.S. Government Printing Office, 1968.

U.S. National Park Service, *Administrative Policies for Natural Areas of the National Park System*. Washington, D.C., U.S. Government Printing Office, April, 1968.

———, *A Brief History and Description of the National Park System*. Washington, D.C., National Park Service, 1966.

———, *The Giant Sequoias of California*. Washington, D.C., U.S. Government Printing Office, 1955.

———, *Our Vanishing Shoreline*. Washington, D.C., U.S. National Park Service.

———, *Point Reyes National Seashore, California*. Washington, D.C., U.S. Government Printing Office, 1967.

———, *The Redwoods*. Washington, D.C., U.S. National Park Service, 1964.

U.S. Office of the Federal Register, *United States Government Organization Manual, 1966–67*. Washington, D.C., U.S. Government Printing Office, 1966.

U.S. Senate Committee on Interior and Insular Affairs and House Committee on Science and Astronautics, *Joint-House-Senate Colloquium to Discuss a National Policy for the Environment*. Washington, D.C., U.S. Government Printing Office, July 17, 1968.

U.S. Senate Committee on Public Works, *Air Quality Act of 1967—Report*. Washington, D.C., U.S. Government Printing Office, 1967.

———, *Steps Toward Clean Water*. Washington, D.C., U.S. Government Printing Office, 1966.

U.S. Senate Subcommittee on Executive Reorganization, *Redesignate the Department of the Interior as the Department of Natural Resources, October 17, 19, and 20, 1967*. Washington, D.C., U.S. Government Printing Office, 1968.

Virginia Division of Parks, *Seashore State Park*. Informational folder.

Wallace, Robert F., and Blake, Daniel R., *Montana Travel Study*. Missoula, Montana, Bureau of Business and Economic Research, School of Business Administration, University of Montana, July 11, 1966.

Waterbury, Lawrence S., *Report to the Committees of Rye and Oyster Bay, N. Y. on the Proposed Bridge Across Long Island Sound*. New York, mimeographed report, 1965.

Westport, Connecticut Public Site and Building Committee, *Parking Study of Bedford Junior High School Area and Coleytown Junior High School*. Westport, Conn., duplicator report, 1966.

William Penn Tercentenary Committee, *Remember William Penn*. Harrisburg, Pa., William Penn Tercentenary Committee, 1944.

Wurster, Charles F., "DDT Goes to Trial in Madison." *BioScience*. Vol. 19, No. 9 (September, 1969), p. 809.

Index

Acadia National Park, 225
Adams, Ansel, 29, 344
Adams, Samuel, 326
Agency of Public Works, U.S., 92–93
Agriculture Department, U.S., 72, 76, 79, 141, 239
Air Force Department, U.S., 68
Air pollution, 33, 109–10, 136–40, 151–52, 180, 246
Airports, problem of, 120–24, 127
Air Quality Act (1967), 138
Air-quality standards, 138
Albuquerque, N.M., 107
Allegheny Conference on Community Development, 178–79, 181, 182
Allegheny County, Pa., 255, 271, 273
Alligators, extermination of, 41–42, 54–56
American Association for the Advancement of Science, 136
American Health Association, 130
American Institute of Biological Sciences, 290
Anthrax, 146, 151
Antipollution programs, 149–54

Appalachian Mountains, 19
Arkansas River, 70
Army, U.S., 144–47, 151. *See also* Corps of Engineers, U.S. Army
Army Department, U.S., 66, 68
Arroyo Seco Parkway, Los Angeles County, 112
Aspetuck Land Trust, 299
Assateague Island, Md., 222–23, 224, 227
Assateague Island National Seashore, 223, 226
Atlantic and Gulf Coast Canal and Okeechobee Land Company, 46
Atlantic Ocean, 17–18, 224
Atomic Energy Commission, 148, 152
Audubon, John James, 18
Audubon Plumage Act, 49
Automotive pollutants, 109–10

Baker, John A., 163, 166
Bald Cypress Swamp, Va., 219
Battlement Mesa, Colo., 148
Beard, Daniel B., 54
Big Basin Redwood State Park, 204
Big Cypress Swamp, Fla., 120

Biological warfare material, 144–47, 151

BioScience magazine, 290

Biosphere, residues in, control of, 143

Bird watchers, 327

Birth control, 157

Birth rate, 156–57

Blatnik, John A., 133

Bloxham, William, 46

Boardman, Samuel H., 230–31, 232, 233–36, 272

Boeing Aircraft Corporation, 192

Bogue, Dr., 159

Bolles, Richard, 47, 48

Bonneville Power Administration, 76

Boone, Daniel, 23–24

Boonesboro, Ky., 23

Boston, Mass., 104

Boulder, Colo., 168, 244, 245

Braddock, Edward, 174

Bradley, Guy, 48–49

Bridge Canyon, Utah, 85

Brooks, Paul, 140

Broward, Napoleon Bonaparte, 47, 48, 49, 50, 51, 52, 58

Budget, national, 289–90, 296, 345

Budget Bureau, U.S., 270, 289

Bueche, Arthur M., 109

Buffalo, extermination of, 23–24

Buffalo River State Park, 82

Burger, Warren Earl, 149

Burroughs, John, 335, 337

Business and Economic Research Bureau, 30–31

Busways, 118

Cain, Stanley A., 271–72

Calhoun, John C., 65

California Development Company, 88

Caloosahatchee River, 52

Cameron Pass, Colo., 95

Canada, 26, 32

Canal 111, Florida Everglades, 57, 63, 290

Canyon del Muerto, Ariz., 125

Cape Cod, Mass., 21, 23

Cape Cod National Seashore, 21, 295

Cape Flacon, Oreg., 234

Cape Hatteras, N.C., 17

Cape Hatteras National Seashore, 225

Cape Kennedy, Fla., 54, 57

Cape Perpetua, Oreg., 236

Cape Sable, Fla., 38

Cardenas, Garcia López de, 324

Carolina Constitution (1669), 22

Carson, Rachel, 141, 144

Cascade Canyon, Utah, 86

Cascade Mountains, 19, 185–92

Cassidy, William, 80, 81

Catskill Mountains, 260–61

CBS Laboratories, 125

Central and Southern Florida Flood Control Project, 53

Chambers Lake, 94

Chelan, Lake, 185, 186

Chemical warfare materials, 144–47, 151

Chesapeake Bay, 217, 218

Cities, problems of, 170–84

Citizen's Advisory Committee, 291

Civil Aeronautics Board, 124

Civil War, 46, 66

Clausen, Dan H., 213

Clausland Mountain, 322

Clean Air Act (1963), 138

Clean Water Restoration Act (1966), 129

Cleveland, Ohio, 128, 131

Cliff, Edward, 264

Coast and Geodetic Survey, 35

Coast Guard, U.S., 199

Cockenoe Island, Conn., 299

Collier, Barron, 56

Collier County, Fla., 59–60, 63

Collins, E. S., 233

Collins, George, 195–96, 199

Colorado River, 18, 84, 87–91, 93, 296

Columbia River, 18

Columbus, Ohio, 112–13
Commerce Department, U.S., 99
Commercial airlines, 123
Commercial resources, 20
Communal rights, 28
Congress, U.S., 54, 56, 57, 59, 62, 66, 67, 68, 70, 71, 74, 75, 79, 116, 117, 122, 127, 128, 129, 133, 135, 136, 137–39, 141, 196, 198, 199, 200–1, 210, 211, 212, 214, 225, 228, 241, 246, 248, 249, 250, 251, 253, 270, 271, 274–77, 281, 283, 284, 287–88, 289–90, 292
Connaughton, Charles A., 243–44
Connecticut River, 332
Connecticut Turnpike, 103
Conservation, 29–34, 160, 301–2, 331–32, 334, 346, 347; government role in, 280–97; private agencies role in, 298–323; technologies, 311–23
Conservation districts, Florida Everglades, 57–58
Conservation 70's, Inc., 61
Conservationists, nature and work of, 324–47
Cooley, George, 340, 341
Cooperative effort, need for, 254–79
Corps of Engineers, U.S. Army, 53, 57, 58, 59, 63, 64, 65–69, 71–72, 77, 78, 79, 80–82, 83, 92, 117, 249, 250, 254, 284, 286, 288, 290
Crafts, Edward C., 251
Crater Lake, 18
Crime in the cities, 171–72
Cuyahoga River, 128, 131

Dade County, Fla., 47, 59, 60, 61, 63, 121
Dade County Airport, 59–60, 63, 120–21, 124
Dams, 75–84, 89, 92, 192
DDT, 140–41, 143, 144, 156

Death Valley, Calif., 19
Defense Department, U.S., 78, 147, 227, 284, 288
Del Norte County, Calif., 205
Del Norte Redwoods State Park, 205, 212
Desert Land Act (1877), 70
Deserts, 19, 69
Detroit, Mich., 128
Devil's Den Sanctuary of the Nature Conservancy, 113, 167
Disston, Hamilton, 46
Donora, Pa., 33, 136
Douglas, William O., 83–84
Drake, Sir Francis, 192
Drakes Bay, Calif., 193
Drug abuse, 172
Drury, Aubrey, 204–5
Drury, Nelson B., 204–5, 328
Drury Grove, Newton B., 206
Dugway Proving Grounds, 144–45
Düsseldorf, Germany, 153
Dwight, Timothy, 23

Ecological Union, 314
Education on conservation issues, 321–22
Eisenhower, Dwight D., 98–99, 100, 281
Electric power, 76, 83, 90–91, 92
Elk Hills oil scandal, 26
Emotionalism, 326–28, 334, 345
Endowment funds, 339–40
Environmental Defense Fund, 144
Environmental Policy Act (1969), 292
Environmental Quality Council, 291–92, 296
Erie, Lake, 130, 131
Estes Park, Colo., 244
Everglades, 34, 35–54, 62–64, 80–81, 92, 93, 225, 254, 267, 279, 288, 292, 294, 345
Everglades National Park, 11, 34, 36, 54–64, 80, 225, 290
Extremism, 326–28

Fairless, Benjamin, 177
Fall, Albert B., 26
Family planning, 162–63
Faubus, Orval E., 82
Federal Aid Highway Act (1956), 98
Federal Aviation Administration, 125
Federal Council for Science and Technology, 126
Federal Farm and Home Administration, 56
Federal Insecticide, Fungicide and Rodenticide Act (1947), 141
Federal Power Commission, 76, 83, 84, 93
Federal Water Pollution Control Administration, 77, 129, 131, 133, 134
Federal Water Quality Act (1965), 129
Fell, George, 314, 315
Fields, W. C., 159
Fish and Wildlife Service, 57, 221, 222, 224, 228, 276
Fisherman Island, Va., 221–22
Flagler, Henry M., 46, 47, 48
Flaming Gorge reservoir, Utah, 269
Flamingo, Fla., 48
Flood Control District, Fla., 53, 58
Flood-control projects, 58–59, 62, 67, 68, 76, 80, 83, 128–29
Florida, University of, 53
Florida Bay, 35, 37, 40, 57
Florida Board of Internal Improvement, 45
Florida Engineering Board of Control, 51
Florida Federation of Women's Clubs, 50, 53
Florida Game and Fresh Water Fish Commission, 57
Florida Internal Improvement Fund, 46–47
Florida Keys, 43
Forbes, John, 174

Food and Drug Administration, 142
Foote, Samuel A., 24–25
Ford Foundation, 272, 340, 341
Forest of Nessine Marks, 263
Forest reserves, 186
Forest Service, U.S., 168, 187, 190–91, 236, 237, 238–46, 249, 250, 256, 257, 258, 259, 263, 264, 270, 278, 293–94, 306
Forests, 20, 22, 26, 27. See also National forests
Fort Duquesne, 174, 181
Fort Lauderdale, Fla., 50
Fort Ord, Calif., 218
Fort Story, Va., 218, 221, 227
Frank Key, Fla., 35–36, 37
Freeman, Orville L., 116, 188–89, 190, 228, 282
Fund-raising campaigns, 315, 331–32, 339

Gallagher, Cornelius E., 145
Garden City, Kan., 70
Garrison, Mont., 136
General Accounting Office, 142, 152, 154
General Land Office, 45, 72
Geological Survey, 53, 70, 72, 128
Georgia Charter (1732), 23
Georgia-Pacific Corporation, 213
Glacier Peak Wilderness, 187–88
Glen Canyon Dam, 84–85, 90
Golden Eagle pass, 249–50
Gore Range-Eagle's Nest Primitive Area, Colo., 117
Government, role of, in conservation, 280–97, 345
Government Printing Office, U.S., 246
Grand Canyon, Ariz., 18, 84, 87, 90, 91, 93, 189, 324–26
Grand Coulee Dam, 192
Gray, Kenneth J., 213
Great Britain, 26, 312–13
Great Lakes, 18, 128, 130, 131
Green Mountains, 19

Guadalupe Hidalgo, Treaty of (1848), 194
Guam, 289, 291
Gulf of Mexico, 18, 35, 40, 225

Hammacks, 41
Hammarskjöld, Dag, 204
Harlem, New York City, 171
Hayne, Robert Y., 25
Health, Education, and Welfare Department, U.S., 77, 128, 129, 138, 142
Hell's Canyon, Ida., 83, 84
Highway Act (1968), 111
Highway Beautification Act (1965), 116
Highway construction, 11, 12, 27, 95–103, 111–19, 135, 152, 207–8, 231–32, 236, 255, 281, 286, 345
Highway Trust Fund, 99, 117–18
Historic sites, invasion of, 115, 117
Hogan, Mark, 148
Homestead, Fla., 36
Homestead Act (1862), 71
Hoover, Herbert C., 89
Hoover commissions, 68, 77–79
Hoover Dam, 75, 89
Housatonic River, 22
Housing and Urban Development Department, U.S., 127
Hudson River, 18, 128, 153
Hudson River Expressway, 115, 117
Hughes, Charles Evans, 49
Humboldt County, Calif., 205
Humboldt Redwoods State Park, 205, 207
Huntley, George E., 233
Hurricane Donna, 37
Hydroelectric power. See Electric power

Idaho Power Company, 83
Imperial Valley, Calif., 88
Indian Affairs Bureau, U.S., 232

Indiana Natural Areas Survey, 316–17
Inflation, 12
Ingram, Lake, 38
Inholdings, 56–57, 263–64
Insecticides. See Pesticides
Interest rates, 277–78
Interior Department, U.S., 68, 76, 77, 83, 87, 92, 129, 132, 141, 150, 191, 201, 248, 252, 288, 289
Irrigation projects, 69–76, 88–90, 91–92

Jefferson, Thomas, 65
Jenkins, Alston, 301
Johnson, Lyndon B., 100, 111, 115, 132, 162, 210, 214, 226–27, 280, 282, 295–96
Johnson, Mrs. Lyndon B., 198, 199, 214, 252, 296
Joint Chiefs of Staff, 285

Kaniksu National Forest, 256, 279
Kennecott Copper Corporation, 189
Kennedy, John F., 248, 280, 282
Kennedy Airport, 125
Kent, William, 204
Key West, Fla., 44
Kings Canyon National Park, 203
Kinzua Dam, 83
Klamath River, 18

LaGuardia Airport, 123
Laird, Melvin R., 283–85
Land agents, 45
Land and Water Conservation Fund, 10, 248–53, 269, 270, 273, 274, 277, 284, 291
Land commissioners, 45
Land Management Bureau, U.S., 201, 202, 254, 258, 306
Land policy, federal, 192
Land preservation, 320
Land speculation, 71, 75, 111, 267–76

Land trusts, 299
Land use, 161, 217–53
Land-use planning, 22, 24, 25
Land Use Survey—Proposed Point Reyes National Seashore, 196
Land value, increase in, 264–78
Lane, Franklin K., 240–41
Laramie River, 244
Las Vegas Bombing and Gunnery Range, 148
Lawrence, David, 177–78
Lee, Philip, 162–63
Lewis, Sinclair, 173
Lindsey, Alton A., 317
Litter and trash, 27–28
Locke, John, 22
London Company, 219
Long Island, 107, 108
Long Island Expressway, 108
Long Island Sound, 101, 106, 134, 335
Los Angeles, Calif., 107
Louisiana Purchase (1803), 24
Lower Priest Lake, Ida., 256, 257, 259, 267
Lumber industry, 190

Mack's Creek, Mo., 96
Management control, 308
Marble Canyon, Ariz., 84, 87, 90, 91
Marin County, Calif., 197, 198, 200
Marshall, Thurgood, 149
Martha's Vineyard, Mass., 122
Mason Neck, Va., 275–76, 278
Mather, Stephen T., 50, 240
McCarthy, Richard D., 147
McCleod, Columbus G., 49
McKinley, William, 186
McLuhan, Marshall, 321
Mead, Elwood, 75
Mellon, Richard King, 177–78, 179–80
Memorial National Forest, 210
Memphis, Tenn., 125–26
Metroliner, 124

Miami, Fla., 50, 59, 60, 63
Miami Beach, Fla., 50
Miami River, 52
Mields, Hugh, Jr., 135
Miele, Ralph, 35, 36, 37, 38, 39, 60, 120
Migratory birds, 26
Military expenditures, 283–85, 286
Minshall, William E., 134
Mississippi River, 18, 66–67, 76
Mohawk Airlines, 123
Mojave Desert, 19
Monongahela River, 128
Monorails, 118
Monroe County, Fla., 60, 63
Mormons, 24, 69
Moss, Frank E., 77–80, 145
Motor vehicle accidents, 110
Mountains, 19, 185–92
Mount Baker, 186, 191
Mount Baker National Forest, 186
Mount Hood, 96
Mount Rainier, 191
Mount Rainier Forest Preserve, 186
Mount Rainier National Park, 186
Mueller, Paul, 140
Muir, John, 326, 337, 338
Muir Woods National Monument, 204
Muskie, Edmund S., 132, 150

Nashville, Tenn., 115
Nassau County, N.Y., 108
National Academy of Sciences, 145–46
National Aeronautics and Space Agency, 222, 227
National Association of Audubon Societies, 48, 49
National Audubon Society, 301, 326
National forests, 26, 162, 186, 210, 236, 238–46, 256, 258, 263–64, 306
National monuments, 204

National Park Service, 36, 50, 56, 57, 81, 82, 83, 85, 125, 162, 187, 190–91, 195, 196, 198, 200–1, 207, 208, 210, 211, 212, 223, 224, 225, 226, 230, 236, 238, 240, 250, 254, 255, 269–70, 288, 289, 290, 293–94, 295, 305–6, 325

National parks, 31, 162, 186–87, 190, 191–92, 203, 209–10, 225, 229, 236, 240–41, 281, 289, 290, 306, 345. *See also* specific parks

National Research Council, 142–43

National River, 82

National System of Interstate and Defense Highways, 99–100

National Security Council, 147

National Timber Supply Act, 213

National Water Commission, 77

National Wilderness Act, 187, 189, 239, 307, 345

Natural Bridge, Utah, 20, 85–86

Natural resources, 160–62, 345

Natural Resources Department, U.S., 93

Natural wonders, 19–20, 85–86, 204

Nature Conservancy, 257, 259, 260–64, 271, 272, 274–76, 278, 299, 300–1, 302–3, 308, 311, 314–16, 318, 319, 320–21, 331, 336, 337, 339–44

Navajo Indian Reservation, Ariz., 84

Navajo Indians, 86

Nerve gas, 145–46, 151

Newington, N.H., 22

New Jersey Concession and Agreement (1664), 22

Newlands, Francis G., 66–67, 71

Newlands Act (1902), 71

New Orleans, La., 114

New York City, 96, 105, 107, 117, 119, 121, 123, 126, 132, 136, 139, 167–68, 170–71, 173

New York *Times*, 92, 322

Niagara Falls, 20

Nixon, Richard M., 11–12, 116, 122, 133, 135, 146, 147, 214, 251–53, 283, 288, 291, 296–97

Noise pollution, 124–27

Norfolk, Va., 217

North Cascades National Park, 191–92

North Tarrytown, N.Y., 115

Northern Regional Park Authority, 276

Norwalk, Conn., 95

Nuclear explosions, 147–49, 152

Ocean City, Md., 222

Offshore drilling, control of, 11

Ohio River, 76

Okeechobee, Lake, 18, 39–40, 42, 48, 51, 52, 58, 62, 80

Old Dominion Foundation, 295

Olympic Mountains, 19

Ordway, Katherine, 113

Oregon Chamber of Commerce, 232

Oregon coast, parks, and highways, 229–38, 278

Oregon Territory, 186

Orick, Calif., 214

Ossining, N.Y., 115

Outdoor Recreation Bureau, 213, 248, 249, 269, 273

Outdoor Recreation for America, 246–47

Outdoor Recreation Resources Review Commission, 246–47

Overprofessionalism, 303–4

Owens Valley, Calif., 96

Pacific Forest Reserve, 186

Pacific Ocean, 18, 193, 230

Paine, Thomas, 326

Paradise Key, Fla., 48, 50

Park lands, invasion of, 115

Parking space, problem of, 103–7, 111, 229

Parks. *See* National parks; State parks

Parochialism, 332, 345
Payne, Sereno, 73
Penfold, Joseph, 255
Penn, William, 23
Penn-Central Railroad, 102, 103
Pesticides, 56, 140–44
Philadelphia, Pa., 23, 114–15
Pinchot, Gifford, 26, 67, 210
Pinchot National Forest, Gifford, 186
Pittsburgh, Pa., 104, 174–84
Pitzer, Kenneth S., 148
Plains, 19
Planning, 22, 24, 25, 305–11
Plant, Henry B., 46
Plume hunters, 49–50
Plymouth Colony, 21–22
Point Lobos, Calif., 219–21, 224
Point Reyes, Calif., 193–203, 214, 226, 252, 254, 255, 264, 287, 345
Point Reyes National Seashore, 198–203
Point Sublime, Grand Canyon, 324–25
Pollutants, 60
Pollution. See Air pollution; Automotive pollutants; Noise pollution; Water pollution
Pontchartrain, Lake, 18
Population increase, 155–70, 183
Portland, Oreg., 96
Potomac River, 130, 275
Powell, Lake, 85–87, 296
Power plants, 328
Prairie Creek State Park, 212
Preston Timber Company, 234
Private agencies, role of, in conservation, 298–323
Private aircraft, 123, 131
Private philanthropy, 273
Progress, 346
Public Health Service, 109, 137, 141, 142
Public lands, 20–21, 70, 71, 73, 74
Public Roads Bureau, 116
Public works relief program, 75

Quetico-Superior Canoe Area, 255
Q fever, 146
Quigley, James M., 130

Radioactive materials, 147–49, 152
Raftrey, John C., 37, 58, 61–62
Railroads, 46, 47, 102–3, 118, 258
Raleigh, N.C., 122
Reagan, Ronald, 215
Realfoot Lake, 18
Reclamation Bureau, 68, 75–76, 79, 83, 84, 90–91, 92, 269, 325
Reclamation Fund, 71, 72–73
Reclamation Service, 72, 73–75, 89
Recruitment of new conservationists, 335–44, 346
Redwood trees, 203–15, 254–55
Redwoods National Park, 210, 212–15, 252, 284
Resources for the Future, 153
Revolving funds, 314–15
Ribicoff, Abraham, 81
Rights-of-way, public, 229
Rivers, 18, 22, 27, 66–67, 68, 83, 87–91, 128. See also specific rivers
Rivers and Harbors Act (1927), 67
Rockefeller, Laurence S., 246
Rockefeller Forest, 205, 206
Rockwell, Norman, 281
Rocky Mountains, 19, 27, 244
Roosevelt, Franklin D., 79
Roosevelt, Theodore, 71
Roosevelt National Forest, 244
Royal Palm State Park, 53
Rural Electrification Administration, 76
Rye, N.Y., 100–2, 107

St. Lucie Canal, Fla., 52
Salt Lake City, Utah, 69
San Francisco, Calif., 104, 195
San Jose, Calif., 204
Sangamon River, 83
Santa Barbara, Calif., 251
Santa Cruz, Calif., 262

Santa Rosa, N.M., 96
Save-the-Redwoods League, 204–6, 207, 208, 209, 210, 211, 212, 214–15, 220, 255
Seashore State Park, Va., 218–19, 221, 224
Seashores, 21, 27, 101, 193–203, 216, 217–31, 235–38, 269–70, 278, 287, 295
Selbyville, Del., 137
Seminole Indians, 43–44, 62
Seminole War, 44
Sempervirens Club, 204
Senate Committee on Public Works, 132, 137, 139
Seniority system, Congressional, 285
Sequoia National Park, 203
Sewage disposal, 128
Sewage treatment plants, 132, 135–36, 152, 153
Shakespeare, William, 312
"Share of market," concept of, 309
Shark River, 38–39
Shrimp industry, 37, 61
Sierra Club, 91, 189, 322, 336
Sierra Nevada, 203
Sikes, Representative, 212
Silent Spring (Carson), 141
Sinslaw National Forest, 236
Smith, Alfred E., 49
Smith, Tom and Dan, 49
Smith, Walter, 49
Smith State Park, Jedediah, 212
Smog, 136, 137, 180, 281
Smoky Mountains, 19
Snake River, 72, 83
Snoqualmie National Forest, 186
Soil conservation, 23
Soil Conservation Service, 53, 76
Sonic booms, 125
South Vietnam, 10
Soviet Union, 281, 283
Spanish-American War, 46
Spectator, The, 322
State parks, 31, 50, 82, 122, 162, 196, 198, 204, 205, 207, 212,

214–15, 216, 218–19, 224, 230, 232–36, 260–63, 276. See also specific parks
Storm sewers, 136
Studies, 307, 322
Suburbs, problems of, 169–70
Superior, Lake, 131
Supersonic jet planes, 127, 152, 345
Supreme Court, U.S., 83, 89, 115, 149
Survival holes, 41–42
Swamp Land Act (1850), 45, 47
Swanson, Ernest W., 31

Tahoe, Lake, 130
Tall Trees, 211–12
Tamiami Trail, Fla., 39, 52
Teapot Dome oil scandal, 26
Technologies, conservation, 311–23
Tennessee River, 79
Tennessee Valley Authority, 76
Ten Thousand Islands, Fla., 56
Teton National Forest, 245
Tetons, 19
Thallium, 142
Thompson, Wiley, 43–44
Thoreau, Henry David, 23, 128, 335
Tidal marshes, 13
Tomales Bay, Calif., 193
Tomales Bay State Park, 196, 198
Town planning, 20–21, 23
Traffic problems, 107–9, 119, 281, 345
Transportation, public, 116, 118–19, 123–24
Transportation Department, U.S., 116, 288
Travels in New England and New York (Dwight), 23
Tropical Everglades National Park Commission, 53–54
Troy, N.Y., 128
Tucumcari, N.M., 96

Tularemis (rabbit fever), 146
Twin Falls, Ida., 72

Udall, Stewart, 91, 130–31, 159–60, 164, 169, 248, 282
Uinta Mountains, 148
Underwood, Oscar, 73
United Fund, Pittsburgh, 181
United Nations, 204
United States Steel Corporation, 181
Upper Priest Lake, Ida., 255–60, 278, 279

Vietnam War, 282, 286, 296, 319
Virginia Beach, Va., 217–18
Volpe, John, 114, 310

Walden, Colo., 95
Walton League, Izaac, 255, 278
War of 1812, 65
Washburn Expedition (1870), 25, 327
Washington Forest Reserve, 186
Waterbury, Conn., 95
Water policy, 92–93
Water pollution, 10, 11, 126, 127–36, 150–51, 152–54, 281, 283, 287, 297
Water Pollution Control Act (1948), 129
Water Resources Council, 79
Water Resources Planning Act (1944), 79
Water rights, 87
Water standards, 77
Waterways, 20, 68

Weather Bureau, U.S., 50
Weaver, Robert, 163, 164, 166
Weicker, Lowell, Jr., 134
Wenatchee National Forest, 186
Western Pennsylvania Conservancy, 181–82, 255, 300
West Indies, 43
Westinghouse, George, 175
Westmoreland, William C., 282, 285
Weston, Conn., 113–14, 167
Weston, Edward, 220, 344
West Point Military Academy, 65
Westport, Conn., 299
Westward movement, 24–25
Whitecap Bay, Fla., 38
White House Council on Environmental Quality, 292
Wilderness Society, 307
Wildlife refuges, 225, 228
Willamette River, 96
Wilson, Alexander, 265
Wordsworth, William, 312–13
Work, Hubert, 74
Works Progress Administration, 317
World Health Organization, 109
World War I, 314
World War II, 52, 54, 140, 175, 281, 314

Yakima National Park, 187
Yellowstone National Park, 25–26, 27–28, 229, 327
Yellowstone River, 18
Yosemite National Park, 203
Yuma, Ariz., 89
Yuma Valley, 89

About the Author

Throughout a busy career as newspaper writer, FBI agent, vice-president of two large commercial banks, and author, Alexander B. Adams has been in the front line of the struggle to maintain the quality of our environment, working actively as a trustee or officer of numerous conservation agencies. Because of the urgency of the problem, he decided in 1959 to give up his many other outside interests and concentrate on conservation alone. In 1960, he accepted the position of volunteer president of the Nature Conservancy and later became the first chairman of its board of governors. During the period of his leadership, the Nature Conservancy grew from a small agency to one that the *Wall Street Journal* has described as "unique among national conservation groups."

Although he recently "retired" as the Nature Conservancy's chairman, he remains on the boards of conservation agencies whose headquarters range from Maine to California. In preparation for this book, he supplemented his already extensive knowledge by traveling 15,000 miles across the country in search of further answers to the environmental problems confronting this nation.

His other books include *Eternal Quest: The Story of the Great Naturalists* and *John James Audubon: A Biography*.